2020

or

"My Name is Jesus Christ and I'm Running for President."

A Divine Comedy
Timothy Cooper

THE DAWN AFTER

The soon-to-be *former* chairman of the Democratic National Committee, Jerry McClellan, woke up at dawn on the morning after the November 2, 2004 presidential elections, and felt like getting drunk. After presumably losing the Big One—the race for the White House, as well as a majority of House and Senate races, he'd gone to bed around 3:00 AM with an angel's prayer in his heart, hoping the Good Lord would cough up enough electoral college votes in Ohio to miraculously put his guy over the top.

Then he went to sleep and dreamed he drove his 1964 red Mustang convertible, recently restored, into a row of concrete traffic barriers placed, for fear of terrorists, in front of the guardhouse at the Vice President's mansion at Observatory Circle. So when McClellan woke, he knew it was over, even before he checked his messages. He knew his candidate's defeat—and that of the Democratic Party's in general—had become the full measure of his stratospheric failure.

As good as it felt to smack into the V.P.'s guardhouse barriers head-on—and it really did feel good, even through his dream—he awoke mildly peeved that his nightmare encounter with concrete had ended any possibility of him getting any remedial benefit from too few hours sleep. Still he was greatly relieved that his vehicular collision was merely a continuation of his election night nightmare, and not reality itself, and that his precious red Mustang—which he'd had lovingly restored at considerable expense at a body shop in Silver Spring run by a colorful guy named Andy, who had a hulking Jesus look about him, and did really good work, even though he made more money selling automatic weapons in a room at the back of the shop, and who enjoyed, notably, firing machine guns into abandoned cars in fields down in Anne

Arundel County on Sunday afternoons with his wife and kids, who, by the way, also unloaded any number of rounds into the side panels, trunks, and hoods—was still parked, without a ding or a scratch, in his climate-controlled garage downstairs. McClellan would do anything for that car. He loved it so much, in fact, that right after it came out of the auto body shop in mint condition, he fancifully considered getting buried in it.

Now McClellan confronted the *real* nightmare, perhaps not one quite as horrifying as totaling his Mustang, but nearly so. He faced the fallout of the Day Before, the told and untold consequences of the defeat of defeats. McClellan needed more than a drink. He required an entire brewery to drown his boatload of sorrows.

Having ably led the entire Democratic Party down to its worst electoral defeat in what?—a century or so?—he, above all others (except for the candidates themselves perhaps), would be held accountable for its thunderous losses. Never again would he be entrusted to hold the reins of party power. It was over. He was through. In light of circumstances, it occurred to him that hari-kari was an even more appealing option than getting plastered. It would be a pro-active—even noble—gesture that would likely result in increased sympathy being heaped on him by obituary writers and pundits when they went to work on him. But since McClellan believed in a just God, he knew that escape was not an option. The God above would make him suffer and His punishment would be severe. Yes, God was a Democrat—that much McClellan knew in the brightest spots of his heart—and now he would be made to pay for handing the political works over to the Republicans.

Faint traces of dim autumn light slipped over the brocade bedroom curtains, spilling into the quiet, plush room. On the French dresser an ornate antique clock ticked as a distant garbage truck rumbled down an alleyway behind his Cleveland Park house, that, incidentally, he'd just had painted "billowy blue" in anticipation of a Democratic victory in the White House. A political corpse, for sure, McClellan lay very still in bed, and considered his fate. He could see but he could not move. His bedroom view was rather limited to one side of the room because his eyes were evidently glued semi-shut by a mixture of secret tears and cigarette residue contributed at no charge by chain-smoking political operatives in poorly ventilated hotel war rooms from California to Virginia during the past 48 hours.

In the unhurried light, McClellan considered the disaster. He mulled over the magnitude of his masterly blunder. The scale, alone, humbled him. It was the Mount McKinley of political bungles. He had done what no man wearing a donkey tee shirt had done before. The slaughter was unique in the annals of 20th century Democratic Party politics. Not that he was wholly to blame, of course. He knew that. John Kerry was no Bill Clinton. Clearly, a well-heeled northeastern liberal senator from Massachusetts who'd lost his rhetorical edge during decades of gentlemanly debate in the U.S. Senate proved to be no match for Karl Rove and the evangelical right.

Nevertheless, he felt ultimately responsible for yesterday's 57 million Democratic voter pileup on US Interstate 2004. He felt responsible for it because, well, he was. It was his strategy that so spectacularly failed them. And he knew well that no one would much remember the high points. They would be lost in the burning debris and wreckage of the Kerry-Hindenburg 2004 political implosion, such as the unprecedented $200 million HE RAISED for the Democratic Party or his SKILLED LEADERSHIP in turning out a record number of Democratic voters to the polls on election day. That should—could— count for something... But he was fairly positive that even his own mother wouldn't be too charitable with him about the historic losses. She was a Roosevelt Democrat, after all. Which meant that she'd probably conveniently "forget" about sending him her usual homemade rhubarb pie for a few Friday nights in a row, the way she always did, just to register her resounding unhappiness with his stewardship. Politics is all about hardball, even with mommas.

McClellan brushed the sticky goop from his eyes, alarmed about the potential absence of rhubarb pie this coming Friday night. As bad as that was, worse would be the verdict rendered by political historians about the DNC's leadership under his watch during the 2004 presidential elections. He'd rather face a firing squad than read about that. Hopefully, though, all the gory little details wouldn't be written until he was long dead. He took perverse solace in the thought that one day everyone who had ever voted in the 2004 presidential election results would be dead too and that his part in the party debacle would be known only to those few who bothered to read footnotes in American political science books. One day—alive or dead—he'd be free. Somehow that thought came as a great relief, even though—let's face it—it was some kind of twisted logic.

But what really blew a hole in his heart was that he'd nearly convinced himself his guy Kerry could actually win at the end by some miracle of chance, despite the doomsday daily tracking polls that said the Good Ship Kerry was taking on water fast, and sinking in uncharted waters. With a loss of this magnitude, there was simply no conceivable way he could have properly prepared himself in advance. He knew of no psychiatrist in Washington he could go to guide him through the rocky narrows of his humiliation. Not now. He'd jumped off the bridge with no bungee cord attached. The professional loss would be staggering: career mutilating, in fact, compounded by the psychological effects of ideological torture on the front lines of political trench warfare. He was screwed.

He would have been capable of coping with less extensive losses much better, of course. With his guy elected to the White House getting clobbered in the House and Senate would have been semi-tolerable. But the shock of losing everything—once again—twice in four years—forced McClellan to reconsider his position and think more creatively. So creatively, in fact, that the thought of taking up life as a Tibetan monk in Lhasa wasn't altogether out of the question. Two corkscrews between the eyes in four years wasn't McClellan's idea of fun anymore. He was inclined to do just about anything to avoid stepping into the ring with the likes of Karl Rove & Co. again. His momma raised a pragmatic realist—not a masochist. Those guys were rough—and mean—mean as Darth Vader.

Whatever his fate or wherever it would lead him, it would not be as the head of the DNC in Washington, DC. Come February, his contract would be up and he would be ceremoniously relieved of his duties. They'd be happy to give him the boot. Failure was intolerable (even for Democrats), and political gallows awaited anyone who'd lost more than their fair share. But it wasn't just the numerical losses that made McClellan feel the need to live the rest of his life on a misty mountaintop—it was *how* his guy lost that dug into him like a pitchfork into peat. Kerry lost not because of his nuisance positions on the war in Iraq, national health insurance, tax cuts, and prescription drugs for seniors. Nor did he fail to catch on because the American public didn't exactly warm to his wife, Theresa Heinz Kerry, who had more money than most third world countries could ever get in foreign aid. No, the issue that carried the water for George W. and Republicans running for Congress, the one that devastated Kerry's presidential dreams and demolished McClellan's ambassadorship to the Court of St. James ambitions could be reduced to a pithy bumper sticker slogan—eleven letters slapped on the back of Pat Robertson's Cadillac, inches above the tailpipe: "Moral Values."

If instant history teaches us anything, it's this: Americans love their moral values. The voting public pulled the lever for those candidates who most conspicuously touted them, as narrowly and curiously defined by the Christian Right.

According to exit polls, 23% of the voting public cited "moral values" as the principle reason why they, in their moralistic wisdom, voted for George W. That percentage was the highest in any other issues category, including the war in Iraq, the economy and tax cuts. George W. and his evangelical right had claimed title to and won the morality superiority contest—a covert war McClellan had no idea was being fought out with such gusto in the hearts and minds of certain U.S. voters. If only his pollsters had been able to get their polls around that issue; if only his guy had worn a crucifix on his lapel instead of an American flag pin during the televised national debates. That might have made a difference. Instead, the time for second-guessing had officially begun. The dawn after came in slow for poor old McClellan as he lay traumatized in bed, having been done in, along with all his kind, by the public perception that Democrats didn't know the difference between the "Ten Commandments" and David Letterman's "Top Ten List."

But this much McClellan did know: He and his Democratic Party would be doing hard time in the Gulag of American Politics for the yet another four years—perhaps longer—unless he and his sorry excuse for a moral values party came up with a candidate for 2008 who could out-moral-values the Moral Right, and then some.

Lying there in the sunken deep of his tsunami shock and titanic guilt, McClellan wondered whether God reserved a special place in Hell for losing DNC strategists, especially since he'd already deduced that his God, at least, took a special interest in the fortunes of the Democratic

7

Party. Yes, McClellan had concluded over one too many beers after hours with his political cronies that Jesus, if He ever did come around again, would register as a loyal member of the Democratic Party. He'd speak truth to Republican power, that's for sure. Which his party could use—badly. The corollary to that, of course, was that the anti-Christ would sign up as a Republican—and in fact, already had—at least according to some who claimed they'd detected the stink of sulfur coming from the general direction of George W.'s White House.

There in the tangle of the shallow morning dark, a green cotton sheet tucked underneath his chin, he also took to musing about his own shaky fate. He saw himself standing at St. Peter's Gate, barred from entering for his notorious political ineptitude, and then condemned by the God of Gods to serve out eternity in the Lower Depths. As a unique form of punishment, designed exclusively for failed Democratic political operators such as himself, the Good Lord would send him on the express train down to the 13th Ring of Hell, which would bear a striking resemblance to another location he knew remarkably well: Washington, D.C. under a Republican-controlled White House and Congress. For McClellan, doing eternity at Abu Ghraib was preferable.

McClellan closed his eyes. He wasn't feeling very optimistic, was he? He opened his eyes. McClellan reached out across the cotton sheets, wondering if they'd become frisky flames licking at the air above the River Styx. Before his imagination drove him certifiable, he felt Margaret's hip, covered in a soft, cool St. Laurent blanket. She stirred uneasily, no doubt trapped in her very own post-election nightmare. Poor woman. Now she'd pay for his birdbrain leadership, too. At least he knew where he was now. And he was comforted to think that the Good Lord would never drag an International Red Cross worker, like Margaret, down to the 13th Ring of Hell. Only failed Democrats, and such other malefactors as the Democratic Lord found worthy, got the heave-ho. And deservedly so.

Outside, McClellan could just make out the pumpkin sky, painted the colors of Halloween. Very fitting. It hung down low above a miasmic silent fog, mingling with the blazing overhead trees, enveloping the bare sugar maple branches in a serene haze, even filling up the potholes up and down Newark Street, where he lived. He breathed in. Yep, the air smelled like sulfur. It always smelled like that in Washington the day after the Republicans won big. At least to him. The trouble was—he was getting used to it. Too used to it.

He looked at the clock on his bedside table. It read 5 till 6. At most, he'd gotten three hours sleep. McClellan had flown in by private jet from Boston to be with Margaret after Florida had gone for Bush and Ohio was still too close to call. In another few minutes, NPR election reporters would be chattering on his alarm clock radio, set for 6, and break the spell of his post-Halloween hell. Daniel Schorr and Cokie Roberts would be commenting on the dry dimensions of the Democrat's defeat. All across America people would be waking up to news that the Grim Reaper visited the Democratic Party last night. McClellan knew that even if he heard all the stats and exit polling data yet again, he still wouldn't believe it. No matter how accurate the reporting, no matter how incisive the commentary, it all would seem, somehow, well, totally surreal, like some dreadful hoax perpetrated by a conspiracy of roving gangs of juvenile delinquents on an unsuspecting nation in the dead of night. But it was real, all right. 100% Made-in-America real. He and his beloved Democratic Party had been shut down—again. The worse case scenario had been made real—thanks to his world-class failure to decipher the psyche of the US voter—to understand their hardcore need to vote for a candidate who spoke to their common sense of moral values.

9

He turned on his side to face the clock, and sighed. If he'd been a deeply religious man, he would have gotten out of bed, knelt down, and prayed. But decades ago he had more or less lost his faith, supplanted by a child-like naivety in the democratic system of public affairs, otherwise known as the cannibalistic world of American politics—a world in which political parties ate their own, whenever necessary. Which was more than a little often. So to get down on his knees and prayers at this late date would appear to run the risk of being declared disingenuous, if not flat-out hypocritical, by someone you'd rather not have hold that against you, too, on top of everything else. But still, it was an option that he'd hold in reserve, just in case there was no other way out.

His mind retreating, standing still, racing forward, McClellan turned to the only line of consideration that could give him a lift: Campaign 2008. He quickly circled back to his predator instincts, his survival impulses, and put the only question that had legs on the table: *Who would his nominee in 2008?* Even the question made him feel good.

Today the future was safe from failure.

Which holier-than-Republican Democrat could the party cultivate over the next four years that would possess the requisite degree of first pew Sunday morning piety, policy wonk street smarts, and commander-in-chief gravitas—starting as now—6:00 a.m. today—to take it all the way in 2008? Where was that one transcendent Democrat who had all the unimpeachable moral values credentials of a Jimmy Carter, the soaring oratory genius of a Bill Clinton, and the graphic good looks of a JFK incarnate?

The answer, of course, was, who the hell knew? Who ever knew? But what he did know was that a Hilary Clinton candidacy would eventually crash and burn, too. She might make a pretty good showing for the party nomination—she'd have the Clinton machine behind her, after all—but even if she wrested the nomination from a redoubtable dark horse candidate—the Republicans would bludgeon her candidacy during the general election with instant recalls of her husband's licentious behavior in the halls of the White House with Monica Lewinsky. Not precisely what the American voters said they were in the mood for yesterday.

In McClellan's snap analysis, the Democrats were totally screwed. Screwed coming and going, across an infinite political horizon: 2000—2004—2008. And beyond. Say, why not just go for it and work real hard to bomb out in 2012 and 2016, as well. Consistency is everything in politics. Maybe the Dems could set some kind of record. Right, go for two decades of total Republican rule. Might as well flunk out in 2020, too. In fact, McClellan mused, having fun now, why not stick the donkey in the stable, dissolve the Democratic Party, and go fifty red states under a One-Party America. The Republicans would certainly endorse it; and he'd lay odds on the Chinese getting behind it, too. His momma would never send him a rhubarb pie again, but there was always a price to be paid for everything, so so what?

McClellan groaned, not so loudly as to disturb Margaret, but loud enough to make her stir. It was a groan that acknowledged his and his party's gross incompetence. If only he and his party standard bearers had been going to church, wore armbands broadcasting their religious denomination and date of baptism or bar mitzvah. If only. Such overt strategies might have siphoned off enough churchgoing votes to shift the electoral math. This was not a capricious thought. Exit polls told the tale. Churchgoers voted Republican 2-to-1. Had he and the top DNC echelon knelt at the communion rail every Sunday instead of lying about in bed watching "Meet the Press," their political antenna might have been more attuned to the moral values issue in the first place. Hell, he might have come across the perfect moral values candidate in the third

11

pew across the aisle a couple of hundred Sundays ago. The Good Book says, "Seek and ye shall find." So, McClellan, get to church. The Lord works in very direct ways. Check out who's saying prayers and singing psalms and volunteering for the Vestry. McClellan breathed easier. He was getting a fix on how to extricate himself from his fix. Get religion into Democratic politics forthwith.

He lay on his side, his head sunken into two bamboo pillows, visualizing, like he once envisaged gorgeous girls tanning on white sands in summer, a whole new raft of slogans: "Dems Do It Better—In or Out of the Church!"; "Jesus was (and is) a Liberal Democrat!"; "Vote the Gospel According to Democrats in 2008!" Those buzz phrases would be improved in committee, but they were a decent taking off point. But the bottom line was clear: The Dems needed to shape conceptions of morality from pithy platform mottoes into concrete public policy. That's what Jesus would do, if He came back. And that's what the Dems should do, too. What would happen to that logic in committee, only the good Lord knew, but McClellan was convinced he had a firm handle on a born again political strategy that was sure to win. He had to hand it to the Republicans, they certainly put the fear of God into him—or was it the fear of looking godless? In any event, he couldn't wait to mix morality, religion, and politics, because what McClellan was most terrified of was having his party go up against Rove & Co. again without it wearing a morality shield.

The truth was McClellan dreaded Judgment Day, November 4, 2008 far more than his own day of reckoning at St. Peter's Gate, whenever the hell his number came up. At least November 4, 2008 was a date certain. His rendezvous with eternity, at least to his knowledge, was not. So, it seemed clear, that what McClellan & Co. needed to do was cultivate a new presidential candidate of considerable moral standing ASAP: Not a John Kerry, or a Hilary Clinton, but a candidate that was Holier than St. Luke and cooler than Matt Damon and Brad Pitt put together. Or perhaps a nominee possessing a mind meld of Mother Teresa and Eleanor Roosevelt. That would be good, too. Certainly, no less would be required to capture the presidency and help resurrect the USS Democratic Party.

What McClellan wouldn't pay, barter or steal for just one more chance to redeem himself, to atone for his catastrophic leadership. All he wanted waiting for him underneath the Christmas tree on Christmas morning was the perfect values candidate in a big blue box tied up in a beautiful blue bow. That hardly seemed like too much to ask for. But, getting back to reality, he knew he could forget about it. Santa wouldn't deliver and the DNC wouldn't give him a second chance. He was history. Come to nothing history at that.

Of course what galled McClellan the most was his own personal humiliation in the face of his opponent's victory. This much was certain: Yesterday's re-elected, six-gun-toting, Moral Values Commander-in-Chief would be reveling in plum pudding and downing eggnog at his ranch in Crawford on Christmas Eve, go to bed with visions of four more years in the White House dancing in his head, and wake up Christmas morning, look under the tree, and find a big red box wrapped in a beautiful red bow waiting for him, containing, well, what else?— Jerry McClellan's head, bagged, stuffed and lovingly gift wrapped by Karl Rove & Co. All he'd get for Christmas was a stocking stuffed with hanging chads.

The lazy fog curled outside his window; it became darker, denser—the opposite of what should be happening at daybreak. But then again, nothing about any of the last 24 hours should have been happening. McClellan's spheres of comprehension were skewed. Light was dark; dark light. There was no retreat; no advance. Where was refuge? Where were his soothing waters of anonymity, his cool forests

13

of obscurity? Wherever the hell bin Laden was hiding out, that's where he'd like to go. For sure, no one would find him there. Especially Karl Rove & Co.

But for all his panic-induced wanderlust, McClellan was only too happy to sequester himself from the world underneath his green cotton sheets. He lifted the covers up over his head and savored the peaceful dreamy white space beneath. He intended to revel in these last seconds of solitude. Soon the gong of accountability would ring and he would be summoned. Sent for by the commands of responsibility. Naturally, the media would be waiting for him, huddled in expectation, waiting to record the ingenious spin of the losing DNC chairman beneath the basketball hoop at the garage door by 7. (He'd been meaning to replace that old shredded net for several years now... Now he could. Now there would be time. Defeat's silver lining.

McClellan's radio alarm buzzed pitilessly. NPR came on. McClellan swatted the buzzer. Carl Castle's voice purred as he announced the morning's top story, sounding more like a family priest giving last rites to the Democratic Party than a newscaster. George W. was the probable winner over John Kerry. But Senator Kerry still had not conceded. The number of provisional ballots in Ohio made it theoretically possible for Kerry to pull out a win in Ohio and shift the Electoral College math. Oh yeah, right. McClellan knew and Kerry knew and the whole damn DNC knew that the odds of that happening were comparable to George W. inviting Kerry to serve as Secretary of Defense after "swift-boating" him during the election. Principally, it was for the sake of appearances that Kerry hadn't delivered his concession speech earlier this morning. By not conceding, it made a not-so close race look, well, incrementally closer. That's about all the Dems had going for them—the momentary power to create the illusion of an appearance of less of a defeat. Cokie Roberts and Daniel Schorr followed Carl Castle's news highlights with perky comment and deft analysis. They too focused on the startling exit poll results. "Voters claimed that their most important issue—rated higher than their concern over Bush's mishandling of the war in Iraq—was about which candidate could deliver on moral values."

No sooner had McClellan heard the words "moral values" fly off Cokie Roberts' lips than he crushed the little red "Off" button with the flat of his palm, cutting off poor old Cokie mid-sentence. Since McClellan harbored the suspicion that Cokie was a closet Republican—which he wouldn't swear to in a court of law, but enjoyed speculating about because he had a sixth sense about the party affiliation of any number of Washington journalists, which—he was certain—nine times out of ten he was right about—it was not an altogether unpleasant thing to do. His impulse banging woke up Margaret.

"You okay?" she whispered, her voice fuzzy with sleep.

"Still standing, if that's what you mean…"

"Technically speaking, you're…"

"Lying down…"

They chuckled into the sheets and smiled the same smile they'd been smiling since they met ten years ago last month at a Democratic fundraiser. Not awfully romantic, but in D.C. it was enough to get the job done.

"Isn't politics marvelous?" she asked.

"It's an insane man's game."

"I told you that."

"Then why did you let me get away with it?"

"'Cause I'm nuts about you."

They moved closer together and kissed in the low light.

"Even the deranged need company, you know," he said.

"So what's your next move?"

15

"Move to Canada."

"I have a better idea."

"And that would be?..."

"Think succession."

"You have in mind the United Democratic States of America?"

"It's better than lying down."

"Certainly would solve all the party's problems."

"No red states."

"Only nice, friendly blue ones."

"Speaking of lying down..."

"Uh-huh..."

"You busy?"

"Not too."

"Really?"

"Definitely."

And life for McClellan was suddenly much more bearable there under the green cotton sheets. The specters of Karl Rove & Co. were eradicated in the unholy dawn breaking over Washington.

Afterwards, they sat together under a Tiffany lamp at the round kitchen table, on the verge of feeling human again. Sane even. Margaret looked nothing if not smashingly non-profit sharp in her crisp, raspberry wool suit, silk white Christian Dior blouse, and sheer nylon stockings. Her brand new sleek, black Ferragamos were a real turn-on. The scent of new leather, fresh out of the box, mixed with freshly brewed coffee never failed to arouse. Still, McClellan couldn't help wondering about the cost. $400? $600? $700? When it came to fine women's shoes, any price was possible. Normally, McClellan wouldn't have given it a second thought, but today—well, today was different. Come January, he'd be either searching for a new job in a company that specialized in hiring

16

failed political operatives cheap or searching out a lofty spiritual roost at 11,000 feet. In either event, $700 shoes were out. From McClellan's vantage, he had two choices: 1) Redeem himself at a cut-rate wages, or 2) achieve spiritual enlightenment and put the era of $700 shoes behind him until kingdom come.

Margaret poured McClellan a second cup of French coffee in his favorite stained Chicago Cubs coffee mug, chipped at the left side lip. He'd downed the first like a frosty glass of freshly squeezed OJ after a rousing session of hot yoga. She knew he required more coffee so he could do more talking. McClellan was on a full-blown verbal rampage. They happened every month or so. Unstoppable. This one was three weeks early. Her job was to keep it going until it petered out due to a meeting deadline. This morning he was a virtual Abraham Lincoln delivering the "Gettysburg Address" as he lobbed colorful invectives at the Swift Boat Veterans for Truth group, praised the Republicans for their pluck in invading Democratic strongholds and picking up targeted Democratic voters with highly tailored messages block by block. He waxed articulate on the substance of their message delivery: It was a thing of beauty—unprecedented sophistication—a work of serious political art. Their direct mail campaigns and voter technology—years in the making—was capable of identifying and zeroing in on potential voters with the laser beam precision of AGM-65 Mavericks. No wonder his Dems were blown out of the skies over Washington.

He bragged, too. Last chance. Well, why not? Democratic turnout: A record 56+ million Democratic voters. Better than that: His 6.8 million new Democratic voters broke all records. Better than that: His $337 million DNC campaign war chest, for which he received the chair's share of credit, had never been topped. After a spate of self-preserving self-congratulations, he groaned, like a whale beached on the Florida shore. If only he'd foreseen and compensated for Bush's voter

17

turnout hike in the exurban and rural counties of Ohio by banging the get-out-the-vote drum incessantly through inner city streets in search of the pitiful 118,000+ votes that were the margin of his key battleground state defeat. If only. If only the Democratic primary hadn't given his guy a cauliflower ear. If only Kerry hadn't been so damn low on cash when he most needed to respond to those shitty Swift Boat ads; if only he'd brought on TargetPoint Consulting to target Democratic voters in *Republican* strongholds. If only. If only…

If only he'd ignored the Democratic Leadership Council's centrist position on the war in Iraq (Yes to the war, but No to going in without the U.N.'s permission.). If only he'd counseled Kerry from the get-go to frame Misadventure Iraq as a lame distraction from a legitimate police action against terrorism. If only Kerry hadn't gone windsurfing…

But the biggest "if only" of the morning brought him back to where he began: If only he'd had a little heads-up on the looming "Moral Values" gap. His morning mantra buzzed again: 23% of Americans avowed how the moral values issue was determinative in their choosing to vote for His Moralist, George W. How moral values and condoning torture could be reconciled in either American or un-American minds, McClellan would never know. A key question lingered like Valdez oil on an Alaskan beach: How the f*#ck did his pollsters miss this one?

Next time, if there ever was a next time, McClellan would properly vet his pollsters: Were they church-going moralists? Would they accept being banished to purgatory as punishment for missing that and other 118,000+ vote questions? If they wouldn't, they could go work for Republicans. He'd use Democratic moral values to fight Republican moral values. Value for value. Moral for moral. He'd get Christianity on his side this time, all right. He already had a righteous slogan in his quiver to deliver: "Vote the Gospel According to Democrats in 2008!" He still liked the sound of that.

If only he'd had the foresight to recast the Democratic policy agenda in terms of a moral values agenda, six weeks ago, 6 months ago, six years ago. Like the Dems could have been out there promoting the moral value of feeding the poor, providing health insurance to all Americans, guaranteeing low-cost prescription drugs to the elderly, making needle exchange programs available to all drug addicts, creating first-class education in public schools, pledging 0% interest loans to everyone for a college education, investing in clean technology and zero emission cars. These were the Dems moral values. And there were more. Like subsidizing HIV treatment for all victims anywhere in the world, especially those hit hardest in Africa, preventing genocide in Bosnia and Rwanda and other tortured places, forgiving suffocating third-world debt, brokering a Palestinian-Israel peace settlement, pushing for a Marshall Plan for peace in the Middle East, and answering the key question of the new millennium: What is the definition of moral globalization and how do we implement it? Like—"

"You should take the day off," Margaret said, as McClellan was about to climb on the kitchen table his post-mortem address to an audience of one. He pushed back his cold plate of Spike-covered soft-boiled eggs and quarter slice of cinnamon toast, conspicuously missing only one bite, preparing for his second mount of the morning. He pushed back his breakfast plate as though he had the power to push back history itself.

He didn't. But he sure looked good trying. Good to Margaret, if no one else.

"As in this is the first day of the rest of the end of my life?" he asked, brought back to planet Earth.

19

"As in be a compassionate Democrat and give yourself a break: You could have lost Ohio by 200,000 votes."

"So by that logic we really had a pretty big win."

"Big, that's right."

"So how does it feel being married to a champ?"

"Big."

"The thing about losing is…"

"You'll have more time for ME!"

"Right. More time for you."

"Your flirtations were utterly wasted on Karl Rove, anyway…"

"Spurned, was I?"

"Definitely."

"So there really is an up side, after all."

"No, there really is a Santa Claus! And he's putting you in a box for me!"

"Blue ribbon?"

"Not red!"

"So I'll just go outside and tell the nice reporters that everything's okay in Democratic politics as of now because I get to spend more time alone with you!"

"Got that right, mister. But first, starting today, you're going to have some quality time with yourself! Because… (roll drum) I've decided that it's officially Jerry McClellan's Day Off! I want you to spend time with yourself so you can get a grip on yourself!"

"A what?"

"You heard me."

"Not possible."

"Hey buddy, I'm your boss now—not the DNC. You do what I say."

"You're serious, aren't you?"

"Go to the gym, browse in a bookstore, go hide out at a Starbucks and start writing your memoirs, for all I care. And just because I love you, I'll even give you my Starbucks card—fully loaded. I don't give that to just anybody, you know. But don't go getting any ideas... I want it back."

"You don't think you're making too hasty a decision here...?"

"I WANT YOU OUTA HERE, MISTER! STOP TORTURING YOURSELF! American civilization hasn't come crashing down—not yet, anyway."

"Really? I thought I heard a bump in the night."

"And there's more to life than winning elections, too."

"Really?"

"Consider yourself fortunate I let you live..."

"Okay, okay I'll try it— but only for a couple of hours."

"FOR THE WHOLE DAMN DAY! And I'll be expecting a written report accounting for every single hour—no detours down to the DNC!"

"Did anyone ever tell you that you should have grown up to be a tyrant?"

"Turn off your cell phone, don't check your text messages—not once—or your email. Especially not your email. And if your cronies call here looking for you, I'll tell them that you're down at the White House interviewing for a job. That should put a stop to them looking for you— fast. No one will bother you. Not even me."

"A day off..." McClellan head tread water around that novel thought. Perhaps no one would call him anyway. He shrugged and bit into his quarter slice of cinnamon toast. Now two whole bites had been taken out. He was zapped already. A day off sounded right.

"In honor of *family* values, I consent," McClellan said.

"That's my family values husband!"

21

"I'm all for cutting life?"

"No, you're all for *living* life!"

"I'll let you know if I survive."

"I have every confidence in you. You will."

"I'll do what normal people do. Take a day off."

"Don't flatter yourself, honey. You were gonzo years ago. It'll take you a lifetime to make up that deficit."

"I really needed that, Margaret, thank you."

"Now get the hell out of my house! Some of us have real work to do—like saving babies with AIDS in the sub-Sahara."

The perfect moral value for Democrats, McClellan thought to himself.

McClellan was hopeless. He really was.

In the autumn cool and the morning quiet McClellan sat in his shiny red Mustang in the closed garage with the top down. It smelled of dirty lawn mowers, gasoline cans and old bottles of insecticide. He breathed in, out. The cold damp smelled good. Garages reminded him of his childhood. He turned the key. The engine fired. The noise consumed the room. It was a sound more beautiful than any basement tapes of the Grateful Dead. On the white bucket seat, redone in Tex leather, lay the garage door opener. He aimed it at the sweet spot above the back of the door, pressed the magic power button, and the door shuddered, shook, and swayed. Then it began creaking upwards, at a snail's pace, curling back in on itself, and lying flat under the garage roof on a set of rusty rails. One eye on the imaginary red racing light ahead, waiting for green, McClellan gunned the engine several times. Paint cans buzzed on upper wooden shelves along the wall, a cracked windowpane rattled. Cobwebs were disturbed. But there was no discernible trace of smoke. Andy was an automotive saint.

McClellan fastened his seatbelt. He was ready to make a run for it.

The spent trumpets vines espaliered against the two sides of the carport frame became visible against the dove gray daylight showing splendidly beyond. The garage door climbed higher. There was something wonderfully surreal about this. The Mustang trembling in the dingy garage, the beautiful fall light spilling down on the other side of the door, the knot of reporters assembled at the very end of the long sloping asphalt drive (put in last month in a fit of unwarranted optimism at the considerable expense of $13,500), ready to strike. Then again, everything seemed kind of surreal to McClellan this morning, except his romp in the hay and, of course, anything remotely relatable to the consciousness of politics. Politics was always ultra, ultra real. But, according to Margaret, all politics was surreal: Actuality today; chimera tomorrow; delusion soon to follow. Abandonment thereafter. Nevertheless, McClellan gladly worshipped at its altar, drank its communion wine down like mineral water: I am the Lord thy God of Politics and thou shalt worship no other gods but me, for I am a jealous God. He was gonzo all right, he and Hunter Thompson. Margaret was right.

How intricately intertwined and twisted his perceptions had become over time. He almost yearned to unravel them. Well, pretty nearly almost. But he sure wouldn't bet the house on it happening by twelve o'clock tonight, even if he resisted cheating and peeking at his emails or stopping by the DNC today. That's because, he knew, he was suffering from a very real—but hardly surreal—Washington addiction: The love of politics over life. Politics *was* life. Well, better than life, actually. It was a form of Divine Life, un-patentable, but highly marketable, if not ruthlessly contagious. To live on the highest plain imaginable, one had to inhale the sweet ether of politics, conscious and

23

unconscious—all the time—except perhaps when, well, copulating. He drew the line there. (He wanted to use another word for it, but his political instincts made him chose a word that could be quotable in a family newspaper, like the *Washington Post*.) Why didn't others get that? Most of all, why not Margaret? He was ready to pushback now that he was strapped into his shiny red Mustang, engine singing, clear daylight ahead.

The garage door chugged up—ever up—it was nearly halfway up. A technical accomplishment of some magnitude given its failing condition. The mist had melted away and the oak and elm tree leaves dancing in the breeze beyond displayed overlapping palettes of dusty umbers, faded crimsons, fawn roses, and dark wines, with bleached rubies thrown in there, now and again. The sparkling Gingko leaves, waving like Chinese hand fans, shown golden yellow, lit from behind by pure sunshine. Sunshine inside sunshine, the perfect harbinger for things to come: The official color of McClellan's Day Off.

As McClellan pushed in the clutch, slipped his gearshift into first, the media—can't live with 'em, can't live without 'em—spotted him. Instantly, the mathematician in him took over. Distance between him and end of drive twenty-five to thirty yards. He'd be doing thirty-five by the time he scraped the top of the drainage ditch on Macomb Street with his tailpipe (he hated that), hung a left, and headed for Reno. As a friendly reminder, McClellan recited His First Commandment out loud: Thou shalt NOT sideswipe journalists. For sure, it was a coward's exit, but he made no apologies for it. It was all part of his new get-real policy. Or was real really surreal? He was getting confused. Whichever way it was, he was ready. Ready for surreal, ready for real, ready to blow past those journalists.

He released the clutch and his little red baby lurched, like a Mustang pony on the range. He owned the drive. Soared under the flaming sky of leaves. Swung onto Macomb Street past the mob of astonished reporters, scraping his tailpipe again (damn) on the drainage ditch, and disturbing his neighbor's pile of freshly raked leaves, swirling them every which way, out into the street. "No comment, fellas," he yelled out, dashing by, his merry face buffeted by the crisp, cheerful wind, "I'm on chairman's holiday!" Through his rear view mirror, he watched the print and radio reporters pitching a fit, kicking stray leaves. But the TV news loved it; they got it all on tape. Far better than recording a boring stand-up interview. Instead, they snagged McClellan making a run for it! The *Washington Times* reporter threw down his 7/11 coffee cup. He was ticked, I mean really ticked. The *Washington Post* reporter got on his cell phone and called his editor. The WTOP radio guy held his recorder up to catch the fleeting sound of the engine tearing down Macomb Street. McClellan knew remorse for about three-quarters of a second, but then learned to live with it. It was either him or them. This time for a change, he chose, well, No. 1. He howled triumphantly to the Lords of Liberty above. It felt mighty good.

It wasn't a block before traffic snarled on Reno and McClellan was stuck in morning sludge. He banged his fist on the horn in exasperation—and a damn good toot it was, too. But the congestion was wholly unmoved. D.C. traffic didn't yield to soon-to-be ex-DNC chairmen, especially soon-to-be ex-DNC chairmen. Imagine that. McClellan rallied, though, taking it like a man. He detoured off Reno to avoid the annoyance of gridlock. He turned onto Newark, one of the great streets. He loved the old Colonial houses on it and the rolling green slopes of the old Rosedale estate that his neighbors had turned into a miniature dog walk. But most of all he adored the colors of its drooping fall trees. Big full trees painting the sky like paintbrushes. Spurring his Mustang toward Wisconsin Avenue, his cell phone rang. He instantly recognized the challenge: This would be his first and most difficult test. It would be his office—he could just tell. He could always sense that very special DNC electricity buzzing through the cell phone towers from atop the Washington Cathedral and into his phone. He dipped his hand into his blue blazer pocket, drew it out, and caught the Caller I.D. Was he telepathic or what? It was the DNC, all right. They were on his tail because he was late—late for everything. Late for his life. Was there anything to be on time for anymore? It was over. Whatever It was. Plenty good and over. Well, at least for four more years—at least. Now came the moment that would test his uncertain resolve. To resist or cave? That was the question. To lead was to choose. He chose. He pushed in the little red button on the side of the phone. His sweet Sony made a high-pitched squeal, and then a pulsing bleep, bleep, bleep, making it the second cutest squeal, and then yelp, yelp, yelp he'd heard this morning. The memory of the first washed over him again like rosewater and honey. It made his surge up Newark seem, well, nothing if not lightly erotic. Now that he'd made the right choice, he was free to feel and think anything he wanted. Life didn't get much better than this. It was almost as much fun as the Democratic National Convention.

McClellan turned left on Wisconsin, only to get caught up in D.C. traffic again, as he headed south toward Georgetown. Being liberated from everything but his conscience, which would never allow him to wrest free now that he'd succeeded in losing on an epic scale achieved by so very few men in American political history, he decided to welcome in the morning at the Georgetown graveyard. It was the perfect place to eat roast beef sandwiches and drink beer with his family on the Fourth of July before the U.S. government rained down several hundred thousand dollars worth of fireworks over the American public gathered on the Mall. McClellan had been drinking beer there and doing other lively things on the grassy slope with girlfriends long since

26

unremembered ever since his preppy days in college. Now it occurred to McClellan that it might be just the spot to be buried in (he'd dropped the idea of getting entombed in the Mustang), because for him it would serve as an ideal metaphor for a political life, triumphant or otherwise. He emphasized the otherwise. In Washington, everyone in power always had one foot in the grave, no matter how powerful they'd become. Power, like people, it turned out was completely mortal, and the graveyard for people with lost power was never very far away.

McClellan passed the Washington Cathedral on his left, the details of its glorious west façade lost to the early shadows. The rose window relayed no rosy light, no inner brilliance, no life-sustaining spirituality. Inside, outside, the light slept or perhaps mourned. It mourned four more years of George Bush.

He passed the Russian Embassy on his right, a peculiar yellow brick blob of architecturally insignificance. Gross, aptly described it. No offense. Its great bland walls caught the morning light, shining like an Iron Curtain made of yellow brick, and dividing Tunlaw Road from Wisconsin Avenue, much as the Iron Curtain once parted East from West Berlin. During the Cold War days, the mild yellow brick embassy fortress walls looked about as hostile as dungeon walls. Today, they looked about as benign as a tennis backboard.

McClellan edged deeper into northern Georgetown, or Glover Park, cutting across Calvert Street, Guy Mason Park on his left. He'd seen his fair share of summer softball games there under the lights—and consumed more beer than could fill a reservoir. Softball put the world to rest. Those were nice memories because his team usually won, unlike in politics. That's the way he remembered it. Coming up, he'd have many more nights to devote to softball and beer under the lights. That would happen.

Intent on hanging right into the Holy Rood cemetery, otherwise known as the Georgetown cemetery, he slowed just past the dumpy Monarch Paint store, where he'd bought paint for his house on sale three summers ago. He'd chosen "Colonial White," which would have been all just fine and everything, except for the fact that he got it into his head to save a couple of thousand dollars by painting the façade himself. In a moment of tradesmen exuberance, he climbed a twenty-foot ladder, leaned too far to the right to slap paint under the peeling eaves, and fell on a yew hedge, chipping his anklebone, and requiring a cast and crutches for five weeks. It was a pretty humiliating experience, much like today. Perhaps it was a trial run for yesterday and today and the day after. The Lord worked in mysterious ways...

The gate was open. McClellan turned in. He loved the smell of the cemetery in the morning. But today it smelled different. Today it smelled like defeat.

On a rise of the hill overlooking the Washington Monument, where the national fireworks exploded like popcorn in popcorn poppers, stood an obelisk grave marker, skirted by a square of small cut stones, set next to a drooping cherry tree. He read the inscription on the marker, which was the final resting place for John and Anne Noone. His birth date: December 23, 1883. His death date: January 3, 1932. It made him feel at ease to know they were there. If they could take death, so could he. Not that he was in any kind of hurry to share their experience. His eyes followed the grassy path to another set of gravestones sandwiched together on the other side of the cherry. If he remembered correctly, this was the spot on which Sally Worthington seduced him. Or was it the other way? Either way, sex superseded respect for the dead. As a Georgetown University student, conquests were as easy as flipping pancakes for McClellan. Now, it seemed, they eluded him altogether. What had happened to the old McClellan magic? Oh, grow up, he yelled

28

at himself inside his head. You didn't come here to beat yourself up. He'd wait for other, more qualified experts to do it. All good things come to those who wait.

McClellan was there to wrap himself in a new positive, a fresh exotic viewpoint, more colorful than a Cleveland Park fall. But he wasn't having much luck yet. He'd climbed the graveyard slope to re-calibrate as he often did. And more often than not it worked. But today there was no instant anything. No instant save. No instant refreshment. He engaged himself in a bit of sophistry, based on the improbable theory that no one ever really lost, that one only had to persevere until the next election cycle to continue on the journey to victory, that defeat was no more than the temporary absence of victory, the inconvenience of delayed victory, if you will, soon to be realized. It was very convenient: An all-purpose theory, just this side of a unifying political theory, which could be applied, when necessary, to all the struggles of history. It went something like this: There were no losers, only those who persevered to take up arms again against a drifting sea of ideology and changed circumstance. Translated in politics as a different candidate in the next election cycle. It was a grand unifying theory of how misery and humiliation finds hope, and visa versa. For all its defects, it worked, worked for McClellan, that is, particularly today. Or so it seemed as he stood on his perch nestled amongst the splendid gravestones above a city that could have been, should have been, his.

The thought of misery finding hope was really very comforting.

McClellan got back into his red Mustang, dug in his black loafer spurs, and was off, galloping on all 4-cylinders down to G-town. Hope, if not Washington, was his.

He shot past the social Safeway, where he avoided shopping ever since Whole Foods opened up in upper Georgetown. He and his charge mounted the last, small rise to R Street, and drew up to the red traffic

29

light, diagonal to the Georgetown Library. The light winked green, finally, and he crept over the crest of Wisconsin; the nose of his Mustang dipped, facing the long slope, which ran down to the waterfront and the Potomac River. The water sparkled, bending toward the tree-lined shores of Virginia, a leafy kaleidoscope skirted by a blue diamond carpet that moved majestically. Wisconsin Avenue flowed like a river, too, bisected by sheltered Federalist streets, populated with two-story clapboard houses, most of them freshly painted—something McClellan always noticed since he took it on himself to slather expensive paint on his own—and three and four story brick homes with white picket fences, metal steps painted with rust-prevention paint, and usually modern sculptures or classic nudes figurines in the windows, showing off built-in bookshelves in posh living rooms lit by recessed lights set on low. Insanely pricey. But what price G-town? Prestige under Georgetown trees beside cobblestone parking spaces ran at entry level at about $2 million. He and Margaret could just swing it, if they wanted to make up for their humiliation somehow. Beyond the Georgetown lanes and the shining river was the Memorial Bridge, visible, if you knew where to look, between the canopies of psychedelic trees that shone above R, Q, O, and P Streets. The electric colors reminded him of a time in Georgetown when the streets smelled of sandalwood incense and the music of Jimi Hendrix, mainly "Purple Haze" and "Are You Experienced?", was piped out second-story head shop windows. Inside Beatle, Bhagavad-Gita and "White Rabbit" posters together with black lights, bongs, and cigarette rolling papers sales fueled the hippie and anti-war movement, of which he was proud to have once been a part in his howling youth. Somewhere in his head McClellan thought he'd kept a microscopic piece of the peace movement alive, but as of right about now, with a guarantee of another four years of George W. in the White

House, that last fragile sentiment of flower power optimism was deader than Janis Joplin.

McClellan rode past the Addison/Ripley Fine Arts Gallery, which this month was featuring an exhibition of gigantic hanging ice crystals made of razor-thin Plexiglas, fitted together somewhat ingenuously and seamlessly in patterns approximating genuine ice crystals as viewed through an electron microscopes. McClellan rolled his eyes. Taste was a subject thing, he knew. But really. He steered on, passing trendy boutiques with fleshy plastic bodies of female mannequins draped in low cut high fashions and looking so very cool. There were also more than a few high-end hair salons, advertising haircuts and blow-dries for $125 a pop, and evidently getting away with it. Perhaps, McClellan thought, he should try his hand…

He turned right on P Street, zeroing in on his final destination and passing a jean store occupying the space where the venerable Georgetown Pharmacy once stood. There McClellan used to buy Bugler rolling papers to make his one-handed joints when he was blowing weed at college, like most other red-blooded Americans of his generation. A joint would be nice right about now, he thought. The clerks behind the counter never even looked at him funny. And it wasn't because they didn't know exactly what he would be doing with them. Those were the days.

P Street was *his* street, mainly because he loved the trolley car tracks, still embedded in some 18th century cobblestone streets. The trolley tracks were a thing with McClellan. Each time he took the corner, he'd steer his Mustang onto the tracks, to get a smooth, flowing ride. It wasn't the kind of fun he'd ever boast about. It was like forbidden pleasure—he just did it.

Hobnobbing with world leaders and Nobel Laureates was sometimes cool, but trolley track surfing was always hot.

31

His Mustang glided across glassy waters, like a swan. So now it was definite: McClellan was officially having fun. Right here, right now. It took the sting out of everything. Election? What election? Defeat? What defeat? He was gliding on trolley car tracks and the way ahead felt smooth as glass.

The sun streamed down; the day was looking fine. Under the fluttering shadows of colorful, blazing leaves, he veered off the tracks at the end of the block, searching for a parking spot. But he could forget about that. The only available spaces were just a little too short for his Mustang. He wouldn't even try. He was terrified that his newly chromed bumper would get dented by a careless parker or that his front headlight would be smashed by a menacing SUV backing up too fast. Parking spaces in Georgetown were as rare as Democrats winning elections lately. McClellan did an illegal U-turn at 33rd St., a controlled intersection, and slid back onto the glassy tracks—his second illegality in the span of less than ten seconds—and swung right into the Filmore High School parking lot. His illegal street adventures reminded McClellan of his college days when he borrowed a horse innocently grazing in the pastures of an estate off Reservoir Road, not far from P St., and rode it down M St. on Halloween night, dressed as the Long Ranger. The DC police gave chase, but he escaped. The *Washington Post* put his picture on the front page above the fold, with a caption that said, "Who is this Masked Man?" McClellan had the clipping framed and it got hung eventually on his office wall at the DNC. Everyone asked about it when they came in, but like the real Lone Ranger, he never coped to the true identity of the masked man galloping down M St., police in pursuit.

He parked under the NO PUBLIC PARKING sign planted in the schoolyard around back. He wasn't worried about getting a ticket. Certainly one more couldn't hurt. He had a drawer of them at home.

Now he'd have time to pay up. No, McClellan wasn't worried about anything but indulging in a store full of books. This was the new Jerry McClellan, master of his fortunes, well, for today anyway. Two white contractor vans, one electrical, one plumbing, sat unashamedly beside his luminescent Mustang. He parked a generous five feet to the far side. If there hadn't been a tree right there, he would have parked even further away, wanting to make triply sure his driver's side hand-rubbed lacquer door didn't get dinged by an electrician in a hurry to get home for the day. Ahead sat a matching pair of decidedly inglorious Goode dumpsters, one was overflowing with broken sections of green board, gigantic piles of crumbling plaster and lathe, and clutches of genuine two-by-fours poking up here and there (they didn't make them like that anymore). There was something virtually exhilarating about inspecting the aftermath of renovation, the contents of perfectly contained destruction. All that demolition so neatly compartmentalized was a wonder to McClellan this morning. If only he could contain the wreckage of his own life in the dumpster of his past. The other was empty, like his future. Filmore High School was the perfect metaphor for what his own life demanded, which was a major overhaul, though he doubted any amount of rewiring or plumbing could get the job done. His was crying out for new construction.

Defying D.C.'s ubiquitous parking enforcers, McClellan put the top up, rolled up the windows, and hotfooted it out of there. In the process, he slipped on his wrap-around Ray-Bans. Man, he looked good, though obviously, at his age, Bono he was not. More like Bono's distant second cousin.

He sallied over the trolley tracks towards Bryn Mawr's Used and Rare Bookshop. He hadn't been there in at least a year. A lapse in judgment to be sure, but he was ready to make up for it. Not even Karl Rove could stop him now. Come pestilence or fire and brimstone of a

Republican kind, he was going book browsing for as long as he damn well liked. No unforeseen moral values issue would shut him down; no candidate's shortcoming would collapse his sweet dream. This was his moment to shine, shine like his Mustang.

McClellan peered into the bowed bookstore window through wavering pane of Colonial-era glass. He looked like a preppie college kid disguised in Ray-Bans, navy blue blazer and classic gray slacks, gawking at a toyshop window at Christmastime, even at the age of 59. His whole body exuded puppy's joy. If McClellan had had a tail, it would have been wagging. As he studied the high-rise displays of eclectic and eccentric books that only a bibliophile could love, and shielded from the judgment of the world by his own false sense of anonymity and inconspicuousness, McClellan felt a poor man's serenity—admittedly a pretty weird sensation for McClellan, but a welcome one nevertheless. A hike on the C & O Canal gave him that same dreamy feeling. It made him soar like the blue heron that lived on the far side of the canal a couple of miles past Carderock. And maybe he should have gone to visit his old friend the heron this morning. But he knew that he would always be there, unlike Bryn Mawr, which like other independent bookstores was an endangered species. They could and mostly would be disappeared coming one night, as happened to his cherished Cleveland Park bookstore at Newark and Wisconsin. Much like its other independent brothers, it too went poof in the long night. McClellan was more than marginally unhappy with Barnes & Noble and Borders over that. He loved life when a certain rough fairness in competitiveness reigned over all, which of course didn't allow him too many days when he felt a gushing tenderness toward it. The books danced a Busby Berkley dance in the rectangular window frames. A big book on Tchaikovsky, an antique edition of *Ticket to the Opera*, a singular curiosity titled, *Beethoven's Hair*, an illustrated copy of *Ancient-English Christmas*

Carols, and a rock 'n roll classic called, *Fargo Rock City—a Heavy Metal Odyssey in Rural North Dakota,* formed an impressive musical Tower of Babel in the left front window. The fact was McClellan was open to taking a stab at anything—even a treatise on Heavy Metal rock, because on his Day Off anarchy of action was In. From his perspective, it was the only thing worth anything anymore. Margaret had succeeded n making a real convert.

McClellan was off to a damn fine start. It was his day for revolution or peace—he didn't know which—nor did he care. Whichever it was to be, he'd find it for sure on the vellum pages of a damn good book in the sunlit shadows of a damn fine bookstore on a day that didn't officially exist.

Up the wrought-iron steps to the front door he went, buoyed by the positive emotion that he'd succeed, win one for the McClellan, his immediate candidate of choice. His shoe heel struck the last iron step, clanging like a cowbell. He'd announced himself, all right. Hanging above the plate glass door like skywriting was the store banner. He looked up. It read: THE LANTERN: USED & RARE BOOKS. Against the brick façade, shaded the color caramel, stood two tarnished brass lanterns on either side. Inside, attached to the back of the door, eye-high, was a miniature picture frame, and home for a faded scrap of writing paper. McClellan reasoned that this ought to be good. Small packages meant interesting things. McClellan would be right. He took off his shades and snapped on a pair of reading glasses he'd bought in an antique shop in upper state New Hampshire one freezing January night during presidential primary season when competing Dems for the presidential nomination were lobbing shock and awe artillery shells at each other like there was no General Election ahead. The fact was they worked great. Old but great. The exquisite quotation typed on fading paper with an Underwood typewriter circa 1960 read: "People say that Life is the Thing, but I prefer Reading." — Logan Pearsall Smith

Well, Logan Pearsall Smith knew a thing or two about life, McClellan concluded.

Replacing his antique specs with Ray-Ban invisibility shields, McClellan reached for the old brass knob; the door fell open. McClellan entered, invisible. But as his foot fell on a gray shag carpet, a voice whispered somewhere over him, "Buried how long?" McClellan startled. What the hell? The voice spoke softly again. This time it came from within, "Buried how long?" McClellan stopped and answered. "Twenty-three years. Been buried twenty-three years, that's how long." Twenty-three years was how long McClellan had been swirling in the belly of the Democratic Party; it was obviously getting to him.

"What was that?" another voice called.

McClellan spun around, confused. What the hell *was* that? McClellan asked. He was more than losing it. He was already lost.

Then came a voice he actually recognized. "Why, Mr. McClellan, good morning! *How are you?*" He knew that voice.

"Imagine my surprise on seeing you today!"

All McClellan could do was smile feebly. Here was the news flash. He was no longer invisible.

"You've been down in the soul of the beast, haven't you? Poor dear! Those Republicans—they're just *too* smart for us! Or too clever by half," she noted dryly. "But not to worry. We'll take them in 2008! 2008 will be the Year of the Dems. So it is written; so it will be done!"

Her blast of optimism and enthusiasm was a salve for McClellan's festering wounds. Seated like a literary sphinx on the far side of her massive oak desk, one of three made for President John F. Kennedy that didn't make the final cut, she looked more like the Grand Dame of the Democratic Party than what she was: An occupier of vellum fields. Her huge ruddy face and aquamarine colored eyes bobbed above the congested desktop. It was as overgrown as the Brazilian rainforests with hardbacks and paperbacks: novels, non-fiction, and How-To-Books in various states of coming and going. There were returns, regular orders, special orders, and piles of minded and un-minded mail. The unwrapped books were destined for the great upstairs; the books in a box beside her desk were condemned to the dark downstairs where they might never resurface; others on the top left-hand side were ready for shipping—UPS and Fedex. McClellan took it all in, the pure literary chaos.

McClellan answered in a small, halting voice, "*Good morning, Mrs. Worthington...*" She held him in her sway. He would have settled to become the Incredible Shrinking Man right then and there. He couldn't quite believe it. His mask of invisibility was gone—as though it had never been there. Today he was more than a little anxious to avoid even the Grand Dame's tender mercies. His body lurched towards the stairs.

Mrs. Worthington was a fulsome woman. Her voice was as deep as February snows in South Dakota. Over the years that they'd known each other, she'd come to read his bookstore moods. She also knew his bookstore body language, when he was poised to buy, when he was about ready to throw in the towel. She certainly knew his book-buying habits. She even knew about his secret parking spot behind Filmore High School. Most of all she knew exactly where he liked to roost: Upstairs, second floor, in the big, comfy chair beneath the sunny window. "The upstairs is yours, Mr. McClellan," she said. "No one will disturb for as long as you like. It'll be especially off limits to Republicans. I don't care if they sue me. We take care of our own at Bryn Mawr."

McClellan was so happy to have a safe place to hide. He could have cried. "Thank you, Mrs. Worthington... That's exactly what I do need today."

The Grand Dame shifted in her seat, as if about to rise to embrace, but McClellan wouldn't have it. He backed away, gesturing awkwardly, signally her not to bother, although at any other time he would have appreciated a hug. Who wouldn't want a hug from the Grand Dame? Her avalanche of gray hair cascaded over her tweedy, shapely shoulders. Her jovial smile and well-read eyes held the room, consumed it, really. And she loomed large, as large as Orson Welles, but when she did walk she walked as lightly as his blue heron on the C & O Canal. John Donne wrote that no man was an island, but it was an open question as to whether she was or was not. For McClellan, she was Aeschylus, Raymond Chandler, Milton, Salman Rushdie, and early Woody Allen all piled into one big, beautiful, knowledgeable woman. If she *was* an island, and right now he believed she was, he'd be delighted to be marooned on her for a time—any time. And just to show how much he appreciated her kindness, he wiped his feet doubly hard on the rattan mat at the base of the stairs before climbing up. However, he left his Ray-Bans on, just in case his invisibility shield happened to pop on again.

With gratitude in every step, McClellan climbed toward his second-story roost. Only good hours lay ahead, he knew. That made him smile. Oh yes, this was going to be good. He paused halfway up the staircase to read another framed quote hanging on the wall: "I've never known any trouble that an hour's reading didn't assuage."— Charles De Secondat. Nice one, McClellan thought.

With that felicitous quote in his mind, McClellan floated further upstream toward a new land where politics would be outright banned. At the landing, he paused to take in the slow, patient light drifting unseen into the center of the room. He'd crossed the great divine. He'd finally arrived: The Lantern was his and his alone. It was this side of paradise.

The rarified air made McClellan lightheaded. Maybe it was the higher altitude or some aerosol form of exotic book dust potion Mrs. Worthington had sprayed beforehand. Or possibly it was the expectation that he would be left alone for an indeterminate period of time. But whatever it was it had the effect of transporting him, putting the world far, far away, a round about way of saying that he felt stoned. Though he honestly couldn't remember what it felt like to be stoned anymore. It had been that long and college was a thousand years ago. Who needed weed with book dust air like this, anyway? He walked into the longish narrow room, its invisible walls gilded with book-lined shelves. They seemed to usher him in, take him on a direct course toward a green velvet chair in the corner under a sun-lit window. McClellan was charmed. So much so that he thought he could smell the sunshine. The room felt ripe, ready for some heavy-duty browsing. He had arrived at the right cocoon, all right. Downstairs he heard a chain jangling. Mrs. Worthington had posted the Do Not Enter sign across the bottom of the staircase. McClellan was officially ALL BY HIMSELF...

He launched into a major survey of the ordinary room's extraordinary contents: There were floor-to-ceiling shelves tagged with magic-marker headings displayed on 8 x 10 pieces of typing paper: Mathematics, Geology, Chemistry, Medicine, Gardening, Political Science and Fiction—the regular didactic selection. Naturally, the old habits of his mind tried taking over. At first, he lusted after the Political Science section. His body was drawn to it like a compass needle toward north. But, like a good man true to his word, he resisted. He'd sworn an oath against all forms of politics today. For today, at least, politics did time at the end of the line. Besides, he'd already read the major poly sci books and a fat lot of good they'd done him, too! The next book he'd bother reading on the subject would be his own—which he hadn't written yet, but one day might. Well, it was conceivable he might. And if he ever did, it would be titled, *The Politics of Losing and Loss*. Or something like that. A lot of politicians could relate to it. There'd be a big market, certainly among Democrats.

He got past the impulse to flirt with poly sci only to succumb to a more dangerous temptation. He was attacked by a sudden, near physical, urge to check his phone messages. He just *had* to look. But only a peek. And only one time. Not actually open any messages, mind you. That would be okay, wouldn't it? Already drawn to the window and the green velvet chair in the corner, he swept aside all oaths to Margaret and went for it, making a soft landing in the big lumpy chair without any regret.

His right hand foraged around in his jacket pocket. Then McClellan felt it. Oh yes. It was his again—his connection to the planet, to life itself.

He pushed the On button. The phone's cheerful little face lit up. That sweet little beeping yelping sound came on again. This was heaven all right. And in an instant the green screen flashed: 36 New Msgs. He was poised to be exhilarated, but then dread set in. The world was after him. What was he thinking? Of course it was after him. Curiosity turned to total dread. McClellan hit the No button. He popped it back in his pocket, silent and lightless. He couldn't and wouldn't face what he couldn't and wouldn't face. The Temptation of Jerry McClellan was over, although it very nearly got him in the beginning.

Despite being a reluctant gardener, he took on the Gardening Section first. He had a love hate relationship with gardening, mostly hate, though there was certainly a lot of love there, too. When his plants grew and grew well, well, he couldn't get enough of it. When they didn't, well, he bawled and cursed it and blamed everything on the poor dead plant. Nevertheless, he always delighted in remembering the Latin botanical names of plants and shrubs and various trees. He never failed to impress, especially himself, when reeling them off, which came easily to him. They stuck like glue to paper. That particular talent came in handy at state dinners at the White House. When he used to be invited. What he wouldn't give for those days to return again. Until they did, he'd pack in more botanical names, holding them in reserve to be beyond impressive at his next state dinner: "Hamamelis *mollis. Cornus florida. Malus floribunda. Pieris japonica. Sophora japonica. Prunus subhirtella* 'Autumnalis'. *Acer saccharum. Rhododendron maximum roseum. Prunus yedoensis. Rhododendron carolinianum. Rhododendron canescens.* Yes, he would master them all—and now he'd have all the time in the world to do so...

McClellan cocked his head, scanning the long spines of the big books sideways, searching out books with bundles of vital green secrets in them. *Crockett's Victory Garden* caught his eye first, but he'd already read it and besides, no book with the word "victory" in its title was going to make his must-read list today. Then came *The Reluctant Weekend Gardener*—which had him pegged pretty good—reason enough for him not to read it. Followed by a slim and tender-looking volume called *Ferns to Know & Grow.* McClellan had never been a fern man, so he passed on that one, too. Not that he had anything against them, mind you. *Gourmet Gardening* sounded novel and rewarding, but he rejected that too as potentially problematic. He was strictly a fair-weather gardener, the plant, water and feed once-a-year kind, so plants that required undo care and attention by virtue of their exotic nature were definitely out. He tried hard to limit his palette to basically petunias and pansies. And oh yes, he had a thing for azaleas, too. It was tough to kill them, really tough, but not impossible. That much McClellan knew firsthand. The most adventurous he got was putting in climbing trumpet vines.

McClellan moved on down the racks. He'd read up on gardening later.

41

He breezed past the Poly Sci section, barely giving it a glance. Still, there were those titles that snagged him: *Power on the Left, Power & Principle, The Abuse of Power,* followed by most incredibly *Misreading the Public.* The Republicans must have planted that title there earlier this morning to mock him. Or so McClellan thought. He railed inside. If it was them, they sure nailed him but good. McClellan sucked it up and soldiered on. He'd have to learn to wear slights and humiliation better in the days ahead. They weren't going to be pretty and he might as well get used to them.

Under the Medicine Section he found a rich assortment of life-affirming titles. Those he could definitely use. Unfortunately, they also reminded him that immortality was not an option. Sobered by the certain knowledge that rising free radicals and gagging arteries were a nasty part of his medical history, he resolved—two decades too late, at least—to slow way, way, way down. Like he had any of choice but to slow way, way, way down now. He snapped up *Aging Well* by James F. Fries, MD; *The Bio-Diet* by Luis A. Guerra, MD; and *How to Live to be 100—Or More* by George Burns. Humor, especially in medicine, had to be a very, very, very good thing.

Next he landed a pint-size book with big ideas called *Balance, a Guide to Life's Forgotten Pleasures.* He ran his forefinger down the index. Life was better already. And on his forgotten pleasures To-do list for tomorrow were the following:

1. Look at shooting stars
2. Blow bubbles
3. Search for 4-leaf clovers
4. Walk barefoot
5. Skinny-dip
6. Pretend you can fly.

This was the right book for the right time for the right person. He took it under his wing. He knew Margaret would love it, too. Plus, it was proof that he was thinking Zen, not just politics. She loved Zen, in and out of bed. Particularly in.

He crossed into the Mathematics Section. Crying out for his attention was a first edition of *Cult of the Atom*, propping up a beat-up copy of *Nuclear Imperatives*. Neither excited. Any talk about nukes gave him hives. He was just that kind of anti-nuke guy. One row up and two books in towered a so-so condition edition of *Physics & Beyond*, as well as a clean paperback version of *In Search of the Miraculous* by P.D Ouspensky. Now *there* was a mathematical title he needed to relate to. Late last night at DNC headquarters—just after heavily Republican precincts reported in from southern Ohio, McClellan could have sold several thousand copies. He plucked it out of the rack. In and out of power, his Dems were always in search of the miraculous. And who knew? It might bring him luck. He'd have it close at hand when Ohio got to counting its provisional ballots.

By the time McClellan ended up in fiction racks, he still hadn't found the right book for reading in the green velvet chair under the sunny window. Such tomes as *New Approaches to Numeracy* and *The Journal of Glaciology (1952-1956)* weren't his idea of a good time. He wanted something to dive down a rabbit hole with for the afternoon. Nevertheless, he'd buy them for those long, dark twilight years ahead, which were coming to his life soon.

Bernard Malamud's *A New Life* stood out first among firsts. A slice of Malamud seemed about right. He read this line: *"If this was spring, Levin knew it because he eternally hunted for it, was always nosing out the new season, the new life, 'a new birth in freedom.'"* If Levin could do it, he could too. McClellan respected Malamud and liked Levin, but then again he hadn't come to psychoanalyze himself through fiction today. He was

43

here to get out of himself, to get out of himself as far as possible. His job was to forget about himself.

Next he happened on F. Scott Fitzgerald's *The Last Tycoon*. He slipped it out of the slot, and came to Chapter 1. He read the opening lines out loud, a ritual he and his old college girlfriend began one Friday afternoon after making love. *"Though I haven't ever been on the screen I was brought up in pictures. Rudolph Valentino came to my fifth birthday party—or so I was told. I put this down only to indicate that even before the age of reason I was in a position to watch the wheels go round."*

Now there was a man who knew how to write character.

Next to *The Last Tycoon* was *The Great Gatsby*. He put back the one and drew out the other. He flipped to the last page. "So we beat on, boats against the current, borne back ceaselessly into the past."

And like Gatsby, McClellan believed in the green light at the end of the dock on the opposite shore, too—well, to be more precise the blue light at the end of the dock on the opposite shore—and the orgiastic future of the Democratic Party that was receding before him. To his distress, it was receding all the more as of today; but no matter— tomorrow he would run faster, stretch out his arms further... And one fine morning—

As always, McClellan felt better after a fix of F. Scott Fitzgerald.

With a regret lovers knew best, he quietly closed F. Scott and put him back on the shelf, before briefly flirting with a novel by Iris Murdock, *The Message to the Planet*, *A Bend in the Road* by Nicholas Sparks, and Anne Tyler's *Saint Maybe*. He was a fan of Anne Tyler's, especially her earlier reads like *Dinner at the Homesick Restaurant* and *Earthly Possessions*. So he was tempted to take her up for the day. Her quirky humor was downright delicious. And humor in fiction, McClellan knew, was every bit as important as humor in medicine. But then he got cold feet. She wasn't exactly right for today. Close, but... He was looking for something, well, cutting edge, a down-the-rabbit-hole escape read.

He glanced up at the top shelf of the fiction section and took in a four-foot swath of Tom Clancy novels—the king of thriller escape fiction. They looked pretty smug up there, lording it over everything. As every literate Democrat knew, Tom Clancy novels were read by far more Republicans than Democrats. McClellan's ilk of Dems snuggled up in bed with Joyce Carol Oates, for instance—certainly not Tom Clancy and his *Hunt for the Red October* suspense techno-thrillers. Real Dems read real writers like Oates and Mailer, and spent their spare time in the arms of poets like Robert Frost. For McClellan, let's face it, his choice of writers was a political thing, as much as anything else. Come to think of it, for McClellan everything was political, even his choice of dress sock colors.

His gaze floated higher. Placed sacrilegiously on top of the Clancy novels lay a slim reed of a book. It was just lazing about, doing nothing in particular, having one over on Mr. Clancy and his big gun super books. He could barely make out its title: *Life in a Putty Knife Factory* by H.—something or other—Smith. McClellan was drawn to it, for reasons as yet unclear to him. From his point of view, any novel set in a factory had to be more or less politically correct, if not outright pro-union. McClellan sensed good things from slim things.

So he reached and reached, first on the flats of his heels, and then on his tippy, tippy toes, but for all his six-foot plus height, he couldn't quite reach. But he hadn't played college ball for nothing. In a burst of exuberant youth revisited, for better or worse, he unleashed the full reach of his basketball player youth. He was going for it. But his control wasn't quite what it used to be and he only succeeded in pushing the book back further and completely out of sight. Worse, he came crashing back down, shaking the floor and unsettling the dust. His first thought was of Mrs. Worthington, of course. She'd be downstairs scowling up at the fresh cracks in her plaster ceiling, no doubt. *What the hell was he doing up there, anyway?* she'd be thinking. McClellan felt distinctly like an idiot.

Unfortunately, his copy of *In Search of the Miraculous* had fallen with him, bouncing end-to-end across the floor, and disappearing between a pair of misaligned bookshelves. That pretty much put him in a panic. He'd already come to think of it as his lucky charm—the spiritual embodiment of the last pathway to miracles and the miraculous the Dems possessed. It was nonsense, of course, but right now nonsense was all he and the Dems had going for them.

McClellan got down on his knees. He was going to fish it out if it was the last thing he ever did today. And on surveying the situation, he noticed another paperback wedged even further back, caught between the shelf and the wall. It was covered in cobwebs and dust and who knew what. Obviously, it had been there for some time. Prying *In Search of the Miraculous* loose was no big deal. It was out with a snap. He brushed it off and set it aside. Gotcha. But then, because he was more than a little curious, he went for the other book, too. He had succumbed to a sense of bookshop patron responsibility. He gingerly slipped one hand between the shelf and the wall and tried to grip the book's lower edge, but it wouldn't budge. Not one bit. It was jammed in there hard and he couldn't get enough grip on it. In McClellan's world nothing succeeded like winning, so there was no way he was giving up now— now that he was on his hands and knees and breathing in dust. So he came up with a secondary approach: A top-down method of extraction. Being a top-down man all his life, McClellan knew it would work for him.

He wedged his hand in between the shelf and the wall, starting about two feet up. There was more than ample space. He began to inch his hand down, turning his hand, arm and body at the same time, while flattening his body against the shelf. The space at the wall grew narrower as the wall bowed out. But finally, finally, his fingertips touched the top ridge of the book. Hallelujah. He was almost there. Just a few millimeters more. Then parting his forefinger and middle finger as best he could, he made a pair of finger tongs, and willed his hand down just that little bit more to cross the final divide. Then, there it was—the mystery book, at the tips of his fingers.

Slowly, he drew his two fingers together. He pinched his prize between them, and brought them up out of the lower depths. Ever so carefully, he inched his hand back up the side of the bowed wall, one, two, three inches until… he lifted it out between the pair of shelves. Success, McClellan knew, was relative, but in his mind, at this hour and on this day, this was big. He stared triumphantly at the cobweb-coated copy of his paperback prize. His eyes narrowed. He anxiously searched for the title. Maybe it was the dust or his racing mind but the first words he saw was not the title, but instead the name of the author. It read: A Novel by Anonymous. McClellan immediately thought of journalist Joe Klein and his 1990 novel *Primary Colors*. It had caused quite a stir as much for being a good read as for the question of who had refused to put their name on it. It had to have been a Washington insider, everyone knew that, but who? Even though Klein was finally outed by the media, it was far more fun not knowing who'd written *Primary Colors*. McClellan's eyes scanned up. And then like an image on a movie screen going from soft to sharp focus, the title appeared before him. It read: *My Name is Jesus Christ and I'm Running for President.*

McClellan's first thought—shameless even for him—was that Jesus Christ *would* make for the perfect moral values candidate in 2008!!!

He scanned the inside copyright page for the author's name, but like *Primary Colors*, it too was copyrighted by Anonymous. The good thing was that McClellan knew that any novel featuring Christ running

47

for president would almost certainly have to feature Him running as a *liberal* Democrat. That Sermon on the Mount bit about the meek inheriting the earth put Him firmly in the Democrats' camp. God love Him.

McClellan stood, dusting off the cobwebs. He picked up *In Search of the Miraculous,* too. He knew he was done. He'd found The Book. Providence, it seemed, had taken him by the hand. There was only one matter left to tend to. As lightly as possible, so as not to give Mrs. Worthington any further reason to glare up at the cracks in her ceiling, he crossed over to the big green velvet chair by the window, and sat down. Through the window, he saw the shining autumn sky—bright beautiful sky blues brimming with passing white clouds. In the sunny breeze, the fiery leaves of *Acer saccharums* pranced and danced. McClellan heard children's laughter up the street. A bicycle wheeled by. It sounded like a vintage Raleigh. Whatever it was, McClellan felt at ease. That's what mattered. Not rested, mind you, but at ease. Something of an accomplishment, considering. Yes, he was at ease in his favorite chair in his favorite second-story walk-up.

And so the time had come.

He removed his shades, and replaced them with his New Hampshire reading glasses. He slipped off his creamy Ferragamo loafers, which felt more like slippers, and positioned himself just so in his chair, after shifting a little this way and that, until he'd optimally positioned himself for reading.

And with the room quiet, his mind sharp, McClellan took charge, as was his want, and went reading. He opened the book before him and the world of politics and books he knew no longer existed. He went down the rabbit hole, and nothing was the same after that.

My Name is Jesus Christ and

I'm Running for President

BY

ANONYMOUS

CHAPTER ONE

After a long and turbulent ride, I find myself dropping, dropping, down, down, down into that most wondrous of all cities, the City of Angels, a.k.a., Los Angeles. I don't mind telling you, in the interest of full disclosure, that I wouldn't be adverse in the least to using the facilities at the nearest men's room. With no rest stops along the way, believe me when I say, it was a long, long, long flight back.

From the first moment I first heard about the City of Angels, I said to myself: It's got to be my very first stop on my Born Again Comeback Tour. No question about it. What better place could there possibly be for me to launch my long-awaited, much-anticipated, often-mocked, but never in doubt, Second Coming, than in the City of Angels? As I touch down on the Avenue of the Stars, standing atop Gene Kelly's bronze star, at 7 a.m. on Christmas Eve in the Year of My Old Man, 2019, I don't mind telling you that I'm more than a little disappointed. The City of Angels is not as advertised. For instance, I don't see a single angel. Not anywhere. If I could, I'd demand my money back.

Otherwise, it's a beautiful city, I'm sure; that is, if I could only see it. But unfortunately, it's buried in smog, which I had been told about, so I came prepared for that. And yes, the heat is pretty bad—global warming and all—but I'd been counting on that, even though the temperature makes those of my old Palestine seem like cold storage in comparison. Arriving as I have straight from the tropics of Heaven, where cool breezes blow 24/7, and are so cooling, so soothing, the heat will definitely take some getting used to. But I look at it this way: If I can live as a Jew under the repressive reign of the Holy Roman Empire, and bear getting strung up on a damn cross in broad daylight in front of my own mother, I can certainly take the L.A. heat and smog and whatever else it wants to give out.

Besides, I came well prepared for it. I did my homework. I even hired a fashion consultant to make sure I struck exactly the right note. Like right now I'm wearing a white linen Panama suit, broad-rimmed hat, and a cool dude pair of Chanel shades, that would make even Bono sit up and take notice. This is L.A., after all, so it's more than a little important to look great. Which I do. We ambassadors of goodwill and moral authority can't take any chances. We must dress for success. Why? Because the stakes are too high for us to fail, and every minor advantage helps. That's the first rule: Look good and speak the truth.

Remember that.

In any event, the L.A. heat is just what I needed to wake me up. I've been on snooze-time for far too long. It's a real-time, slap-in-the-face reminder that my vacation time's officially over, and that it's back to punching a clock for the King of Kings and Lord of Lords, your truly tardy Jesus "Better Late Than Never" Christ.

It's good to be back. If you'll remember your Biblical history, you'll recall that when last I was back parading about on Earth I plied my curious trade mostly in those emerald hills of Palestine. However fondly I remember them now, they were <u>not</u>, underscored <u>not</u>, the good old days. Not by any measure. Not by any definition of the word good. In short, there was nothing particularly good about them. Mostly, it was just a huge amount of work for me (not that I'm complaining), with no pay or health insurance, everyday headaches like you wouldn't believe, and unfathomable responsibilities and an agenda sky high, which if scrutinized objectivity would lead the sane man to only one conclusion: I could live a thousand-and-one lifetimes and I still couldn't get it done. Not even close.

Again, not that I'm complaining. I mean, it really is a true privilege to be the Son of God, and all, but right here and right now I'd to lay to rest the notion that being Christ means I've got it made. It doesn't and I don't. Sure, it's a great big honor having to carry the weight of the world on my shoulders and doing good all the time, but it's no dance of the veils, for sure. Even while on my hiatus, I had to work hard to recover from the trauma of my crucifixion, as you can well imagine. There were those interminable doctor visits and counseling sessions and therapies and various and sundry stress management techniques, such as acupuncture, slow breathing, and positive imaging. You name 'em, I did 'em. I even went into psychotherapy. I did the Works. And none of it was easy. I'm still popping Vitamin B12 and D and rubbing hand cream into my palms to soften up the nasty scars of my stigmata. I only raise this to call attention to the fact that it's tougher than you might think being me. I mean, if you don't believe it, you try getting crucified. You try giving up the ghost. You try rising again from the dead. And perhaps most difficult of all, you try explaining to the Old Man that nothing you did went quite according to The Plan...

But look, that's all water under the River Jordan, and like I said, I'm not complaining. Essentially I have it good. Plus I agreed to take on these big responsibilities—not that the Old Man necessarily gave me much choice in the matter—which He didn't, but that's another conversation for another day.

So like it or not, I've come to accept the many lumps and the odd bumps. Besides, somebody's got to perform the role of the Supreme Savior, right? And if not me, who? If not now, when? Because, let's face it, in the end, no matter how you slice it, how you dice it, the world's just gotta be saved...

Which is why I came back—to save, save, save...

The only mistake I'd like to avoid this time around is getting strung up on that damn wooden cross again, which was no Madonna-like music video experience for me, believe me. That was a *real* crown of thorns I wore. And those nails? Genuine as they could be. No, I'm not in the least bit interested in going down that path again. Not if I can help it. If I am to ever take it in the neck again for humanity, I'd like to find a third way. Originality is everything. It never pays to repeat. But let's not even go there. Let's think positively. While we all know that my mission is pretty much a mission impossible, I'm certainly in the mood to try. That's what two-thousand-year breaks will do for you. They can make for affirmative adjustments in one's attitude. Being gone for so long did me a world of good. It restored my objectivity, recharged by batteries, and allowed me to put a positive spin on the past. I have no regrets. And as a result, I'm ready for bear.

There were plenty of times, looking back down on Earth and watching the misery make its advance here and there, that I was, well, discouraged, not at all optimistic that anything good would ever come of the human race. That my earlier mission had failed. Who can blame me? Not that that opinion is particularly unique, or anything, because it's not.

But coming from the Son of Optimism Himself, I think that we can all agree that it's fairly disturbing. Not good news.

Frankly, I'd hoped for a more profound impact. I did. Though of course I didn't fail utterly and completely, neither did I even begin to succeed up to and including my wildest expectations. I have a right to certain expectations, you know, even wild ones. And while there have been plenty of decent reviews about my command performance in those early days in Palestine, the concrete results were, shall we say, lacking. Worse, the picture I got up there of things gone wrong down there no longer justified any further extensions of my recuperation period and vacation time. To put it bluntly, hoping for the best and saying prayers was no longer a substitute for policy. Which is why I'm finally back. I'm back to set new policy and make my mandate—the Old Man's edict—a bit more... what's the right word?... binding. Yes, that's the one.

But before I start, I'd like to give credit where credit's due for all the modicum of success I've experienced since I've been away. Of course, I owe it all to my original twelve disciples—Matthew, Luke, Paul and John, et al. Spreading my Gospel here, there, and everywhere the way they did was nothing short of awesome, as the young folk like to say. More like miraculous. I could never have done what they did. And I'd be remiss not to mention those anonymous authors of the original Greek version of *The Bible*. Allow me also to flatter their good work. It just goes to show that one doesn't necessarily need a hefty advance and a fancy publishing house to write literature that climbs straight to the top of the all-time bestseller list. Those guys kicked ass, all the way into the 21st century. That's saying something.

Still, we could have and should have done better. So we'll just consider that whole period to be our first draft, shall we? This next time round, we'll revise and condense, smooth out all those rough edges, add a few more characters here and there, give the narrative a new *mise en scène*, in keeping with the times, maybe write a new ending even—a happy ending. Maybe not. Who knows? In any event, we'll go for it. After all, the world could sure use a lift after enduring the likes of George W. Bush in the White House. But don't even get me started talking about that man. I must remain calm...

One thing's certain, yesterday's strategies just won't do anymore. I can't very well ride on the back of a jackass, preaching in prairie towns and big city ghettos and downtown business districts from here to Beijing and expect to be taken seriously. Things have changed. But having just put down on the Avenue of the Stars, it's not clear to me what that strategy should be. Whatever it is, it should be dynamic enough to put me in a position to tackle the big picture (and big ticket) items: problems of war and peace, hunger and disease, greed, equality, global warming, racism, pollution, the clash between socialism and capitalism, issues of primary, secondary, and college education. To say nothing of universal health insurance! My word, there's no end to the problems. Which makes achieving a happy ending for everyone somewhat problematic, to say the least, but they don't call me the Miracle Maker for nothing.

In any event, Let the Word Go Forth: I'm back.

And not a minute too soon. To tell you the truth, I was getting on my Old Man's nerves a little bit—and visa-versa, I might add—being back at home and living together for all that time. Some of it was my fault. It's pretty easy to forget about picking up your socks and doing your dishes and washing and taking out the trash and recycling on Tuesday nights. In those areas, I'm not always perfect. I could have done better. But when you're home, I mean really home, it's easy to let go and overlook your everyday responsibilities. Ask any kid. So, yes, I think that it's best for both of us that I got back to Earth and on with my life.

54

Besides, I always did like a serious challenge. And with a little bit of luck, maybe this time I'll succeed. Though I'm going to miss the Old Man, I sure won't miss His nagging.

Here on the Avenue of the Stars, standing on Gene Kelly's star, beside a lamppost similar to the one he danced about lovesick in the pouring rain in *Singin' in the Rain*, I can't see my hands in front of my face, let alone my Tony Lama boots. The smog's thick and sticky, like the feel of cotton balls slathered in Vermont Grade A maple syrup. I'm thirsty, very thirsty, and I'd welcome a glass of water, even L.A. tap water. It was a long, long way down this morning and I didn't have a drop to drink.

I adjust my Panama hat and tie, smooth out the wrinkles in the sleeves of my jacket. I pull up my socks. Good grooming is everything. First impressions make all the difference, particularly in my line of work. I'm happy to report I don't feel any drastic affects of inter-galactic jet lag. Not yet, at least. I'm feeling just fine, and so very glad to have my feet back firmly on the ground. The good news is my Second Coming was easier than expected, a significantly gentler ride than my original Resurrection, in fact. If I'm ever faced with the necessity of coming or going again—either in the form of a second resurrection (God forbid) or a Third Coming—either will be a snap. There's just no substitute for experience. Not that I'm in any hurry to go there, mind you. Living through either is more than a fellow—even me—should be expected to take in a single lifetime. But then, I suppose, I'm a man of multiple lifetimes, if you think about it, so I'm in the category of what people call being different.

Atypical as it may be of me, my first thoughts turn to the question of money and how well endowed I am because, well, I'm hungry. Very, very hungry. They didn't exactly provide meals on the Express Bus down. And it's not like in the olden days down here when I could go out into a field and pick an apple. No, nowadays you need bucks and bank accounts. More than one sometimes, like primary checking accounts, secondary accounts, savings accounts, and a line of credit in the form of a home equity loan, if possible. Just to be safe. And it's always best to get overdraft protection, too. And definitely, credit cards are a must. I've been told most places don't take cash, so the Old Man saw to it that I had a pack: American Express, Visa, MasterCard, and Discover, with generous credit limits, thank God. Not so high as to make me unconscious of cost, but not so low as to put a dent in my activities, either. I need to get things done, and fast. Oh, I know what you're probably thinking: Christ of old wouldn't be caught dead with a credit card. And you're probably right about that. But that Christ lived in a very different world compared with one. These days credit cards are the rage. I can do a lot of things, but I can't turn back time... I'm simply a victim of the new age, just like everyone else. So forgive me, please, as I forgive you: This is what the Old Man and I have decided. I go everywhere with my American Express Gold Card without apology. I'm on a schedule now. The planet needs saving and I don't have the time to rely on the kindness of strangers or the fruits of the fields or even soup kitchens. And I refuse to drain my miraculous powers to make myself a bowl of French onion soup. These are the days of conservation. Conserving fuel, conserving electricity, conserving water, conserving the precious natural resources of a choking planet... I have only so much energy now, given my age, so I'm duty bound to conserve that, too. Tackling all the world's problems, not just the problems of Palestine and the Holy Roman Empire, will require everything I've got, and then some. No, I don't have time to worry about the political correctness of carrying credit cards. Let's just chalk it up to one of those modern-day compromises.

So I'm off, heading west toward Sunset Strip because I've heard so much about it. And as I slog through the low smog, I have one thing and one thing only on the forefront of my mind: The salvation of masses? Not just yet. Lifting up the boats of the impoverished? Well, not exactly. Lobbying the Episcopal Church to reinstate the *Book of Prayer* and the *1940 Hymnal*? Definitely not that. Well, then, what exactly, you ask?

Blueberry pancakes and a strawberry sundae. That's what. With me it's first things first. The first shall not always be last!

After breakfast, I intend to mull over my next moves, devise a grand strategy and, (time permitting before prayers and bed at the Tropicana Motel down on Santa Monica Boulevard I booked via Orbitz.com), try to get in some quality saving time out on the streets, if I'm up for it... I'm actually quite nervous about cranking up my more miraculous, saving-the-people side again, because, well, let's face it, I'm likely to be rusty; but I'm also fairly confident that it won't take forever and a day to get me back in the groove, either. As my Old Man told me before showing me the door, "It'll be as easy as riding an ass up and down the streets of Jerusalem again..." I know that He's probably right. What am I saying? He's always right! Which is another reason why—off the record, of course—He's pretty near impossible to live with. But I have no doubt—no doubt whatsoever—that my miraculous powers and soul saving techniques will come shining through again pretty quick, probably faster than I can say "Pontius Pilate" three times backwards.

Slogging west on Avenue of the Stars, searching for Sunset Boulevard, carrying my well-stickered, classic wicker suitcase, circa 1930, given as a farewell gift to me by my friends back in Heaven, a wondrous thing happens to me. More wondrous than even the gorgeous solar systems and misty galaxies I passed by this morning on my way down.

As I walk a silver Rolls Royce slows down beside me. The face of a woman, as dreamy as Grace Kelly's, appears at the rear window. Her eyes lock onto mine. She lowers the back window; she smiles. And in a voice that sounds just like Grace Kelly's, she whispers, "All you need is love… Isn't that right, Mr. Christ?" Before I can respond, her window rolls up as her car glides away as she winks at me. Then she's gone, her face, her smile, lost to me like yesterday's dreams, her voice disappearing like the voice of a stranger heard from a slow passing train…

Of this I'm certain: She's why L.A.'s known as the City of Angels—because she's one of 'em.

I turn back to see her silver car slip into the low smog; it makes me smile. I see her neon license plate flashing in the dim light. On it is a phrase I recognize. It reads, "All You Need is Love."

It's no wonder the Beatles were more popular than me. They got the big picture stuff exactly right. According to my Gospels, and in the end, that's all that counts. Quite candidly, I never said it any better than they did. So good onya, John, Paul, George, and Ringo. You'll always be tops in my book.

CHAPTER TWO

I tuned Him in on my 100" Sony Quaditron flat screen TV, catching Him land on the Boulevard of the Stars, like a fly in my hands. I did that by hacking into the L.A.P.D. police surveillance camera system. I pride myself on my technological acumen. It always puts me one step ahead. As expected my stepbrother's showboating again, in an updated guise,

I'll grant you, but showboating He is all the same. This time, instead of wearing His poor man's rags that stank to high Heaven, He's all duded up in a white linen suit—a very well cut one—I'll admit. His hat and shades were fairly okay, too. I particularly like the addition of the Tony Lama boots. He's actually become quite a fashion horse, but so what? He's still about as commanding a figure and consequential-looking as the second captain of the USS Rowboat.

Okay, so it's true. I never have, nor will I ever give the Lord of Lords and the Bore of Bores, a break. It goes against my nature. Being his older, more sophisticated and infinitely superior, let alone talented, stepbrother, it's impossible for me to shake the fact that though He's been gone all this time, He's still managed to get the lion's share of attention in the media, in the history books, everywhere it counts. So you can see that cutting Him slack would add to my consternation, not help. Besides, His return means one thing only: I've got trouble on my hands because, believe me, He's not here to make me a better person, or invite me to brunch, or take me out for a beer after work in the evening. No, He's come back to challenge me to a chess game. I just hope I'm up for it.

This looks like it's shaping up to one of the worst Christmases I've had in a couple of thousand years. And after being a comparatively good boy all year, too! I don't know why someone would want to put a lump of coal in my stocking!

So I'm watching Christ march along the Avenue of the Stars, groping his way through the smog toward Sunset Strip. Even though I'm bunkered down in my safe house buried below the wastelands of Mexico, located outside of that sweet, little town of Juarez, where even I'm afraid to go by myself at night, I don't feel safe. Because as we all know, Christ looks more harmless than He really is. In my opinion, He should be on the FBI's Most Wanted List. It's good I had a heads-up

59

about this. Otherwise, the news of His return could have given me a heart attack. I don't like surprises at my age. Well, only the ones I choose to dish out, that is.

My deep-throat, garage sources were kind enough to provide me with advance notice of my stepbrother's return so I've had time to gather my thoughts and consider a response. It's a cinch He has one thing and one thing only on His mind this time: To mount a vigorous attack on my inalienable right to wrong the world in whatever way at whatever time I choose. Why doesn't He just leave me alone? What's in it for Him to make my life miserable? And just when we were getting along so well with Him being gone, leaving me to my own devices. Now that He's back, He'll be all obsessed with making the planet safe for things like little blue flowers, Red Wolves and Bald eagles. He'll want to end every last one of my messy little wars and cut out genocide entirely, to say nothing of enforcing human rights! The nerve of the man! And oh yes, He obviously intends on feeding the starving children—just to get the credit—and campaigning for the end of AIDS, and of course He'll probably be wanting to purify the air and water and end global warming—just when the planet's mean temperature is getting much more to my liking! Wouldn't you know it!

Lord save us from the Planet Savers, up to and including the latest and greatest, the Lord Jesus Christ, and with particular emphasis on His Ecological Holiness, Al Gore. I'm still bitter about that man. I would have been much further along if he hadn't butted in with his slide show and stepladder and Academy award-winning movie. Whatever possessed him to do such a thing?

In any case, dream on, little stepbrother. It's all illusion, all confusion, anyway. No way this planet ever gets saved! No way, Jose! They're just too many ways for me to make hay... too many vulnerabilities for me to exploit... which is why, in the end, I have it made, no matter how many Planet Savers go up against me.

I was up all night, waiting to catch the first act of Christ's Second Act. I rightly named it, *The Return of the Lord of Bores*. I know, you don't need to tell me, it's obvious, I have a natural flair for coming up with good titles. I had considered, *Borelujah*, but decided against it out of my respect of J.R.R. Tolkien. His favorite character of mine was, that's right, you guessed it: Gollum. Why? Because he was so very, very p-r-e-c-i-o-us... Just like me.

Now let's tune in on my stepbrother's progress, shall we? Knock back Bombay Rum and watch His homemade, G-rated movie. If nothing else, the rum will enhance the entertainment value, which otherwise—you betcha—will be right down there with watching crabgrass grow. Granted it may have its moments: Like I assume He'll throw in a gratuitous miracle or two, just for show, like feeding Hollywood's homeless and hungry with McDonald's Happy Meals, instead of loaves and fishes. He'll also probably do His fair share of showboating, just because He won't be able to resist—never could, never will—like walking across the Grand Canyon without a wire and pole. Anything's possible now that His divinity's been re-charged! But there's no way Jose that His little hand-held camera movie is going to be another *Indiana Jones and the Raiders of the Lost Ark*. More like C-Span coverage of the House of Representatives budget hearings. So I guarantee you, we'll be snoozing by lunchtime, maybe sooner. But at least the picture quality will pretty much be great. What with my Sony 2160 Hi-Def resolution TV screen. Believe me, His every wrinkle will look sharper than my intellect. It'll make Him look the way He really looks: Old. Very, very old. At least forty-five. Maybe forty-six. His youthful savior days are over. And worse, it's all downhill from here. That's all there is to it. There's no hiding those gray streaks anymore, not unless He dyes His hair, which He won't, because the Lord of Bores will always do what purists do, go *au natural*. And there's no covering up those scowl lines, either. Or maybe they'll smile lines—I can't tell. Who cares? They make Him look old, that's all that counts. Not even Botox can save Him now! He's been scowling or smiling for too many centuries! No, there's no running away from the obvious, as I said: That good-looking, youthful savior look is long gone. Like the water at the bottom of the Dead Sea. People won't buy it, so He shouldn't try to sell it. Red alert: Christ is middle-age...

Not so sorry to say, no number of spa days will be enough to rid Him of that ancient, mercury-contaminated look. I was almost shocked when I saw Him again. Compared to the last time I saw Him, when He was getting nailed to that beautiful, beautiful cross, and even with no beard, and neatly combed hair, He looked like no spring chicken, believe me. Which is understandable. If I'd been crucified and died and dumped in a tomb behind a big rock for three days in the dark and then put on a bus back to Heaven, with my tail hanging between my legs, I'd look wrinkled, too. As it is, despite my long, silky beard, and lengthy Hells' Angel hair, I don't believe I look a day over... Well, forty-three... or so.

Which brings me back to me. As always.

Basically, I'm as lean as Harrison Ford was in "Raiders" and do my Nordic track workouts every morning before breakfast. On weekends I even throw in stair-steppers and some upper bodywork. I also do a yoga classes in Juarez on Sunday afternoons, which I credit with keeping me flexibility, especially in my lower back, and a lot less cranky than I might otherwise be. Sure, I have my aches and pains—don't we all?—but because I have such a healthy attitude about life and have learned to take the knocks and practice slow-breathing techniques and, above all else, still love my life, love what I do, I'm in remarkably good shape, even though, I confess, I can still be persuaded to do the occasional line of coke, for health reasons only. That I can't quite resist. And I'd like to think that it actually helps keep me looking, if not young exactly, than at least, well, not too terribly old, either! Not like my stepbrother. What was good for Edgar Allen Poe is good enough for me!

Anyway, wintering in Mexico has been beneficial for me. I've been coming here since the War of 1812. My safe is dry and cool and the air down here is remarkably fresh. The dry air and high heat upstairs is helpful in keeping my allergies at bay and my arthritis in check. I have no complaints. At least it's not Siberia.

For food I live on a high protein diet of beans, lentils, and lots of fresh fish, which has very high concentrations of DHA and Omega-3's. My doctor says they're great for my heart. And my first health priority has always been and will always be, if I can help it, my heart. So I eat healthy and stay healthy with a daily diet of exercise. I also enjoy my quiet time. My most peaceful hour of the day is when I fish. I drop a line in the fresh water pool at my feet, strike up a Lucky Strike, and blow smoke rings into the night. I can't tell you just how nice that is. It's my happy time, like singing in the shower.

I pity him, I really do. My stepbrother slogs through the L.A. heat, weighed down by His ridiculously ancient and over packed suitcase, without a water fountain or rest room in sight. I take a shot of Bombay Rum just because I can. Christ's problem is that He was an only child and as we all know only children they're gluttons for attention. The entire world is their surrogate parent. So basically that fact alone has ruined Him. Add to that He's never even gone on a date in two thousand years, let alone gone all the way, and there're insufficient words in the Oxford-English dictionary to describe how pitiable His life has really been. What's in it for Him, I'll never know. If you ask me, somebody, somewhere, somehow, sold Him a big bill of goods. Now I wonder who that could have been?... Hmmm.

By exuberant contrast, my life has been, well, worth living. It has been the picture of vitality, the essence of creativity, a never-ending series of accomplishments on a vast geo-political plane. Oh sure, there have been the occasional setbacks. They're always setbacks, no matter who you are, even God. But I've learned to live with them and learn from them. And like the mature leader of a great cause that I am, I've succeeded on a scale unimaginable, overshadowing from time to time even the likes of my stepbrother and His doting Old Man. I worry them more than even they're likely to admit. Which makes my joy all the more profound. I've gotten good at this while Christ has been on the lam. Goryjulah!

So exactly what have I been doing since He's been getting pedicures in Heaven? Let's look at the record, shall we? At the highest levels, I work closely with the highest heads of authoritarian governments and specialize in my relations with dictatorships. Not that I ever violate their sovereignty. No, I wouldn't do that. Not unless I absolutely had to, like if they began to backlash on their solemn commitments to oppression. Then and only then I might step in and put a stop to it, but not before. No, those guys are perfectly capable of running the show and getting the job done right—the first time out. Oppression is best carried out down at the grass roots level by local authorities. They understand the psyche of the populace and know where to push and where to press. I learned that long ago. Outsiders, like myself, are generally frowned upon. Our presence can even lead to acts of repression backfiring! Not good. So I like to keep my distance. In the name of subjugation, I'm nothing if not discreet.

The beauty of 21st century is that I can achieve great things right where I am. Transnational crime, international riot, human trafficking, you name it; I can get it done with the brush of a keystroke. Whoever said that crime doesn't pay didn't know what the hell they were talking about. Of course it pays! My profits from human trafficking in one year in Cambodia and Vietnam is sufficient for me to retire on, should I ever wish to, which of course I don't, and won't, because I REALLY REALLY LIKE WHAT I DO. Always have, always will. It's a marriage that will know no end, a marriage of crime and convenience.

And the nice part is that any cash I make through my good works brokering arms, selling narcotics or facilitating transfers of stolen intellectual property rights can be wired anywhere in the world to any one of my secret bank accounts with a keystroke, and there it will remain hidden bearing pretty decent interest out of reach of the taxman. Singapore, Switzerland, Panama, they all have such wonderfully discreet banking laws, you know, and they welcome my money with open arms. For these types of modern conveniences and many more, I owe this age an immense debt of gratitude. Is this a great century, or what?

Oh sure, the 20th century had its high points, too. Did it ever. The many genocides, two world wars, Korea, Vietnam, Afghanistan, and the Cold War. And some perfectly beautiful little guerrilla wars. It wasn't called the bloodiest century in history for nothing. My allies and I put on quite a show. It doesn't get any better than that. And while I always regretted that the Cold War never climaxed in a full-scale nuclear conflagration, I've come to believe during these ensuing years that it was just as well. Look what I would have missed! E-mail. Instant messaging. The IPhone 7G. My 100" Sony Quaditron TV, with 2060 resolution no less! THE INTERNET, for God's sakes! I can even encrypt my satellite phone against NSA intercepts anywhere in the world these days! The spooks at Fort Meade don't know what I'm thinking! For sure, it's a technologically rich environment, the 21st century. God love Bill Gates. He's my kind of wonder boy. And then there are, of course, the big

65

picture items that I excel in nurturing, like terrorism, Sudan, Iraq—that was a beautiful hoot: George W. fell for that one!—and oh yes, need I mention one of my newer enterprises—global warming and its smoldering glories! Someone upstairs must be smiling down on me! Until you-know-who landed on Gene Kelley's bronze star on the Avenue of the Stars this morning, and called out like He'd just arrived home from camp, "You-who! I'M BAACK!", the 21st century was in the running for my second or third favorite century. They're just so many to choose from! But unless I act very, very decisively, that could all change. I perceive peril. I sense extraordinary danger. I believe that the bottom could fall out. Thanks a lot for nothing, little stepbrother! Go stuff yourself! Could it have hurt for you to extend your vacation for another century or two? We were all getting along just fine down here without you! I was so looking forward to shaping another round of coups in Fiji and Thailand early on next year! Now it's clear that I'll have to turn my attention to getting rid of you, just like before...

It's so unfair. So totally unfair. On top of that, Christ's probably going to ruin my Christmas, too. Who the hell asked Him to put coal in my stocking?

I adjust the color of my Sony Quaditron that I've set up on an old Château Neuf du Pape wine crate to the right of my fishing hole. My stepbrother's countenance changes from grotesque orange to cheerful blood red. I like that look; then I decide I don't, so I move on to a gory green hue, which seems perfect. Yes, I like. You can never put too much ghoulish green into anything, especially complexions. Deeply strange is good. And I must admit, exaggerating flesh tones is good fun! Messing up my stepbrother's coloring is even more amusing than playing Grand Theft Auto!

I sit back down in my REI trail chair, content with having messed up Christ's face on the screen. I stole the chair last year from a campsite north of Aspen. I couldn't resist. REI is my favorite. I pick up a hunk of bait and hack at it in two with my bait knife. I mount it on a fishhook, drop in my line, and wait for the nibble that is breakfast, one eye on ghoulish-looking stepbrother.

The truth is, I'm a little cranky. Which is understandable, considering. It's way past my ordinary breakfast time and I haven't even had fried crickets to nibble on since hours before dawn. I just couldn't eat, knowing He was coming. Which is understandable. The stress is rather unforgiving…

Christ veers too close to the curb. A transit bus going by nearly takes Him out. Shoot! Now that would have solved all my problems. But I don't have that kind of luck. Had He been hit and killed and sent back to Heaven, we could have saved ourselves a whole lot of trouble. Who wants all the fuss and bother of internecine squabbles, anyway? Besides, it would have been a classic win-win situation. But that damn bus missed and Christ plods on. I really have to admire His magnificent bladder control! He must really need of a restroom by now.

I've never seen the L.A. smog come down so deep; it looks like bubbling potato soup. It'll take a miracle for my stepbrother to find Sunset now. What were the lyrics to that George Harrison's tune? "There's a smog upon L.A.…." They went something like that. He needs a GPS tracking system. But of course you can forget about that. He's hopelessly out-of-date in His use of 21st century conveniences. It'll take Him a year or more to get up to speed. You would have thought Heaven would have been wired for Google. I may have more time to organize than I thought.

I get no nibble, no bite, no breakfast, down below. I park my rod and reel to get up and stretch. I stare into my stepbrother's pea green countenance on the big screen. Not one bead of sweat rolls down His cheek. With the remote, I zoom in for a closer look. No, no sign of sweat. So cool and calm. This is what makes Him such a formidable adversary and an unflappable do-gooder. Money can't buy cool like that. You either got it or you don't.

This is the day I wish the Lord hadn't made.

Which means only one thing: I snort a line of coke. I simply can't resist. I'd been a good boy since 3 a.m., too, but now I need an assist. I snort it through a plastic straw from a white powdered line I laid out on a white piece of paper I put on top of another old wine crate beside my chair. It gives me a pretty decent lift, makes me feel better about everything. There's that lovely rush again. There's that first moment of exaltation. Goryjulah! Now I can believe, truly, truly believe—that I can take Him on. It's no problem really, though of course it still may be some inconvenience. I only wish I could look inside His mind, hear His thoughts, know His plan.

There's a tug at the end of my fishing line.

Breakfast! My luck seems to have changed. That's gotta be a good sign. Maybe this century won't turn out too badly, after all. It could happen… because I have faith, faith in my manifest destiny and a good line of coke.

CHAPTER THREE

Mel's golden sign, turning slowly above Sunset Strip, blazing as bright as an Olympic torch through the Beijing smog, lures me on, beckons me toward the cool sanctuary of the culinary temple that is Mel's Diner. Yes, it seems to be reeling me in for the $21.95 blueberry short stack breakfast special. Now I ask you, how can a guy resist? And I've promised myself that if I mind my table manners and remember to say grace, I'm entitled to a treat: Specifically, a strawberry banana sundae with nuts sprinkled on top. You have no idea how much I've longed for one ever since I came across a picture online. Heaven's kitchens just don't do strawberry, chocolate or vanilla ice cream sundaes. Sure, they'll whip me up a soy ice cream sundae any time I want, but you and I both know soy isn't, well, ICE CREAM! Even though we can all appreciate the fact that health-wise soy's hands down much better for you.

I make for Mel's frosted double doors, coated in sprayed-on snowflakes. Even Mel's windows are sprayed with frosty rime, obscuring inside views, making it impossible to see in. Above the frost lines on the windowsills a glowing ambient light, as warm as a Lapland sunrise, adds to the atmosphere of the Hollywood holiday season. My hunch is that anything could be happening in there—restaurant or riot. For the sake of argument, I'll assume that it's still going to be a family restaurant inside. I trade on optimism. Always have.

I brush aside the hot cobwebs of Hollywood smog, while resisting my impulse to make a beeline for the door, running like a colt with the scent of hay in his head toward the barn door. I want it all: Cool air! Blueberry Pancakes! Strawberry ice cream sundaes. The men's room! I hear the strains of "Away in a Manger" floating across Mel's full parking lot. Instantly, I recognize that voice: It's the voice of the Material Girl herself. "The little Lord Jesus lay down in his bed..." Oh... gee whiz. She sounds so sweet, so divinely child-like. That pumps me up pretty good. All is not lost on planet Earth if Madonna has come round to singing Christmas carols!

As I crack open the frosted front door, an unseen choir belts out the "Hallelujah Chorus." A rush of cool air zaps my system and I'm engulfed in a blaze of bright white light, brighter even than the front porch lights up in Heaven. Even my cool dude shades are useless against the onslaught of light. It's that intense. (Rest assured: I'm definitely

69

asking for my money back.) Then, as quickly as they came on, the high voltage lights snap out, plunging the space into newfound night. Like, say, Mel, did you forget to pay the light bill? The choral voices fade and I'm left standing very still, waiting for something to happen, waiting perhaps for Gôdot. I wonder: Now how am I going to find the men's room? Not to put too fine a point on it, but my bladder's about to burst.

Behind me, I hear the sliding bolt. The double glass doors lock tight. That may or may not be a positive indication of good thing to come. Like a surprise party, maybe? Even if they mean to do me harm, I'm not likely to mind, since that nice cool breeze I'm currently experiencing is blessed central air conditioning. Overhead, I sense the wide open sky. Not that I can actually see it, mind you. I hear a distant swirling, whooshing noise up there, like winds dancing with the stars. I stretch out my arms protectively because I have no sense of where the doors or walls or anything else is other than the floor. I'd like to avoid breaking my nose, if I possibly can. A splint combination bandage would put a pretty big dent in my celestial image.

I sense only darkness and more darkness beyond my outstretched hands. I perceive that dark spaces and still darker places are within reach: It's out there... I could be in an open field or on an isolated country road, on the other side of everywhere and nowhere. I could be standing atop vast rocky planes that lead to everywhere in particular or nowhere in general. Who can say for sure? Not me, that's for sure. This is all new territory for me. I don't even own a guidebook. But wherever I am—on a studio back lot or in a cloistered sound stage—it's a cinch Mel's itself is long gone. That's because there's an air of Hollywood magic about. I'm ready for whatever razzle-dazzle may come, so long as it eventually leads me back to Mel's for my well-deserved pancake breakfast.

Let's face it: I'm a big, big fan of old Hollywood classics. As a result, I have a very vivid celluloid imagination. For instance, I half expect Cary Grant to give me the drop as I step forward into the night, just as he did poor old H. Bartholomew through the trapdoor of the opera house stage in *Charades*. Well, after everything I've been through, you'd be paranoid, too.

Back in Heaven, we got all the Hollywood classics through Netflix. Name one, and I've probably seen it—multiple times. I watched *White Christmas* before coming down, just to put me in the right frame of mind. It goes without saying that I'm a sentimental softy at heart, especially at Christmas time. That's off the record. I wouldn't want it getting out. A man in my position has to maintain his reputation as stern but loving. Sentimental just won't do.

Suddenly, below my feet, the floor gives a start. It's as though I'd stepped onto a moving walkway at LAX, or a Gold's Gym treadmill. A smooth, wide rubber belt flows beneath my Tony Lama boots, ushering me away from wherever I was. I'm drawn into a cool, dark place, but with a far vaster sense of space about it. For instance, above, I sense a starless sky and a long river of unseen stars. And the air smells of fecund earth. Not manure, mind you—more like rich, dreamy loam. It's the loam of life. Yes, life! The Motherland of Life! Wherever I'm heading, this could be good. I'm riding on a rubber tide, sliding into a strange new spatial night. I can't be certain why. All I know for sure is that I'm floating away from a place that was once Mel's and am moving toward a new space that may or may not be purgatory—or Hell, for that matter, but is, thank the Lord Almighty, still very, very well air-conditioned.

Inexplicably, then, the conveyer belt slows. Am I approaching the end of the line already? Or am I to be left alone under a dead sky? Abandoned to the loamy darkness. Then, without warning, I'm hit from behind, cut down at the back of my knees. They buckle; I crash. I fall

71

back into the seat of a carriage car, which breaks my fall and scoops me up. A metal guard bar slips across my waist, holding me firmly in place. Then we're off. I'm whisked away on a brand new kind of ride. It's a carnival ride. I put my suitcase on the seat next to me and settle in. It's like taking a Haunted House or Pirates of the Caribbean ride at Disneyland, I imagine.

We scoot forward fast. I'm projected into an extraordinary night, where time bends and the winds of the world swirl. Someone or something, I dare say, is taking me out for a world-class ride. So okay. Why not just relax? The worst they can do is kill me. And I already have an anecdote for that. And since I've waited this long for a *real* ice cream strawberry sundae, I can wait another hour or two longer without fear of losing it. Besides, I'm really, really curious about who's behind all this— who's in charge here. Yes, I've accepted my light-less state of mystery with a certain equanimity. Who needs a strawberry sundae when I can breathe unsullied air and move through fantastical, dark spaces? This experience is as rare as snowfall on Santa Monica Boulevard and I should make the most of it. Besides, I've had a hankering to go to Disneyland ever since it opened. This could be my only chance to get anywhere near it. I'll grab it.

The stage night gets still darker as we hurtle ahead. My carriage grips the tracks; chains turn below; rubber wheels twirl. Sometimes we slow; sometimes we're catapulted forward, jolted when the chains catch and rocket us on. Then, as if to convey an ominous mood, a drumbeat dirge sounds, coming as though from the open graves of recently released ghosts. Oooooooooh, spooky! I love it. I can't always just get behind all things warm and fuzzy and light, you know. It's always good to mix it up.

Middle Earth. That's exactly where the sound sounds like it's coming from. Boom, boom, boom. Or maybe it's more like doom,

doom, doom. With drums it's always difficult to say. Whichever it is, it's not very Christmas-like. And I was so in the mood for all things Christmas after viewing *White Christmas*. I really was. Boom, boom, boom, doom, doom, doom. It comes from below; from on high; from the edges of the empty horizon. What I wouldn't give to hear "O Little Town of Bethlehem" now! I'm not sure I like where all this is going. It seems to be going nowhere. Absolutely nowhere that I know of.

Now it gets a little fun again. We bank left and veer right. We accelerate, brake, then surge again. They even throw a hairpin turn in there. Actually, this could pass for a relatively decent roller coaster ride. After being cooped up in the cloistered hallways of Heaven for so long, I guess I'm about due for a dose of amusement. I know that being the Son of God sounds great and everything, but the Old Man doesn't do amusements very well, so I guess I'll take it whenever and wherever I can get it.

Yeah, baby! We're rockin' 'n rollin' now! Like a garden snake slithering through stands of tall grass, we zig this way, zag the other way, all of which puts a big smile on my face. Then comes a straightway, as flat as a Kansas highway, leading towards the mouth of a tunnel rising up out of the ground. We go into it and down. I have to tell you: I've never been too crazy about tunnels. Tunnels are a downer, you know. I definitely don't have a good feeling about this. I grip the bar across my waist, and hope for, well, what else? The light at the end of the tunnel.

Which comes on much faster than expected. Soon I see it, the light at the end of the tunnel. Beyond it I see starlight and a great open field that rolls out forever. And as we fly down the tracks, the air cools, the darkness lifting lightly, the stars growing brighter, too, I swear it looks like the real sky. But this being Hollywood, who really knows for sure? Those set painters at IATSE Local 724 can really work wonders. There's the Big Dipper, the Milky Way, the North Star shining over what must be, yes, it must be Bethlehem. Oh, how nice, they've brought me back to Bethlehem…

But Bethlehem it's not. Not even close. We shoot out the end and into the Dead Zone, not the little town of Bethlehem. How do I know it's the Dead Zone? Because scattered across the loamy soil are millions and millions of bones. As in the dried and brittle bones of dead people. I don't do death rides. Life-after-death rides, yes, certainly; resurrection rides, oh, absolutely; but no death rides. I want my money back. Oh, I forgot. This ride's free.

This is the perfect ride for my stepbrother, but not me. They must have gotten the wrong guy. Beelzebub would like this just fine. Yes, he would. Me, I'd rather be eating breakfast or walking through a field of daffodils. I really hope they won't mind turning me around and sending me back to Mel's.

Wouldn't you know? Next my carriage slows, just when I'd like it to get me the hell out of here. Like right now would be very nice, fellas! I look for a reverse gear to shift. I can forget about that. I look for an accelerator to push. Not a chance. I'm as helpless as the day I got strung up on that damn cross. Something tells me I'm about to take a ride through the House of the Dead, or worse. A sign above the creaking front door will read, "Woe Be Unto Ye Who Enter In… Warning: Check your jokes at the door." Someone's set me up. Terrorists?

I hope the Old Man isn't looking down. I'm not in the mood to hear His guff. Not until I get to the men's room, at least. Where the hell am I? Where the hell is Mel's? I can't believe I've managed to get myself lost first thing back on Earth!

My carriage slows; a dry wind blows. I lift my eyes to a tapestry of stars above. They curve down to the edge of the sky like a parachute fully open, down to the bone yards. Somewhere I've seen a gruesome field like this before…. Cambodia, Rwanda, Uganda? What movie did I see it in? I can't quite put my finger on it. There's nothing Hollywood Light about this, nothing in the least artificial… They convey a sense of dread and evil. I'm not crazy about being here.

Would someone kindly get me out of here?

Down along the graveyards of the world we move. Down the Dark-Fantastic Highway we pass, picking up velocity. From my perspective, the faster we get out of here, the better. A regular amusement park ride was okay by me—fun actually. But this, well, this is a different matter. My carnival carriage blows back corkscrew dust in swirls. I press my hand down hard over my hat. I'll need that. My sense is that the manure's gonna start falling heavy and fast. There's no question now: I've been set-up. Who would want to go and do a thing like that? After all, I just got back! Show me a little mercy, will ya fellas?

Along the Dark Fantastic Highway billboards appear on the right of the road. They burn bright holes in the lower edge of night. Above the loamy fields littered in seas of white bones, the billboards stand one behind the other, running to the thin line of the midnight horizon, standing at attention like soldiers at a firing squad. As we come upon the first of them, my carriage mysteriously brakes, slows for literary emphasis. One way or another, my joyride's over, the handwriting's on the billboards. This is the Land of Serious Stuff. So wipe that smile off your face.

The first marquee reads:

Mel's Drive-In Theatre Presents

The second:

The Golden Age of Genocide

The third:

Now Answer Us This, Jesus:

The fourth:

"Where Were You in Rwanda in 1994?"

The fifth:

"In Bosnia-Herzegovina in 1992-1995?"

The sixth:

"In Cambodia in 1975-1979?"

The seventh:

"In China in 1958-1969?"

The eighth:

"In Poland in 1940-1945?"

The ninth:

"In Nanking in 1937?"

The tenth:

"In Ukraine in 1932-1933?"

The eleventh:

"In Turkey in 1915-1923?"

The twelfth:

"WHERE WERE YOU WHEN WE MOST NEEDED YOU?"

The biggest billboard of them all reads:

"55 MILLION DEATHS, JESUS."

The thirteenth:

"ALL BECAUSE YOU WERE M.I.A."

The fourteenth:

"WHAT DO YOU HAVE TO SAY FOR YOURSELF?"

Nothing good, I'm afraid. The truth is while I was basking in the warm bosom of the bright lights of Heaven, nursing my wounds, etc., and, well, let's face, procrastinating a little too, waiting, I suppose, until the time was ripe to get back on the donkey and ride, ride through the streets of wherever I could do the most good, the bloodiest, grisliest century came and went, without me spamming an updated version of the Gospel over the Internet. I really should have hauled ass back to Earth much earlier on, but then again, I had my reasons for holding back, which I'll get to sometime later on.

My carriage grinds to a halt as I glide past the last accusatory billboard. It's as though a circuit breaker down below or up above had just been pulled. All the billboards go dark at once. Above, even the stars blink out en masse, bringing about a new show of double darkness. I'm assuming that my joyride's officially over. But no. Off in the wings, wherever the wings are, I hear the beautiful strains of a cello played live. If I'm not mistaken, it's Elgar's Cello Concerto, second movement. Could be Dvorak, but I'm certain it's Elgar the more I hear. Whoever it is, it moves me to tears. Such loss, such suffering, such abiding sadness.

I wipe my tears on my sleeve. Since there're no reporters out here, I don't even try to hide my tears. We all remember what happened to Edmund Muskie after he cried on a snowy day in public. That was the end of his political campaign. I won't let that happen to my campaign. This time, I mean to win.

I suppose there's a fairly good chance that I'm also weeping for my own soul, sobbing over my own failures, because I permitted the Golden Age of Genocide to proceed without intervening. Whatever was I *thinking?*

For now, what I was thinking will remain classified as a divine secret.

But I swear on my mother's house in Heaven I'll never let it happen again.

My carriage jolts. My head jerks back as the chains catch the gears underneath. Then we're off, flying down the tracks, propelled into a whole new—a maze. A movie maze. A maze composed of long, narrow hallways and open anterooms, the walls laminated with silver screens showing movies—ghastly, horrific scenes of genocide. *Now* I think I understand why I've been brought here.

"Mel?" I call out. "Was this your idea?"

There is no answer. Not from Mel, nor anyone else. Neither does there appear to be any escape. A safety bar across my waist, I'm locked in good and tight. Whatever the length of this ghoulish ride, I appear to be in for the duration.

Welcome to Mel's *Rocky Horror Picture Show*. Welcome to what looks like the Wonderful World of Genocide, brought to me in Technicolor by none other than the human race. God bless it.

Into Cineplex Genocide I, I go. Down into the First Circle of Genocide Hell I descend. This isn't the fun part, not the least bit amusing. No smile to be found anywhere. But it's time for me to face facts. This is the tragedy of what I let happen, without so much as an email intervention, while I was upstairs clipping my nails in Heaven.

I should be ashamed of my M.I.A. status only slightly less than the human race should be ashamed of permitting the Golden Age of Genocide to happen in the first place.

My carriage takes me down, with a swirl and a surge, down to the bottom of the First Circle of Hell: Cineplex Genocide I.

On the wrap-around IMAX screen, glowing in Technicolor:

Muslim Turkish soldiers round up dozens of Christian Armenian politicians, writers, clergymen, diplomats, and intellectuals on a balmy April evening, rousting them from sleep and delivering them into the jaws of the street. An

Armenian writer, his wife trailing after him pleading for his release, is dragged away in bedclothes, much to the delight of a gaggle of Turks, dressed in fine cepkens, ziugas, and Ottoman Fez hats, and seated across the street at an outdoor café, smoking hookahs and drinking black coffee.

Throngs of Turks gawk at the dangling bodies of Armenian men hanging from makeshift gallows, constructed of long poles roped together at the crown, like a clumsy Teepee. Standing on either side at ceremonial attention are Turkish soldiers guarding the Ottoman Empire new crown jewels: The Armenian dead. A subtitle appears: **Constantinople, Turkey: April 24, 1915**

This is not my idea of a Walt Disney production. I shift uneasily in my seat.

Armenian prisoners prepare for a group picture in front of a Turkish jailhouse wall. A Turk photographer dips under the blanket of a mounted camera, holding up a crude powder flashgun above it. A burst of light, a raft of smoke: The fifty Armenian prisoners lie still by the prison wall in their long dark winter coats and old carpet hats, executed only moments before by Turkish soldiers. A burst of light, a raft of smoke: A sepia photograph of the Armenian soldiers as they were, standing before the Turkish jailhouse wall. A burst of light, a raft of smoke.

This is giving me something of a headache.

A photographer prepares to take a portrait of a pair of Turkish military officers, in full military regalia. They show national pride in their eyes. Pan down. A low wooden table ornamented with two Armenian leaders' decapitated heads. A burst of light, a raft of smoke: A sepia photograph of the two Turkish officers standing over the decapitated heads hangs on a peeling plaster wall.

I sigh, but do not look away.

Turkish infantry lower the naked bodies of three Armenian doctors, arms splayed, feet bound, over the edge of a bridge by rope. Then they're left to dangle upside down, their bodies in the shape of human crosses. A burst of light, a raft of smoke: A sepia picture of the gruesome event displayed on a Turkish army desk.

I shift nervously in my seat.

Armenian deportees under military escort stagger, starving and dehydrated, across baked desert sand below a clear blue Syrian sky. The caravan stretches for as far as the eye can see. Here and there deportees fall, their bodies left to fry, like fish washed ashore at low tide. A Turkish photographer, looking regal in his white osmaniye islik and black zinga, surveys the scene before him. Then he turns towards me. I know that face. I recognize this man. It's my stepbrother, Beelzebub.

He smiles, turns away, and dips down under the blanket of his bellows camera, powder flash raised, at the ready. A burst of light, a raft of smoke: A framed sepia photograph of the death march hung on a library wall.

I breathe in deeply, holding my breath.

Alone in an oak-paneled study, former U.S. Ambassador to the Ottoman Empire Ambassador Morgenthau speaks into a Dictaphone: "When the Turkish authorities gave the orders for these deportations, they were merely giving the death warrant to a whole race. They understood this well, and, in their conversations with me, they made no particular attempt to conceal the fact. I am confident that the whole history of the human race contains no such horrible episode as this. The great massacres and persecutions of the past seem almost insignificant when compared to the sufferings of the Armenian race in 1915..." Ambassador Morgenthau closes his eyes, trapped in own his disturbing thoughts. He puts down the Dictaphone on the red leather desktop, reaches across to the edge of the desk and pulls the chain on the green banker's lamp. The room falls dark. Blessedly dark. Ambassador Morgenthau and the Armenians disappear.

The lights remain on at the Genocide Cineplex.

My carriage takes me down, with a swirl and a surge, down to the bottom of the bottom of the Second Circle of Hell: Cineplex Genocide II.

On the wrap-around IMAX screen, burning in Technicolor:

Flowing fields of hard red winter wheat roll out under a smiling blue Ukrainian sky. Towering corkscrew clouds, pushed by southern Caucasus winds, ride the morning light over fairytale fields full of natural abundance. They're as big as floating giants. Kulak women, young and trim, wearing long flowing skirts, kerchiefs knotted at their chins, slice swathes of wheat with sickles. A Kulak girl, pretty as morning sunshine, takes a break. She stands in the open the fields, taking in the full measure of their autumnal glory…

That, at least, makes me smile.

NKVD agents—Stalin's secret police—and Russian grain collectors converge on a little village in Kirovohradska Oblast late one night. Hulking metal cars, Russian-made, with muscular, serpentine front fenders, running boards, and large, dirty windows rolled up to keep out the swirling dust, swoop in like ravens, followed by a caravan of army trucks, their headlights bright as searchlights, making white the night. At the village edge, the growling engines stop. Caught in the caravan headlights are the village granaries and food barns, flush with the Kulak's harvest.

Russian grain collectors batter down the granary doors. Inside, they seize everything in sight—sacks of winter wheat, bags of barley, stores of sugar beets, corn, potatoes, even bags of sunflower seeds. Everything is stripped, as meticulously as barracuda strip bone. They lay bare the granary shelves as resistant Kulaks are pistol-whipped, others shot. Everything gets loaded onto waiting trucks. Stalin's drivers depart into the dark swirling dust. A subtitle appears: **Kirovohradska Oblast, Ukraine, 1932**

I grip my safety bar. Hard.

Another village, another night. Grain collectors raid an old woman's kitchen in Zastavna, sacking her pantry, stealing food off her table, even taking half-baked bread from her oven, leaving nothing—only an old woman in tears.

I grip harder.

Midwinter. Starving Kulak families, desperate to get away, try to board a train with young children at Tomakivka station in Dnipropetrovs'ka Oblast. NKVD agents bar the way. "You have no proper passports," she snaps, her manner tenebrous and sharp. "You are forbidden to leave!" The family stands frozen, shaken. A seven-year-old girl swaddled in rags, fingers blackened by frostbite, detaches herself from her family and steps forward to confront the NKVD agent. Her little leg

81

shakes, her small voice quavers, "My name is Elena and I want so very much to live, you see… so please allow my family to leave Dnipropetrovs'ka Oblast… We're very hungry because for reasons I don't understand they have taken away all our food and we have nothing to eat anymore… so please, let us leave. There is so much to live for, so much to do…" The NKVD agent brushes her aside as Kulak parents lift their failing children's bodies up next to the train windows, hoping passengers inside will take pity, feed them something, anything. But the passengers recoil. They're revolted by the tiny, ancient faces, imploring them for food through the frosted glass. Hands brittle as icicles, skin as translucent as tissue paper, bellies bloated and distended, the bodies dangle in the reflections of the windows, pleading for life.

I squirm in my seat and ask myself: Where the hell was I in 1932?

A steam engine chugs along unplanted Ukraine fields in springtime, carrying feted Russian passengers through Stalin's starvation fields. Kulak children, as thin as marsh grass, chew on clumps of spring grass; others feebly scrounge around for bugs. Most, too weak to chew, too frail to crawl, stare up at the empty spring sky, their eyes not moving.

My mouth is dry.

On the outskirts of a small Ukrainian village, a Russian general, wearing a russet Papakha winter hat and a regulation brown leather greatcoat rimmed in fur, unbolts a Kulak granary door. Starving peasants look on in disbelief as tons of grain spill in lusty torrents onto the bare, cold ground. The general gestures to the grain, his voice swollen with contempt, "Look, you fools, it's been here all along!" Then he laughs as the Kulaks scramble to consume the grain. I get a good look at the general now. But he's no general, that for sure; he's not even Russian. No, he's Stalin's most beloved soul mate: My stepbrother, Beelzebub.

In the Kremlin. Stalin, Winston Churchill chatting over brandy and cigars long into the night. Through a stupor of smoke, Churchill casually asks, "Have the stresses of the war been as bad to you personally as carrying through the policy of the Collective Farms?" Stalin smiles, sparkles in his eyes, "Oh, no… the Collective Farm policy was a terrible struggle… Ten millions," holding up his hands as if to *emphasize his great burden. "It was fearful. Four years it lasted, but it was absolutely necessary... Absolutely necessary." A subtitle appears:* **Moscow, 1942**

I feel sick to my stomach. Will no one end this ride?

My carriage takes me down, with a swirl and a surge, down to the bottom of the bottom of the bottom of the Third Circle of Hell: Cineplex Genocide III.

On the wrap-around IMAX screen, flaming in Technicolor:

Kneeling, hands bound, a Chinese POW lowers his head above a freshly dug pit. He extends his neck as far as possible, as a courtesy and demonstration of courage. An Imperial Japanese Army officer looms above him, clad in a single-breasted yellow-khaki colored tunis, knee breeches, high leather boots, and a flat-topped peaked hat, draws his Masamune sword with all the precision of an artist from his scabbard. Gripping the sword's stingray skin tsuka with two clenched hands, he gently taps the edge of his two-foot blade, gracefully curved, on the nape of the prisoner's neck. It glitters in the last of the sunlight. Then he raises the sword above his head and with one powerful downward thrust decapitates the POW's head. His arteries explode, sounding like escaping gas... So fine is the swordsman's art that the thinnest tissue of uncut skin is left at the base of the man's neck. It holds his head to his torso, allowing the two to tilt forward together, before collapsing to the bottom of the grave. Severing on impact, the Chinaman's head rolls over, exposing his pale face and empty eyes. They stare up at the white winter sky. A subtitle appears: **Nanking, China: December, 1938**

I avert my eyes, too late. I lift them up to the sky, but there is no sky.

A Western diplomat, outfitted in a double-breasted, dark blue, heavy wool pea jacket and Breton fisherman's hat, peers through binoculars at the ancient, walled city of Nanking, smoldering in the late December light. From the deck of a naval vessel anchored on the Yangtze River opposite the Bund and Nanking's Hsiakwan Gate, he watches occupying Imperial Japanese soldiers corral fifty Chinese POWs at bayonet point. They wrap them in bristling rings of shiny barbwire, binding them together like human bales of hay. Further down shore, a machine gunner sets up an air-cooled, full automatic, heavy machine gun. Then he unloads 450 rounds of rimless ammunition into the bound mass in less than sixty seconds. As the last man falls onto the stack, soldiers skewer any remaining survivors with 20-inch bayonets attached to their Ariska rifles. The rifle's receivers are stamped with the Japanese Emperor's mark: A 16-petal chrysanthemum.

I struggle to maintain my composure.

Atop Zhongshan Gate, at Nanking's south end, Chinese POWs are made human targets. Imperial soldiers bayonet the prisoners standing in columns along the high stonewalls of the flaming city. As each one buckles, they're shoved over the ledge, falling down to their deaths.

I blink, but it does no good. The scenes remain; they get worse.

On Central Avenue, near Nanking's Big Circle, an infantryman struts about, marching as if in a one-man parade. Over his shoulder, he totes a 6.5-mm cavalry rifle. Impaled on the end of the bayonet is a Chinaman's head. At his feet lie the headless remains of men, women and children, strewn about like fallen acorns from an oak tree.

And worse.

On Zhongshan Avenue, Japanese militia tie captured Chinamen to a wooden pole beside the ruins of the city's breached wall. Then for fun, they lob a hand grenade at them from behind the corner of a bombed-out building. It explodes. When the smoke clears, they eagerly look, ready to enjoy their handiwork. The blast has grated the skin from their bones. They get such a kick out of this.

And worse.

Outside the city-limits of Nanking, Chinese POWs are forced to shovel dirt on fellow prisoners who lie bound at the bottom of slaughter pits. Japanese officers look on nonchalantly from the sidelines. Soon prisoners' muffled screams are heard— after that—silence.

I start to hyperventilate.

A column of Japanese KE-RI light tanks rumbles down a dusty road toward the stone archways of Hsiakwan Gate. In the center of the road, buried up to their necks in dirt, is a line of Chinese POWs. The tanks advance. As they approach, the POWs' eyes widen in terror. The tanks roll over them, bursting their skulls like watermelons. The tank drivers cheer.

Cruelty like this I have never seen before.

From the deck of a naval vessel, the Western diplomat peers through binoculars at the ancient, walled city, still burning in the early morning. Running for as far as the eye can see, are the distended bodies of thousands of Nanking's unburied dead. The Yangtze River is a ribbon of red. The Western diplomat lowers his binoculars, and for the first time, his face stands revealed. One thing's for sure, he's no diplomat. Not by a long shot. He's the Ambassador of Holocausts—my stepbrother.

I'm moved to get up out of my seat to strangle him. But then I'm reminded that this is just a movie. Just a movie.

*Japan's former Justice Minister Shigeto Nagano answers a reporter's question, "The Nanking massacre is a fabrication. Japan did not wage a war of aggression. Japan liberated colonies to create a co-prosperity sphere." Incredulous, the reporter nearly drops his microphone. Another reporter in the room raises his hand and declares, "I don't know Mr. Justice Minister: I know what I saw; I was there."
A subtitle appears:* **Japan, 1994**

My carriage takes me down, with a swirl and a surge, down to the bottom of the bottom of the bottom of the bottom of the Fourth Circle of Hell: Cineplex Genocide IV.

On the wrap-around IMAX screen, smoldering in Technicolor:

Dawn. A freight train crawls through creepy fog, dragging boxcars packed with Jews through the yawning mouth of Birkenau's Death Gate. Tiers of fences line the tracks, standing like barbwire forests and bristling with 6000 volts of electricity. Guard towers, manned by soldiers with machine guns, loom beyond. They cast down menacing eyes. On the far side of the Death Gate, a SS signalman can be seen

85

holding up a STOP board. Brakes squeal. The train slows... slows. It sounds like pigs at slaughter time in the train yard. On the unloading ramps, SS officers, camp guards, and attack dogs mill about. You can see the dogs' breath in the cold. In the station platform wings, Sonderkommandos prepare to pick up the carcasses of the Jewish dead who failed to survive the journey. As the train groans to a standstill, truculent SS officers converge at the boxcar doors, forcing them open, spitting out orders. Bleary-eyed and confused, somnolent Jews stumble out. "Männer!"; "Frauen und Kinder!"; "Männer!"; "Frauen und Kinder!" The Selection begins... "Gesund!"; "Ungesund!"; "Gesund!"; "Ungesund!"

The last train in, his work over for the morning, the SS signalman drops his STOP board on the station platform. Removing his peaked visor hat, marked with eagle wings and skull insignias, he surveys the dark wash of order before him. It's a signalman's feast: His Schadenfreude. He grins. Now it's time for bed.

I know that grin and I sure as hell know that face. My stepbrother's the signalman, of course. A subtitle appears: **Auschwitz-Birkenau, Poland: 1943**

I stir uncomfortably in my seat: *Where the hell was I in 1943?*

Inside a windowless concrete chamber, with low ceilings and dark, very dark, hundreds of naked Jews stand naked and trembling, clutching bars of soap, holding towels. Above, showerheads hang down. The walls are rough, bare, tinged with ghoulish green. The shower door shuts, locks. The children whimper and cry; their mothers try to reassure them.

On the flat roof of the facility, SS officers empty canisters of Zyklon-B through narrow induction vents, spanning the length of the roof. The heavy, granular pellets roll down long, dark shafts, raining down on the helpless people.

Jews, so many Jews, gasping for air. Those nearest the vents die instantly. Those further away die more slowly, more painfully. They stagger about, screaming, banging at the door to get out. A disinfector looks through the peephole. All's well.

I lower my head in shame. Unqualified shame.

Grotesque piles of lifeless Jews lie jammed into an elevator in a warehouse. It's moving up to the next floor. Inside is a team of Sonderkommandos. Hairless women lie dead at their feet, jaws pried back, gold fillings removed. The elevator doors part. They've arrived at Krema 2.

Sonderkommandos shovel dead Jews in the ovens, two and three at a time...

Above Birkenau, malodorous smoke invades the azure skies, hooded crows rising to make a path of black wind.

I put my head in my hands.

Sonderkommandos push a rickety cart weighed down with mounds of human ashes along a quiet, country road. They stop beside a pond to dump the load of ashes. It takes a long, very long time. At a watchful distance, a young SS officer picks his teeth with a pocketknife. He nervously watches the dark sky, worried about afternoon rain.

I cry, and feel no shame.

Inside the Oval office, behind his oak desk, President Franklin Roosevelt berates John McCloy, Assistant Secretary of War: "Bomb Auschwitz? Shut it down? Why, the idea!... We'll be accused of bombing those innocent people! We'll be accused of participating in this horrible business!" Taken aback, McCloy's momentarily silent. At length, he nods his head, "Yes, Mr. President. Of course. The war effort must come first."

Seated in the wings, a White House staffer takes notes. He seems to breathe a sigh of relief. He bears a striking resemblance to the SS signalman on the Birkenau platform, though I can't be absolutely certain.

My carriage takes me down, with a swirl and a surge, down to the bottom of the bottom of the bottom of the bottom of the bottom of the Fifth Circle of Hell: Cineplex Genocide V.

On the wrap-around IMAX screen, aflame in Technicolor:

Midwinter. Starving Chinese peasants huddle around an unlit kitchen table, gnawing on stripped tree bark and ground-up twigs, in a village in Liaoning Province.

Another village, another house: Famished family members chew on the tender body parts of one of their neighbor's children.

87

Across the street, another Chinese family consumes the remains of their neighbor's child, exchanged for their own, saving them all the pain of slaughtering their own children.

Looking on, through the frosty window, getup in a peasant's field hat and blue cotton national uniform, buttoned at the top, is the Cannibal of the Ages himself: You-know-who. He smirks as he chews on a handful of twigs: Exemplary entertainment. A subtitle appears: **The Great Leap Forward: China 1960**

I push at the safety bar at my waist, but it won't budge. I getting used to it: I'm a prisoner of Hollywood and I'm not going anywhere until the movie is over and the lights come up.

On the edge of a windy field under color-drained Chinese skies, a column of blindfolded counterrevolutionaries faces a Red Guards firing squad. A student commander cries, "Death to all counterrevolutionaries!" The firing squad fires; the column collapses, joining their fallen comrades on the fields of Hebei Province.

I wince; I nervously tap my foot.

Red Guards on a rampage. They burn textbooks and ancient artifacts in Beijing streets. Bonfires light the night; Red Guards chant, "Mao Zedong Thought is the source of our life... Whoever dares oppose him will be hunted down—and erased."

Across China, in hundreds of cities, towns and villages, Red Guards torch Buddhist temples, mosques, and Catholic churches. The flames touch the night, making burning nooses in the smoky sky for as far as the eye can see...

I adjust my hat. I pull it down a little over my eyes.

Chairman Mao Zedong stands atop Tiananmen Gate. Millions of Red Guards march before him, waving their Little Red Books, hailing him as their god. "May Chairman Mao live ten thousand years, ten million years!" Mao drinks in the exultation like green tea. Leaning against the granite Monument to the People's Heroes is someone we all know by now. Dressed in a bright olive-green PLA uniform, a Mao hat shades his dark, Oriental eyes. He looks at Mao with terribly jealous eyes. He cannot take his eyes off him.

I nod knowingly. That's the man I intend to take on.

President Lyndon Johnson delivering a foreign policy address to a Washington, DC-based think tank: "Lasting peace can never come to Asia as long as the 700 million people of mainland China are isolated by their rulers from the outside world. We persist because we believe that cooperation, not hostility, is the way of the future. That day is not here yet. It may be long in coming, but it is clearly on the way, and come it must." Clad in a spiffy gray Hickey Freeman pinstripe suit, punctuated by a silk silver tie knotted over a shimmering white button-down shirt, the Lord of Violent Revolution, my stepbrother, snoozes at the back of the auditorium, snoring really rather loudly.

My carriage takes me down, with a swirl and a surge, down to the bottom of the bottom of the bottom of the bottom of the bottom of the bottom of the Sixth Circle of Hell: Cineplex Genocide VI.

On the wrap-around IMAX screen, afire in Technicolor:

The Khmer Rouge evacuates Phnom Penh, removing city dwellers and merchants from their homes and workplaces at gunpoint. Youthful soldiers herd hundreds of terrified inhabitants into chaotic lines on muddy, congested streets, marching them on foot toward the city's outskirts under hard driving torrential April rains. A subtitle appears: **Year Zero, 1975, Cambodia**

I bite my lip.

Phnom Penh lies empty, roasting in the rot of neglect. Abandoned cars clutter empty sidewalks; dead motorbikes lie about like junk; bicycles, discarded hastily on street corners, rust. Main street shop shelves are stripped bare; outdoor cafes and sidewalk restaurants look like graveyards. Norodom Boulevard: a canal of snarling weeds interspersed with islands of broken glass and debris. Wild dogs bark at Central Market; rats roam about as free as birds; flies feast on dead cats. The people of Phnom Penh have vanished.

Thousands of Cambodian city-dwellers advance in long lines under armed guard through the hot, humid Asian countryside. The young cry; the old and frail collapse, dying off like fleas, in the steamy, roadside dust. Heads down, submissive, the strong push on as best they can.

I smack my lips. I need water. Now.

Tuol Sleng. South of Phnom Penh. Schoolhouse compound walls encased in corrugated metal sheets strung with electrified barbwire. Within the fortified walls, cheerful yellow lights shine through schoolhouse windows, making merry the look of the night. Inside, torture victims scream now and again; terrible screams; voices beg for mercy, long into the damp summer night...

In the schoolyard courtyard, nothing moves, not even a mouse.

I breathe deep. I look up at the low ceiling. I breathe out.

Khmer Rouge prisoners transported in the back of a covered truck down a country road in the Asian dark. Headlights feed off the night, nibbling at its edges. Columns of red dust swirl up, like instantaneous tornadoes. The truck finally turns into a rural compound, identified only by a rough wooden sign: Choeung Ek.

I breathe in.

Dawn. People from Phnom Penh digging shallow graves in the open fields: Doctors, diplomats, priests, monks, aristocrats, teachers, and children. They dig, they dig, they dig. Done, a Khmer Rouge soldier, not quite eighteen, cries out, "What is rotten must be removed!" Then black-clad executioners attack them, bludgeoning, stabbing them to death. Others pick up screaming children, bashing their heads against mango trees, staining them with blood for good.

Beyond the scene of the morning massacre, seated under a blooming mango tree, and whittling bamboo with a crude knife is, of course, my stepbrother. He wears a Khmer Rouge uniform and looks as though he hasn't a care in the world. Another subtitle appears: **Year Zero, plus three: Choeung Ek, Cambodia, May 1978**

Now I need a drink. I real honest-to-goodness drink.

International tourists file past a Buddhist stupa erected in the center of Choeung Ek's killing fields. 9,000 human skulls, placed side by side on wooden shelves, lie sealed behind glass. Arranged according to age and gender, some shelves are piled very high.

I need a Scotch.

At a foreign policy conference, Zbigniew Brzezinski, President Carter's former national security advisor, states matter-of-factly, "I encouraged the Chinese to support Pol Pot... Pol Pot was an abomination. We could never support him, but China could." A news photographer snaps Brzezinski's picture, then lowers his Leica and throws him an incredibly cynical look and a wink. It's my stepbrother again. He's on top of everything.

My carriage takes me down, with a swirl and a surge, down to the bottom of the bottom of the bottom of the bottom of the bottom of the bottom of the bottom of the Seventh Circle of Hell: Cineplex Genocide VII.

On the wrap-around IMAX screen, ablaze in Technicolor:

A small brick church in Ntarama. Inside, Hutu tribesmen club Tutsis to death. Families cower between church pews, pleading for them to stop. Machete-wielding Hutus hack at children, even babies. They seek them out in the aisles, at the crossing, in the choir. Even at the altar. Most savagely at the altar, below a humble cross, where a figurine of Christ hangs, looking down on the slaughter. A title appears: **Rwanda, 1994**

I put my hands up in front of my eyes.

Washed in morning rain, a turbulent African sky. Below, bloated bodies of Tutsis carried away like logs down the swollen Kigara River. They flow toward Lake Victoria. On either side of the riverbanks, barefoot Hutu children give chase, as distended bodies surf Rwanda's killing streams. Sitting on a stool on a bridge over the gruesome river is a Huti, his fishing line in the water. He chews on a piece of river grass, watching the bodies pass in droves below. He's an African carbon copy of Beelzebub.

I remove my hands from my eyes. The tears are gone; only guilt remains.

President Clinton waves goodbye to White House staffers as he, Hilary and Chelsea cross the south lawn to climb aboard Marine One. Off to Camp David for the weekend. The helicopter lifts off—a strange dragonfly against the swampy sky. The helicopter pilot flashes a thumbs up to the crowd gathered on the White House lawn to bid the First Family goodbye. Even behind the aviator goggles and helmet I know. I know... How the hell did he ever get security clearance, anyway?

My carriage takes me down, with a swirl and a surge, down to the bottom of the bottom of the bottom of the bottom of the bottom of the bottom of the bottom of the bottom of the Eighth and Last Circle of Hell: Cineplex Genocide VIII.

On the wrap-around IMAX screen, on fire in Technicolor:

Newsreel footage of Gen. Ratko Mladic, commander of the Bosnian Serb army, mingling among Muslim civilians on a warm July day. He pats a Bosnian boy on the head, gently reassuring him. "Don't be afraid... Take it easy. Thirty buses are coming... to deliver you... No one will hurt you..." He's a gentle as a pastor on Easter Sunday. A subtitle appears: **Srebrenica, Bosnia: June 1995**

I sigh, expecting, at last, relief.

Rough footage of six Muslim men and boys in dirty shirts and jeans being forced at gunpoint from a truck by Serb Scorpion militiamen on a country road in broad daylight. They're made to lie facedown in a ditch, hands bound. More Serbs arrive... Taunting them, the Serbs escort the men and boys into an open clearing. Sunlight streams down lighting the tall grass, making the meadow sparkle and glow. Haltingly, a Muslim man steps under the trees. A soldier shoots him in the back. He falls.

Another captive shuffles ahead. Rifle fire; he, too, falls. A third and a fourth. They lie dead in the open field as flies buzz round.

I look down.

The surviving men carry off their comrades' bodies and place them in a concrete shack, somewhere east of Sarajevo. A Serb soldier demands they lie down next to the corpses. Then he fires at them through the doorway. Their bodies twitch.

92

I look up, I look down, anywhere other than at the screen.

In a celebratory mood, the militiamen amble off down the village road with their Kalashnikovs slung over their shoulders like Serbian flags. One of the Kalashnikov-toting soldiers going by is definitely Beelzebub, looking more than a little self-satisfied.

I push at the safety bar, but it won't budge. All I want to do is take Beelzebub down, anyway I can.

Gen. Ratko Mladic is conducting an impromptu interview on Belgrade TV. He can barely contain his exuberance. "We are giving this town to the Serbian people. The moment has finally come for us after the 19th century rebellion against the Turks, to take our revenge on them..."

Then—as if someone had suddenly stopped the projector— Mladic's image freezes, melts, burns through from the center out, and the IMAX screens go bright white. The room becomes totally awash in light, brighter than Serbian sunlight.

I can't emphasize the relief I feel crossing out of the dark.

Then, instead of going down, down, down, my carriage reverses direction, and takes me up, with a swirl and a surge, up past all the bottoms of the bottoms of all the Circles of Hell, right back into Mel's. Sweet Mel's! Never did a diner look so damn good!

I guess Mel finally paid his light bill!!!

I'm finally back in the land where I belong, in a place where they serve beautiful blueberry pancakes. The only issue is—there's no one here. Not one soul. It's just me and my conscience full up with the knowledge that I screwed up.

I shoulda been there... woulda been there but for... No, I plead the Fifth. I can't reveal my hand... Not just yet.

Then through the Pioneer speakers mounted in the ceiling comes a voice from Oz. "Welcome to Mel's..."

93

Oh I just know, this is going to be good. Don't ask me why, I can just tell.

"We have one question," says the voice, a deep baritone voice that commands respect.

I've always loathed pop quizzes whenever the Old Man sprung them on me, but answer the voice as politely as I can, "Yes, and what might that be?…"

"What's your name…?"

Naturally, I resist the temptation to prevaricate because, well, I'm Christ. Nevertheless, even I have to think twice before answering candidly—and who wouldn't after being excoriated on silver screens a thousand miles high for failing to save the 20th century from genocide?

So I let it all hang out.

"I AM THE CHRIST…," I say.

Then all joy breaks out.

"AND I AM MEL!" the voice bounces back. Then comes Mel. Out from behind the cash register, hopping more merrily a kangaroo, in black tie and tails. "OH, YA BEAUTIFUL BASTARD YA!!! YA BEAUTIFUL BASTARD! WHAT TOOK YA SO LONG?" Mel bounces over, hugs me like an old war buddy presumed dead, and later discovered—very much alive. "I told those whackers ye'd come! I told them ye would. And ye have! So bite me, Dave Letterman! And ye, too, Connan O'Brien! Bite me!"

"Nice to see you, too," I say, trying to get a fix on who the hell this guy is.

"Which is why, despite being made the butt of their merciless jokes on late night television fer TEN YEARS, I WAITED PATIENTLY EVERY CHRISSIE EVE FER YA TO COME!

"I TOLD 'EM, I TOLD EVERYONE, THAT THE DINKY-DI CHRIST WOULD RETURN TO EARTH ONE DAY AND WHEN HE DID HE'D COME BY MEL'S! SO GO GAG ON A CROSS DAVE AND CONNAN AND ALL YE OTHER NONBELIEVERS! MY CHRIST—THE FAIR DINKUM JESUS—CAME BACK AND WENT TO MEL'S!"

I can only hope for Mel's sake that none of that Aussie slang was as offensive as it sounded. I'm in no mood. I've had obscenity for a lifetime after that ride, believe me.

Mel looks at me gravely, his dark eyes bearing secrets and gifts. He lowers his voice in strict confidence. "So ye want to know why I believe ye are who ye say ye are? Why I know beyond a reasonable doubt that ye're the fair dinkum Christ Himself?"

I nod my head yes.

"Ye may not know it yet, but this being Hollywood, there're imposters and impersonators everywhere! I mean everywhere! So be on guard, beware..."

Actually, the Old Man said the same, so I believe it.

"Every Chrissie Eve, I'd be waiting and waiting fer ya, and because Dave and Connan would make fun of me on late night T.V., about me waiting at my restaurant fer ye to come back, after I made my movie, one or two would show up at the door, claiming to be ye. And always they would be dressed the same way, in rags and long hair, and sometimes carrying a cross. So maybe they were telling the truth and maybe they weren't. We really couldn't say. Until we decided to put them to the test. Which was to put them on the Golden Age of Genocide ride...

"Before the ride, it was always the same with them: I AM THE MESSIAH. But after the ride, it was like, 'Who me, Christ? Not a chance. Say, my goodness, *look* what time it is. Got to go! Merry shopping you know! Bye now!'

"I think we both know why they did that: No one but the real Christ would ever take the rap fer the Golden Age of Genocide. That's why when ye did, I knew that ye were the One. The Real One. The Fair Dinkum Himself! Because only the dinky-di Christ Himself could tell the truth about something like that! Admit to making such a beaut of a mistake! Get my logic?"

Whoever Mel is, he's impressive. "Good thinking," I tell him. Then more than a little curious, I ask, "How did you get involved in all this?"

Mel looks stricken. Somehow I've offended him. Don't ask me how. I suppose I should know who he is but I don't. At least, I can't remember.

He looks at me with pleading eyes. "I'm Mel, like I said. The Mel of Mel's and also known as Mel Gibson, the writer, director, producer, and yes, gourmet caterer fer 'The Passion of the Christ!!!' That little boffo movie that shook the world! Surely, you saw it on Netflix!?"

Oh, now I know who he is... yes, yes, now I remember... I *thought* I recognized that face.

My first impulse is to genuflect. The truth is *The Passion of the Christ* single-handedly rescued the sinking ship of Christianity in 2004. The Old Man and I owe Mel big time for that. Back then was one of Christianity's bleakest periods—not as bleak as the Inquisition, naturally, but still pretty bleak. Our polling numbers were in freefall, priest sex scandals were in the headlines, and the Catholic church's position on abortion rights and the use of contraception weren't doing us any favors either, to say nothing of Islamic fundamentalism going head-to-head with us. Those were precarious days, for sure. And Mel's movie saved us. Saved two thousand years of evangelical work in nine months at the box office. To be sure, Mel's a hero back in Heaven.

96

Truly impressed, I say, "I saw your film seventeen times… It's an absolute classic."

Naturally, those are the very words all filmmakers live for.

"OH YE BEAUTIFUL BASTARD YOU!" Mel beams. "THANK YOU! THANK YOU!"

Mel starts to cry. Even I practically start crying along with him because I'm so happy for him—and of course for Christianity, too!

"The thing is," Mel says, embracing me again, "even though ye were gone for too long and shoulda come back to stop all those horrible genocides before they happened, I think ya'll find that people, by and large, will be very forgiving because, well, that's what ye taught us to do—forgive one another's transgressions. What's more we've also learned in yer absence, and I personally think that we've learned it a little too well, that WE CAN'T LIVE WITHOUT YOU!"

It's then that Mel hollers over my shoulder, as if to the billboards floating above Sunset Strip, "NOW HIT IT, MEL'S ANGELS!"

And as the overhead lights flash off—Mel, what's with the light bill?—and then back on again, everything's miraculously changed. A chorus of singers clad in white leather jackets and shiny leather pants, appears on a platform stage behind the cash register, singing, well, what else? Handel's "The Hallelujah Chorus."

"And He shall reign forever and ever; King of kings! and Lord of lords! And He shall reign forever and ever; King of kings! and Lord of lords! Hallelujah! Hallelujah! Hallelujah!"

And everywhere I look Mel's is full up, jammed stem to stern with Hollywood's elite, the likes of which would make the average movie star fan faint.

Now, this is more the kind of reception a guy like me would expect!

But the truly great news is Mel takes me by the shoulder, cranes his neck around, and looks me in the eyes, and says, "King of kings and Lord of lords, brekkie's on me!..."

"Good onya," I reply.

"Oh ye beautiful bastard ye, what took ye so long? *I've been waitin' fer ye forever!*"

With visions of blueberry pancakes dancing in my head, Mel escorts me over to the star-studded receiving line to shake hands with his star-studded friends. Who am I to mind? The way I look at it, any friend of Mel's is a friend of mine.

CHAPTER FOUR

IAS 600 knots. Cruising at Angels 40 in my G-suit. President Bush strutting across the deck of the U.S.S. Lincoln in his puffed-up flight suit never looked so good. Hunkered down, reclining at 30 degrees in the single-seat cockpit of my Fighting Falcon F-16, I feel as snug as crabgrass in tall, weedy grass. I'm sailing, sailing due west towards that dream town, L.A., my aluminum cloud screaming at super sonic speeds. Twenty-knot headwinds, ceiling and visibility unlimited. NOSIG. Feet dry. Yes, siree, Bob. The pilot's life is good to me.

I squeeze my side stick controller, just because. My Viper banks right, as responsive as a woman in the right mood... That's all it takes— my gentle hand, the kiss of my wrist. I love this bird. She soars under me; she roars. A few years back I pinched her from the Davis Monthan Air force Base Bone Yard in the heart of the Sonora Desert outside Tucson. As good as new she was when I lifted her. And today she's still capable of hurtling some very nice ordinances—a whole quiver of arrows, if need be, like the AGM-65 Mavericks and the AMRAAM sidewinders and the AGM-119 Penguins. They make a lot of noise and put on quite a show. And just for my kind of fun in the left wing root there's a really, really nice M61 Vulcan 20mm Gatling gun, that I'm dying to unload. This broad has everything. We make for quite a team.

Passing over Lordsburg, New Mexico. Latitude: 32.20:50.665N, Longitude: 108:42:31.244W. ETA LA, seventy-six minutes. It's a perfect morning. The perfect morning to bomb my little stepbrother back into the Bronze Age. I pry open my visor, rip off my oxygen mask, and crack a bottle of Bombay Rum I purloined at a liquor store I can't remember where. I unscrew the top and knock back a couple of hits. Fucking Magic. Definitely.

Forgive me, for I have sinned. Flying stoned is just my kind of thing.

My music and ECM on, I'm flying invisible at Warp One. I'm a cloud inside a cloud, a shadow on top a shadow. Yes, siree, the Viper's a drop-dead beautiful machine: Fly-by-wire controls, lots of countermeasures, cockpit upgrade, a pretty decent little computer, and a data bus to die for. Considering the price, what more could I have asked for? Truth be told, she's one hundred percent FM. For those who don't have a clue about fighter lingo, that's short for Fucking Magic. She's definitely all of that.

I knock back another belt. These are good times. Then I hit the blower. I hit it hard. Really crank this broad up. And up and up. Speed of Heat, Warp One... Then onto Mach 1. Bravo Zulu: I'm really getting my kicks now.

I love the taste of Bombay Rum in the morning.

Like rawhide dried across a rack, my skin draws taut. I'm pulling a full 4-Gs, maybe more. I'm the 800-pound gorilla in the room. Am going, going... under... Oh yes, def, I'm losing my bubble now. Slipping, slipping away from consciousness. Right: I'm blacking out. Eject? Eject? Oh please, unholy ghosts, don't make me a full-fledged member of the Martin-Baker ejection club! Then mercifully, my speed jeans start to do their glorious thing. Now comes that nice sensation: Compressed air massaging my ankles, nursing my legs, massaging my abdomen. I'm back in my bubble again. Not even a crash diet of ephedrine could shed my G-force pounds any faster. In no time that I can tell, I'm back to being 200 pounds again. Farewell you Martin-Baker Fan Club suckers. They'll be no bail out for me today. I can take it like the best of them.

My thoughts return to my mission: To taking out Mel's. I really could use a little target practice. Like, I'm ashamed to say, it's been more than a little while since I took out a whole family cruising down the highway in their SUV with my Gatling gun. Some might even say that I've exercised considerable self-restraint.

Now I take in the inordinate glory of the blue skies. I look north, then south: Vast territories of endless space. Today they all seem mine. I'm in a good place right now, at the doorway to grand events. In fact, for the first time in a long, long while, I find being alive acceptable. Which is a very nice change of pace. So long as I've got my Bombay Rum, I imagine I can fly this big sweet broad forever.

I slam into some turbulence. We rattle about like a car without shocks down San Francisco streets. I brush my side stick controller and she obeys my desires. She takes me down. I retreat to Warp One. I don't do Mach 1 the way I used to. Perhaps it's my age or something.

Cruising nice and even like, I switch on my satellite TV, just for the sake of company. That's right, if I'm perfectly honest about it, I can't do without it. Not many of us can these days. We're all visual junkies. It's a curse that goes with the times, I'm afraid. And what comes on?

100

What's the first thing that pops out at me, disturbing the tranquility of my flight? That's right: My fucking stepbrother. He's already grandstanding on KTLA-TV. Live. Happily, at this hour, it's only local coverage, but still, He's got press, and He looks pretty good, considering He's a couple of thousand years old. To be frank, He doth shine, especially under that shining umbrella of floodlights. It looks like a media Love Fest over there. And that's going to be a problem for me. He's got more magnetism than the North Pole. More star power than the North Star. Simply said, I'm in trouble.

I spike the volume. Sadie Sherwood of KTLA-TV is conducting an impromptu interview with him. This I got to hear: "Why should any of us believe that you're Christ and not just some Hollywood imitator?"

Mel butts into the picture frame, saying, "Because no one but the Real One would take the rap for lolly-gagging in Heaven while the 20th century went to genocide in a hand basket! That's why!!!"

"Well, is that what you say, Mr. Christ, or is that what he says?"

Her camera zeros in on Christ. "Si enim dimiseritis hominibus peccata eorum dimittet et vobis Pater vester caelestis delicta vestra. Si autem non dimiseritis hominibus nec Pater vester dimittet peccata vestra," He answers, forgetting that Latin isn't exactly a live language around these parts anymore.

Seeing the perplexed look pass over Sadie's face, He tries another choice: English. "For if you will forgive men their offences, your heavenly Father will forgive you also your offences. But if you will not forgive men, neither will your Father forgive you your offences."

Oh brother. Tantamount to a public confession that last yarn is. His non-denial affirmation that he really, truly, positively, and forever SCREWED UP. I have only this to say to Him: *Qui s'excuse s'accuse!* His polling numbers should be in the toilet before noon.

"Meaning what exactly?" Sadie presses.

"I was unavoidably delayed..."

Oh yeah, I shout at the screen. Try telling that to Pol Pot's victims! Like that's gonna make the dead at Auschwitz feel any better! You didn't do a thing! Not one thing! Over all those decades! You should be ashamed of yourself!

Sadie moves on with her mild interrogation. Well, what do you expect? This is local news, not a Bill Moyers PBS Special.

"So what will you *do* now that you're back?" she inquires, a little too respectfully for my tastes.

Christ shifts his weight and lifts His eyes toward the lights—never a good thing on television. Didn't anyone ever tell Him that? It makes Him look befuddled. Well, that's generous. It makes Him look slightly daft. Which is actually quite a good thing since it's in front of millions of Angelinos. He's definitely not ready yet for primetime TV. Obviously, He needs a media consultant. And He needs one bad.

When He finally gets around to answering Sadie's question, after a bout of looking loopy, He doesn't sound too much like a knucklehead, which is what I expected.

"No one lights a lamp and puts it in a place where it will be hidden or under a bowl," He says. "Instead he puts it on its stand, so that those who come in may see the light. I hope to light a lamp."

"Hear Him! Hear Him!" Mel yells on camera. It's as if he'd hit the lottery and wasn't afraid to tell everyone. "He comes to light a lamp! He comes to a lamp! That's exactly what I told Jay Leno He'd do when He returned! Exactly that!

"Did he believe me? Oh, no! Of course not! He made fun of me in his monologue instead! 'That's right, ladies and gentlemen, Mel's spending yet another Christmas Eve at his diner on Sunset waiting for

Christ to come back... And to pass the time, he's showing his customers Loony Tunes...'

"So I want an apology, Jay! A public apology, you whacker you! You won't have Mel Gibson to ridicule anymore! You're through!"

Sadie stares through Mel, continuing her interview. "Couldn't you be a bit more specific about your intentions now that you're back?"

Christ obliges. "Do not think that I have come to destroy the law, or the prophets. I have not come to destroy, but to fulfill."

Oh, yeah, right. A fat lot of good your light's gonna do all those starving Kulaks back in 1932!

"And how do you intend to accomplish this fulfillment exactly?"

"Ask and it will be given to you; seek and you will find; knock and the door will be opened to you..." he says far too cryptically to be worth a damn.

"Hmmmm," Sadie says, more than a little out of her depth.

"Well, what else is on your agenda then, Mr. Christ? What other plans do you have for the people of your faith?"

"That they may be the children of their Father who is in heaven, who maketh his sun to rise upon the good, and bad, and raineth upon the just and the unjust."

"But specifically, Mr. Christ, do you intend to support a constitutional amendment that would guarantee, for instance, Christians the right to display Nativity scenes in public spaces alongside menorahs at Christmastime?"

He says this: "Their father raineth upon the just and unjust."

Whatever the hell that means.

"Will you give us other hints about your plans? Will you run for Pope? Take on the job of U.N. Secretary General? Maybe head up Amnesty International? What exactly will you do?"

This much He answers. "It is written, not in bread alone doth man live, but in every word that proceedeth from the mouth of God..." And that's it. No more, no less. After which Mel barges in again waving Sadie away. "You heard the Man. He's traveled a long way today and it's time he sat down and had his brekkie!"

Ignoring Sadie as she does her on-camera closing, Mel takes Christ at the elbow, escorting Him to the head of a receiving line of Hollywood's rich and famous that stretches from one end of Mel's to the other. What strikes me is that Christ appears to be so at home and so very much at ease in His new Sunset Strip surroundings. He's got that easy feeling about Him that I couldn't imitate ever. Of course, it helps a lot that He makes the sign of the cross over everyone's forehead that he stumbles across. That's bound to win Him friends and expand His circle of influence. Allowing myself a very brief moment of generosity of spirit, I actually find it quite moving.

"Mr. Christ! Mr. Christ! Choose me to be your new disciple!!!!" someone in the crowd shouts.

"No, me! Me!" another calls.

Still another, "I wanna be one, too, Mr. Christ! Me, too!"

That gets my stepbrother going. He responds in a voice sweet as wine, "Come ye after me, and I will make you to be fishers of men and women. I will choose twelve among you to be my disciples..."

I should have seen this coming from a thousand miles off. I should have known He'd try to pick up the best of the best first round Hollywood draft picks. Damn Him. Damn my little stepbrother. I liked it a whole lot better when He was dead.

Mel's first up, which is what you'd expect. He's been waiting all these years, after all. Fair's fair.

"Please, please, dear Christ," he says, "choose me to be yer first disciple. I'm ready. Am I ever ready. I've been waiting nearly twenty years fer this chance. I suffered humiliation, was mocked and ridiculed, because I believed, truly believed, that ye would be returning to Earth one day... And today—yes Jay Leno ye better go hide yourself!—I've been proven right! Exactly right! Plus, as ye already know, I produced and directed—even co-wrote—'The Passion of the Christ!' I did all the catering, too! Imagine that! Just so I could make the best possible movie about YA! But that was only the theatrical manifestation of my love fer ye! My love goes deeper, much, much deeper. Did ye know that in Malibu I built a chapel with my own money to celebrate my faith? It's a beautiful place, where only Latin Tridentine Mass is celebrated. And every day I attend mass, which doesn't make me perfect, but at least ye've got to know I'm trying!

"Like I'm sure ye heard about me getting busted doing 87 mph in a 45 mph zone in Malibu, being drunk and trash-talking that cop with my anti-Semitic ravings. But that wasn't me speaking! Ye and I both know that in my soul of souls I'M NO BIGOT!!! THE FACT IS, MR. CHRIST, I LOVE JEWS! I LOVE YA! AND YA'RE A JEW! THERE, THAT'S PROOF! AND I TOOK WHAT I SAID BACK: JEWS ARE NOT RESPONSIBLE FOR ALL THE WARS IN THE WORLD!

"So now I'm off booze completely. I haven't had a gut full of piss—not even a weenie coldie—since forever. Ye can check my breath if ye don't believe me! I only partake in a weenie bit of communion wine at Tridentine Mass, which helps fill me with the Holy Spirit! What's the harm?

"And though politically I've lived a Republican life, unlike ye who's probably a Democrat by birth, I'm good friends with Michael Moore. We're cobbers, best friends. That says something positive about me, I'm sure, because Moore's more liberal than George McGovern!

"And I have done Democratic things before: Like I marched against the Iraq war! Spoke out against federal funding fer embryonic stem-cell research, too. Definitely I'm against all cloning! I also spoke out in favor of saving Terri Schiavos's life. There's no way she should have been taken off that respirator! Bless her soul! And yes, though I used to be a supporter of the death penalty, I'm perfectly open to reconsidering my position because as ye know the Roman Catholic Church is adamantly opposed to it. I'm always up fer tender mercies. It's the Christian way.

"Now I know ye might have also heard about my attitude towards gays. And it's true, I've said some things—some unprintable things, but I've made amends. Like I invited homosexual and lesbian filmmakers onto my set to teach them about how Hollywood really works. I did that on my own, without prompting by my publicist! On the pathway to love and understanding, tolerance is a way station, right, Mr. Christ?

"One last bit of self-promotion. This is Hollywood, after all, where self-promotion is a recognized art form… Everyone knows that I've stopped pulling pranks on the set, fer which I was more than a weenie bit famous. And everyone's forgiven me fer all of my past stunts. Julia Roberts's forgiven me! That says a lot. And Jodie Foster's forgiven me fer licking that wagon wheel on the set of *Maverick*! Thank you, Jodie! And I've also canned my Elmer Fudd voice. I swore on the cross that I would never again direct a funeral scene using Elmer Fudd's voice! And if ye still don't believe me, ask Helen Hunt: She's the one that put me straight! Bless you, Helen!

"So believe me, I'm all grown up, Mr. Christ. And I'm so rapt that ye're back! I know now that JEWS ARE THE BEST!"

He doesn't hesitate to welcome Mel into His discipleship. He carves an invisible cross over his forehead and, in a voice filled with the sunshine of righteous, says, "Ask and it will be given to you; seek and you will find; knock and the door will be opened to you. For every one

106

that asketh, receiveth; and he that seeketh, findeth; and to him that knocketh, it shall be opened. Yes, Mel Gibson, maker of *The Passion of the Christ* and genuinely reformed anti-Semitic, you will be my first disciple..."

Hopping up and down like a roo, Mel throws his fist triumphantly, saying, "The passion of Christ is BACK! Hallelujah! Hallelujah!! Christ, the Lord! HE HAS RISEN INDEED. TAKE THAT JAY LENO!"

My stepbrother shuffles down the receiving line. I want to drag out a bottle of Pepto-Bismol. I must have a touch of airsickness. Besides, what lies ahead doesn't bode well. If He can get Mel, He can get anyone. But now for some fun; I deserve a little fun, don't I? Yes, I believe I do. I squeeze my side stick controller, taking my Viper down, down, down. Down through clouds burnt around the edges like crisp marshmallows. When I finally break through, I receive my reward for putting up with Mel, my first target practice. I get a visual on a Mercury SUV. A family of five sings Christmas carols inside, barreling down Interstate10, northeast of Dos Cabezas, Arizona. I line up behind it, lock and fire.

Splash.

All that remains is a pothole as wide as Fifth Avenue—a smoky lake. Santa needn't bother to climb down their chimney tonight. I suppose that means they'll be more presents for yours truly?

I return to Angels 37, leaving the road kill far behind. I tune in my stepbrother again. Hands down it's got to be the best TV out there today. KTLA-TV's carrying him *live*. *Live*, I tell you, *live*. Do you have any idea when the last time was I got any *live* press coverage? I'll tell you when: After the fall of Baghdad, up to and including the time U.S. Special Forces nailed the Butcher of Baghdad, my pal Abu Musab al-Zarqaw, in his safe house with a 500-pound bomb. Some safe house that turned out to be. Say what you will about Abu Musab al-Zarqaw, he was a genius extremist's extremist.

Christ presses the flesh, like a regular politician running for city council. In a nice bit of grassroots campaigning upgraded for the occasion, He carves out cute little invisible crosses over people's foreheads as he makes his way down the receiving line.

Actor Tom Cruise comes up next, wearing an "I Take Zoloft" tee shirt. Uncharacteristically, he looks more kind than cocky. Clearly, something revolutionary has happened to him. As the television lights shower down on him, he slips into character—his Generic Tom Cruise character—only this time in reverse. Instead of being his customary cocky, egocentric character right from the get-go, he radiates the sunshine of humility. He pours it on faster than you can say "Dianetics." He's so, so selfless that, at first, I don't recognize him. His first act as disciple-in-waiting is to embrace Christ like a soft cashmere blanket. Then he kneels and offers him all his earthly possessions, among other things.

"Welcome to Mel's, dear Jesus. You know I'd do anything for you. I'll co-star with you in any movie. I'll even be your gofer or chauffer. Whatever you want, I will do. No job is too small, no assignment too menial. I'm your guy. Just please answer me this: "How's my guy L. Ron Hubbard doing up in Heaven?"

Christ smiles, which is enough to relieve Tom's curiosity.

"Don't get me wrong. I'm no longer one of his apostles roaming the earth, spreading the Gospel—according to L. Ron Hubbard. I just appreciate everything he did for me. I was one of his biggest success stories. His Scientology Study Tech cured my dyslexia! Of that I'm convinced! But I'm done with him and the Church of Scientology now—I swear. I've given up any leadership role I might have had in the Church, having resigned my leadership role in the hush hush secret

secret Operating Thetan 7 years ago. And I have been faithful to my pledge ever since: I divulge its secrets to no one. Not even you.

"I'm rid of them! I haven't written them a check in ages. Not one! That's because I became disillusioned. Disillusioned about their illusions, though I must confess there're those days when I'm tempted to fall back in with them.

"Which is just one more reason why I want to be YOUR disciple, Christ. Your disciple! I gotta have a fresh start. Gotta believe in something again! Scientology, Christianity, it's all the same to me! Illusion, delusion! What's the dif? For you, I'm willing to get back on the stump! Willing to campaign for you and your New Wave Christianity! Praise Jesus! Praise L. Ron! It's all the same to me!

"Still, I've got to get him out of my mind. If I could only sleep at night, just a few precious winks. But he's always there. Always, always there. I wake up in cold sweats every, every night because he's always there, staring down on me—the Master of the Universe, with those bright eyes. Yes, it's always the same, always L. Ron Hubbard, asking me the same question: 'Why have you forsaken me?' It's too much! Too much to take! But now that I know he's safely squirreled away in Heaven, maybe I'll be okay. Yes, I can be okay again, especially if you make me one of your disciples. I'd give almost anything to see *your* face in my room at night. I've definitely had enough of seeing L. Ron Hubbard's. And I know now that I should have knocked on your door first, Christ—not his. I should have come to you to cure my dyslexia! How could I have been such a fool?

"I know that you might have heard a little something about what happened to me with the French a long time ago, which might have a bearing on whether you choose me for your team... It's always something with the French. And in my case, it's possible that I might not have exactly ingratiated myself with the mayor of Marseilles on the subject of Scientology because it's true the Paris City Council did issue a proclamation declaring me—ME, TOM CRUISE, of all people—persona non grata, stating publicly that it would never again quote receive the actor, Tom Cruise, spokesman for Scientology and self-declared militant for this organization unquote.

"And it was quite true, of course: I was *way* over-the-top in those days! Like, *WAY OVER-THE-TOP!* Still, I did try to apologize. I studied French late at night so I could write a pretty decent 15-page letter of regret to the City Council, and I guess it worked, because they let me come back into the country later on so I could propose to my beloved Katie Holmes at the top of the Eiffel Tower. And as you know, she said, 'YES!' So as you also know, I'm not afraid to apologize.

"And while we're on the topic of apologies, I've also made amends with my good friend Brooke Shields, after I publicly slammed her for using drugs to treat her depression. I freely admit that I do believe in Lithium now! And I believe in Prozac, Praxil, Tegretol, and Depakote, too! As well, I'm also a pretty big fan of psychiatry! Katie's post-partum blues put me straight about all that.

"So yes, definitely, I'm not perfect, and I apologize for it, but I've had some good contacts with Christianity already, which just might help you decide in my favor. I attended a Franciscan seminary in Cincinnati once upon a time and even considered the priesthood before going the way of Hollywood. So I'm practically pre-wired for the highest rungs of discipleship. It could even be hidden somewhere in my genes. And given my association with the Church of Scientology, I'm already wide open to the awe and majesty and splendor of religion in general. And, just so you know, if you hadn't guessed it already, I have what you'd call mega-bucks. Many more gross receipts in deposit than you could ever possibly imagine. And I promise to put them all at your disposal because now it's all about you: The awe, the majesty, and

110

splendor. Forget that old L. Ron Hubbard. I don't see him rising from the dead... I don't see him coming back down to Sunset Strip. No siree. I'll play my aces with you, dear Christ... You're the King of Kings. You're the Dude."

Tom searches Christ's face for some slight sign of affirmation. None as yet apparent, he launches into Tom Cruise Pitch Phase II.

"Of course, I'd understand perfectly well if you harbored some minor reservations about me because of that little couch incident you probably heard about. These things get around, I know. But you have to understand from my perspective: I was a young fool drunk on love when I got to hopping up and down on Oprah Winfrey's couch! Yes, I readily admit that I was coo-coo! In front of all of Western civilization, no less! Lord knows it was certainly no career booster. I went from 11th Most Liked celebrity to 197th in just six months! Even my publicist sister couldn't save me from my own well-earned humiliation. But in my defense I just have to say: I WAS GA-GA OVER KATIE!

"But there was a positive side. Because of my public humiliation over that, I became as humble as a groundhog. Yes, I think I can safely say this about that: Thanks to Oprah Winfrey's couch, I'm now one of the humblest men ALIVE!!!

"So please, Jesus, make me one of your disciples. I promise to be your cash cow for Christianity. I promise I'll never go hopping on Oprah Winfrey's couch again! I promise to keep my face turned away from L. Ron Hubbard's, so help me JESUS!"

Christ, now more than a little anxious to get a move on, resigns himself to the inevitable. He carves an invisible cross over Tom's forehead, and says, "Ask and it will be given to you; seek and you will find; knock and the door will be opened to you. For every one that asketh, receiveth; and he that seeketh, findeth; and to him that knocketh, it shall be opened. Yes, Tom Cruise, cash cow for Christianity, you will be my second disciple…"

Deeply humbled, Tom lowers his head in thanksgiving as my stepbrother takes another step down the receiving line.

I'm gonna love taking out both Christ and Cruise because in times past Cruise rejected every one of my fundraising letters.

I see that Oprah Winfrey's next. My stepbrother's got all the luck! Oprah Winfrey? Are you kidding me? She's the best! On too many depressive winter afternoons, she's lifted up my spirits. And her cohort Dr. Phil: He's a psychotic's dream. When I listen to him speak in that low soft voice, I can believe that there still might be some hope for me!

Wearing the exact same slave dress she wore for her role as Sethe in the movie version of Toni Morrison's novel, *Beloved*, sporting a broad-brimmed Frederick Douglas Panama hat with the date 1619 stamped across the brim, commemorating the 400th anniversary of slavery in Jamestown, Oprah clutches Christ's hands. She draws him close, so very close to her. Close enough to make her pitch. "I'd like to invite you to be on my show next week, Mr. Christ. If you like, I'll have my people call your people soon…" An envious cry sweeps up and down the receiving line. "Goodness sakes alive, He got a invitation to be on the Oprah Winfrey Show next week!" Those words rush over the room. Yes, it's an invitation to die for, and I'm more than a little jealous. I call out to her from my F-16, though she hears me not: Why not me, Oprah? Why not your No. 1 fan?

Christ remains noncommittal. Oprah doesn't take his silence for an answer. "Of course, we'll fly you up to Chicago on my Gulfstream and put you up at the Drake, articulated elegance and the first choice for celebrities and heads of state for eighty-five years! We'll give you your own limousine and driver and provide you with a contingent of bodyguards because in America you're nobody without them. I mean nobody. I'll reserve a corner table for you at Charlie Trotter's—Chicago's finest. Average tab $300. Chef Trotter's an absolute genius—a culinary Einstein. His gastronomical creations are so organically righteous that I can eat there twice a day and still not blow up like a rhino! Which really is saying something, since I have a history.

"But, look, I'm easy. If you decide not to do my Show—turn down the opportunity of a second lifetime—well, that's okay, too! There'll be no hard feelings. Believe me. I mean, you're the Lord of Lords, after all, and I'm only a good-hearted entertainer! But if you won't come on, then maybe, just maybe, you'll consider me for one of your disciple slots because all you've done so far is sign up a couple of rich white guys, no offense intended, believe me. Which leaves a perfect opening for me: So how 'bout bringing on a good-hearted African-American female entertainer, who also happens to be very, very, very rich? I mean really filthy rich. Look, you could do worse. Besides, not to pressure you or threaten you, but down here in the political jungle that is America, there's no wrath like the wrath of the Congressional Black Caucus. Believe me. Trust me when I tell you that you never want to be on the wrong side of the Congressional Black Caucus. They can make your life *m-i-s-e-r-a-b-l-e*! Just like that.

"And you and I both know you're a merits-based system kind of guy and that my credentials to serve you are this side of impeccable. Did you know that by the age of three, I was reciting whole hunks of sermons by heart? I could even recite so many thick passages from the *Bible* that they called me The Preacher! The three-year-old preacher! They'd put me on the Sunday program and the minister of the church would get up in front of the congregation, and say, 'Now little Mistress Winfrey will render a recitation.' And then I'd get up and mesmerize the church with something like 'Jesus rose on Easter Day, Hallelujah, Hallelujah, all the angels did proclaim.' *Oh, I was good!!!* Believe me. That

113

was because my dear Baptist granny—God rest her soul—taught me to read so very early on when I was blessed to live with her down on the farm in Mississippi.

"But by the age of fourteen, I'd gone to live with my daddy up in Nashville. And there I was asked to deliver the beautiful sermons of the great Negro preacher, Rev. James Weldon Johnson—all by memory. My lips to God's ears, they said. *I was a sensation!* And ever since I've been sermonizing: Over the radio, on television, in the movies, via the Internet. While you were gone missing, I did your work for you—that is, I mean, while you were unavoidably detained! Believe me when I tell you that I was the most sermonizing woman in America! And as a result, America rewarded me, making me through my show the CEO and majority stockholder of Harpo Productions (If you don't know, that's Oprah spelt backwards). And now, now I sit atop the Mt. Sinai of American media empires. Yes, that sweet memorizing girl in pigtails from Kosciusko, Mississippi has become more than an empire, more even than a legend: She's become OPRAH.COM, averaging over 200 million page views and six million Internet hits each month! Now beat that, King of Kings. Beat that! So close your eyes and dream about those possibilities for your line of work. Imagine if you could harness the power of the Internet for your salvation agenda. Try to picture all the people you could communicate with and influence from my couch on the Oprah Winfrey Show!

"So, now it's all become clear to me: My whole life has been about preparing to become one of your disciples. That's because I've always tried to do the right thing: On my show, I've wrapped my arms around the sexually abused; I've stood up for battered children; I've cared, how I've cared, for victims of AIDS, and even prayed for them on national television. I've helped hunt down pedophiles and lock up child predators. I've extended an open hand to the newly divorced. And

114

oh yes, I've raised millions for thousands of those poor displaced Hurricane Katrina victims. I hosted a Nobel Peace Prize Concert with my good buddy, Mr. Tom Cruise, whom I genuinely adore. Love you, Tom!

"And there's more. Much, much more."

Christ's eye express infinite patience, endless endurance, which He's gonna need.

"At the 2002 Emmys, I received the first Bob Hope Humanitarian Prize. No small thing. And I was also nominated for a Nobel Peace Prize. I know, I know, anybody can get themselves nominated for one of those things...

"And then there was the time my best friends and I flew to South Africa to visit orphanages and broken down schools in nowhere places on the other side of the world. And we played Santa Claus—Santa riding his Gulfstream reindeer—distributing gifts to over 50,000 impoverished children, doling out dolls and soccer balls and other toys and plenty of practical stuff, too, like socks and shoes, underwear and undershirts. We were a full service Santa operation that year, Jesus. And we filmed the whole thing and then later back in Chicago we aired the show and asked our viewers to donate to Oprah's Angel Network. That's what I called it. Good name, uh? And guess what? We raised over $7,000,000 for the poor and needy! And believe me, I personally supervised how every red cent of those millions was administered, made sure that it went right to all the meek and the lowly. Your kind of people, Jesus. Right up your alley!

"So dear sweet Jesus, as you can see, I preach the Gospel According to Oprah from pages torn right from your own book. So please consider me for one of your slots. I can help bring your Word into the living rooms and bedrooms of millions of Americans. I can even introduce you to Dr. Phil, who can maybe help you with some of your own problems... Not that you have any, of course!"

Then somewhat miraculously, Oprah clams up. Which means there really is a loving God. Okay, just kidding. All I can hear is the roar of my F-16 as it careens towards West L.A. It's a sound to make a baby sleep. Well, one of mine, at least.

Being no fool, my stepbrother, who could use a little time with Dr. Phil, extends his gentle hand, scratching out an invisible cross over Oprah's forehead. In a voice as smooth as olive oil, he says, "Ask and it will be given to you; seek and you will find; knock and the door will be opened to you. For every one that asketh, receiveth; and he that seeketh, findeth; and to him that knocketh, it shall be opened. Yes, Oprah Winfrey, CEO of OPRAH.COM and Gulfstream Santa, you will be my third disciple..."

She collapses at his feet, overcome with emotion. My stepbrother edges on.

But for all her bliss, OPRAH.COM can kiss her empire and discipleship good-bye. In nineteen minutes, according to my clock, she's gonna be toast.

I snap off my monitor. I've had more than enough for now. I pry down my oxygen mask, raise up my visor, and fire up a joint. At Angels 37, there's nothing like lighting up. Thin air and sweet cannabis go right together. A couple of tokes and I'm stoned out of my gourd. Playtime.

I kiss my side stick controller with my palm and take this beauty down. Down through dense carpets of smog, down until she breaks out into the open. I train my sights on my new plaything: A BMW Roadster Supreme doing 123 mph in a 70 mph zone. Should I let it live?

Arming the M61 Vulcan 20mm Gatling gun, I unload some practice rounds. I dice up a Joshua Tree with a couple of quick bursts; I

116

shred to bits a patch of Crucifixion Thorns; I massacre a mound of Mormon Tea shrubs with the flick of a trigger; and just for fun I explode the belly of a black-tailed jackrabbit scrambling for cover. That was so much fun I decide to let the BMW off the hook. Why put a pin scratch on such a nice new paint job?

I climb back up. Soon I'm flying higher than what seems like the International Space Station. Love the weed. Love the jet. I tune into my cockroach stepbrother again. Well, why not? I'm still feeling the peace, knowing that tucked beneath me is a righteous stash of AGM-65 Mavericks. No better friend a fighter pilot could ever have than the AGM-65s.

Ready for fifteen-minute hack.

My stepbrother's gone on down the line; Sadie's cameras following his every cockroach move. I guess I'm in for the duration, so I settle back. But I decide not to light up another joint. Who needs dope when you can watch for free the Greatest Dopes on Earth sign up to walk beside my cockroach stepbrother?

Christophe of famed Fekkai's Hair Emporium butts in next, coming on strong—
very, very strong. It's no wonder Fekkai's is Salon to the Hollywood Stars, including, among many, many others, *7th Heaven* idol, Jessica Biel; Sandra Bullock and Barbra Streisand; or anyone goofy enough to cough up $600 for a basic shampoo, layered cut, and blow dry. Stacks of 18 k gold Tiffany Celebration rings, implanted with round brilliant diamonds, full-circle and half-circle, ornament Christophe's left, limp hand. Though I can't absolutely make it out for sure, I do believe that there's a lapis lazuli ring tossed in there on his middle finger for good measure. Oh yummy. I love lapis lazuli. I'm envious.

Christophe's open-neck mustard silk shirt, pinned with bone buttons, left partially unbuttoned three buttons down, reveals his

117

handsome Byzantine cross, hung from a sheik single strand of leather bootlace, which lies flat against his bristling hairy chest. His thousand dollar linen slacks, beige and freshly pressed, rest comfortably atop his old, rough pair of Birkenstocks.

"You really *are* the Dudie of Dudes, aren't you, lovie?" Christophe joins in, catching Christ in his feathery fey net. "Those dark chocolate eyes and your Romanesque nose sends me all a-quiver inside! But really, hon? *WHOEVER* does your hair??? It's a travesty. It's this side of hair cutter blasphemy! A plague of split ends, with no supple body, and a wanton, even cruel, disarray of gray. You poor thing! You need lots and lots of coloring. Perhaps not a little bit of tinting, too... Still, for all your faults, hon, you're drop dead, moon glow G-O-R-G-E-O-U-S! And just wait till I tell the boys! They'll be *so* envious!"

Then, unable to resist, Christophe scoops Jesus' face into the jeweled palm of his hands and lays a kiss on him. Right where it counts. To His credit, my stepbrother doesn't resist or even appear to be the least bit uncomfortable. You go, boy! You go!

"Welcome to L.A.," says Christophe as he gives Christ the wink of winks, "where gays do it better..." To his dismay, Christ fails to wink back. No hard feelings, Christophe hands Christ a Fekkai's goodie bag packed with a very special gift certificate, good for a year's supply of weekly facials and manicures, monthly coloring and tinting packages, and offers of soft layered cuts, shampoos, and blow dries good for any time of the day or night. There're even a dozen or so Fekkai's Spa Days tucked in there for Him, too, in case He's ever feeling decadent.

"We also want you to know that you're invited to walk in our Gay Pride Day parade any time you want! Once invited, always invited, lovie!"

That said, Christ graciously accepts his package, marks the invisible sign of the cross over Christophe's forehead and proceeds nonplused down the line. Meanwhile, Christophe bumps and grinds, belting out an avant-garde version of the "Hallelujah Chorus," using his own creative new set of lyrics.

"My Lovie shall reign forever and ever,
Dudie of Dudes! And Lordie of Lords!
My Lovie shall reign forever and ever,
Dudie of Dudes! And Lordie of Lords!
Hallelujah! Hallelujah! Hallelujah!"

He puts on quite a show for the cameras. That one should go into show business!

In line, two Hells Angels await Christ. If they're countin' on getting discipleships, I'd advise them to pretty much forget about it. For one, they're dressed for failure, not success. Even I wouldn't be so dumb as to show up wearing black leather jackets. Stamped across their jacket backs are the quintessential emblems of trouble: The oblong Deathhead, the initials M.C., meaning motorcycle club, below it; still further down is the charter's location: OAKLAND. Now I *know* they won't stand a chance. Oakland's notorious. Like He's gonna pick a couple of desperado Hells Angels from Oakland to advise Him on his do-gooder campaign when He can have pretty much any mega-star celeb in Hollywood? Yeah, right.

Nevertheless, Christ being courteous greets them respectfully— as though they were just regular folks. But I suppose they have a plan of their own because when He turns to face them, quick as wit, they unzip their black leather jackets, revealing—surprise! surprise!—their His and Her matching Tee shirts, with the words "Mel's Angels" sprayed across the fronts in what appears to be fool's gold. So much for them being degenerate Hells Angels. Probably they stole those jackets off some *real* Hells Angels while they were sleeping. Either that or Mel put them under some kind of Tridentine spell.

119

"I'm Sparrow, this is Dago."

"We used to be Hells Angels, until we saw his beautiful movie."

"*The Passion of the Christ.*"

"It changed our lives."

"Forever."

"From that night forward we just knew we had to meet Mel."

"Serve Mel."

"Be with Mel."

"It was just *so* L.A."

"Where else could you get called to a higher calling by a movie?"

"It was at the Wilshire Cinema."

"In Westwood."

"From silver screen to Mel's door..."

"And now we're at yours..."

"Yours..."

"Where we hope to ride on your highways."

"Just not on Harleys."

"We'll ride anything but Harleys."

"Vespas, mop-heads, Razors, whatever you like, just not Harleys."

"We'll even ride a Prius."

"Just not a Harley."

"Our Sonny Barger days are over."

"No more debauchery."

"No more drugs."

"Not even sex."

"We gave that up."

"To serve."

"Serve Mel."

"And hopefully, you."

"Even though we really wanted to."

"We'll make good disciples."

"We've learned a lot under Mel."

"He showed us how."

"And he got us straight."

"We gave up angel dust for him."

"Heroin, too."

"And stopped binge drinking."

"Stopped pot."

"LSD and amphetamines, too."

"We even gave up armed robbery."

"Rampages, too."

"We haven't hit one convenience store since that night in Westwood."

"Our rolling thunder days are over."

"We told Sonny Barger to go jump in Bass Lake."

"And to take his Lean and Mean Lager six-packs with him."

"We even burned our copies of *Fear and Loathing in Las Vegas* in a bonfire."

"Yeah, that one hurt."

"Not that we still don't love and admire Hunter J. Thompson."

"We hitchhiked to Colorado to attend his funeral."

"And watched his can of ashes get shot out of a canon."

"Gonzo, man, gonzo..."

"It was awesome."

"I hate what the Angels did to him."

"Beat the crap out of him."

"Thompson was right: Only punks slap women and kick dogs."

"He never should have ended up in the hospital."

"With all those broken bones."

"Conrad was right: 'Exterminate the brutes.'"

"The Angels were bad news."

"We know that now."

"Thanks to Mel."

"And through Mel, you."

"You're the Man."

"We know that now."

"So are we in?"

"Or are we out?"

"Either way, we're not going back to the Hells Angels."

"I hope it helps that we gave up sex for you."

"Helps a lot."

"So are we in?"

"Or out?"

"We wanted to be pure as rain for you."

In all my days, I've never heard such a pitch! Neither, evidently, has my stepbrother because just then He does the unthinkable. He etches out invisible crosses over their foreheads, and says, "Ask and it will be given to you; seek and you will find; knock and the door will be opened to you. For every one that asketh, receiveth; and he that seeketh, findeth; and to him that knocketh, it shall be opened. Yes, Sparrow; yes, Dago, Hells Angels come Mel's Angels lately, you will be my fourth and fifth disciples…whether or not you choose any time soon to have sex."

Then He moves up the line, leaving Sparrow and Dago in sweet delirium behind.

"SWEET JESUS!"

"HOLY MEL!"

"TONIGHT'S GONNA BE THE NIGHT, HONEY BUN!"

"WE'RE GONNA FINALLY GET IT ON!!!"

Sparrow crows to the roof of the world; Dago picks her up and swirls her around. Everyone in Mel's cheers, they are so happy for them. Even I feel all soft and buttery inside.

I've just crossed over L.A.'s outer city limits, about 150 miles due east of my target. Gather ye freebies while ye can, little stepbrother. Party up while you can. Sixteen minutes and ready for hack. I tune in my trusty monitor again. It's a bit like watching daytime soaps. Even though you know they're trash, still you can't resist them.

Next in line, Democratic Congresswoman Nancy Pelosi, representing the 8th Hippie District of San Francisco. But she sure doesn't dress like a hippie. Has on a sleek black velvet suit, a nice white blouse with a ruffle going down the front and new Bally shoes to die for. What I can't understand is why with all her wealth she wants to waste her time being such a do-gooder? It's a mystery to me. Always has been.

As any good politician would, she welcomes Christ by shaking His hand. Naturally, it's a political professional handshake. "Welcome to L.A.," she says. "I'm Democratic House Majority Leader Nancy Pelosi. My Chinese dissident friends call me Nancy. I wish you would, too. I'd like to put my oar in to be one of your disciples. At my age, I could use a good career move."

She holds onto Christ's hand, grasping it tenderly like only she and Bill Clinton can, giving the receiver that special feeling of having known them and loved them since time began.

"Why choose me? Let's go to the record: I was the first woman in the history to lead a major political party in Congress. Prior to I was a senior ranking member of House Appropriations, where I always sided with the American family. I have been a family values politician always. I toiled for decades to improve public education, support worker rights, and push the country towards universal health care. Even when the Pontius Pilate of all Republican politicians House Majority leader Tom

123

DeLay stood in my way, I didn't give up. Even when the Republicans controlled all of Congress, I filibustered when I had to. I was as obstinate as an elephant stopped in morning traffic. But even then I managed to get double funding for the National Institutes of Health, and hold fast against those backward Republicans gutting my overseas family planning programs. I'm all for preventing AIDS in Africa with condoms and proud of it. You can forget about relying on abstinence to get the job done, unless, of course, Sparrow and Dago are shining examples of good new things to come.

"While we're at it, let's not be afraid to review my record on AIDS—the leprosy of the 21st century. One of my very first legislative victories in the House was to ensure that people with AIDS had housing opportunities! I fought for that, like I'll fight tooth and nail for your agenda, too, if you choose me to be your sixth disciple.

"I also got expanded access to Medicaid for people living with HIV. Plus I won big increases in funding for the 'Ryan White CARE Act', and plugged the 'Minority HIV/AIDS Initiative.' I'm not ashamed to admit that I threatened, cajoled, and maybe threatened on rare occasion to kill a few Washington bureaucrats in order to get NIH to move its ass faster to come up with a new HIV vaccine. No one ever said I was introverted.

"On the ecological front, I've been as green as Al Gore, but it was those filibustering Republicans who blocked my green ways legislation. Oh, I've tried to be a good Jewish mother to Earth! But what's a mother to do when the country's governed more often than not by Republicans?

"I was also one of the few members of Congress to vote AGAINST authorizing George W.'s use of military force against Iraq in 2002! I got up on the floor of the House and said, 'America must be a light to the world, not just a missile!' It's in the Congressional record, if you don't believe me. And I introduced an amendment to the 2006 Defense Appropriations demanding that George W. specify *exactly* what their exit strategy was going to be to get us the hell out of Iraq!

"On human rights, I've been a saint. I was practically a den mother to those poor Chinese dissidents after the Tiananmen Square massacre. I got them in to this country by the boatload by sponsoring the Chinese Student Protection Act. And I told Zhang Zemin and Hu Jintao exactly what I thought of them. I've been a Kimono dragon for human rights, ask anyone.

"And given a chance, I'd be a Kimono dragon for you, too. Just cast your ballot for me—Nancy Pelosi—and I'll roll up my sleeves. Make me one of your sixth disciples and I'll go fight for your causes, just like I've fought for this country, the Great State of California and, above all else, the 8th Hippie District of San Francisco!

"So vote NANCY! NANCY! NANCY! I'm your gal in 2019!"

Like, who could resist a pitch like that?

Unsurprisingly, my stepbrother carves an invisible cross over her Botox-smooth forehead, and says, "Ask and it will be given to you; seek and you will find; knock and the door will be opened to you. For every one that asketh, receiveth; and he that seeketh, findeth; and to him that knocketh, it shall be opened. Yes, Nancy, defender of human rights and dissenter on the War in Iraq, you will be my sixth disciple."

Christ slips down the line as Nancy speed dials her press secretary. "I want a press release out on this IMMEDIATELY, you hear Me!?"

She's one together cookie that Nancy Pelosi. I'll actually be sad to see her go. Ready for eleven-minute hack.

Now cover your children's ears and eyes—up next is Madonna. I'm not talkin' about the Madonna of Madonna and Child, either. This one's the original Material Girl, as hot today as she was when she kissed

Britney Spears live on stage at the Grammies. She introduces herself by giving Christ a sloppy, wet kiss that, understandably, He doesn't appear to mind.

"In case you've been dead for the last two thousand years, my name's Madonna," she says, in a low, suggestive voice that would make most mere men beg for mercy. She wipes a bright red splotch of lipstick from the right corner of his parted lips. "There," she says, satisfied with her good job, "Now the Pope won't throw a fit!"

"Say, the thing is, I could use a job, because people don't get shocked by my act so easily these days. It's not like it was in the olden days—and the pay in Vegas absolutely sucks! So I was thinking that maybe you might want to consider me for one of your discipleships. The time is ripe and I'm available. Oh, yes, I know what you're thinking, and I don't blame you a bit: You're thinking that I sang that irreverent pop song strung up on a mirrored cross on my 'Confessions Tour.' Admittedly, I took liberties, lots of liberties with that. But I was young and mercenary then. Now I know it was very wrong of me to sing that song up on that nutty cross, wearing a crown of thorns. What made me do it, I can't tell. It probably has something to do with my upbringing and early traumatic childhood. Like, my mother died of breast cancer when I was only five. You can understand that that might have played havoc with my emotional development, making me always hungry for attention—*any* kind of attention!

"And then there's the fact that I went to a Catholic school, which can bring the devil out in a girl, you know... Surely that's no secret! I'm not saying that the nuns made me do it, but the Mother Superior experience didn't exactly make me embrace confession. The tragedy was there was just so much worthy of confession! So I was thinking, maybe if you heard my confession and you found it in your heart to forgive me, you could, you would sign me as your disciple?"

126

My stepbrother nods His consent. This I gotta hear.

"Confession #1: Father forgive me, for I have sinned. I once posed in the nude when I was living in Manhattan as a starving artist a long, long time ago. That was very, very wrong, I know. I know I should have stayed and worked at Dunkin Donuts and made an honest living.

"Confession #2: Father forgive me, for I have sinned. I once produced a music video for my album, *Like a Prayer,* that wasn't exactly, well, like a prayer... It mixed a little bit of eroticism with religion... well, more than a little bit actually. Which got me in trouble with the Vatican. They called for a boycott of my Italian tour, which now I fully endorse, but at the time was really ticked about.

"Then there was that little matter of my statue, as nude as Baby Jesus, being unveiled at Pacentro, in a nice Italian hill town in Maiella, a couple of hours east of Rome. When the Vatican found out, of course it went ballistic again, which in turn prompted Pepsi to cancel its ad deal with me, even though they'd already forked over five million to have me swig their stuff on television. The dolts. But in my own defense, I'd like to say that if David can stand in the buff alone in Florence, why not me in Pacentro? Anyway, here's the kicker. Because of the Vatican dust-up, 'Like a Prayer' suddenly skyrocketed to the top of the charts, going Number 1 around the world, including a six-week roost on top Billboard's Hot 100 Singles Chart! All because of the Vatican. Ironic, isn't it? I get banned by the Church, but am more than a little blessed by Commerce. Of course, even without you having to say it, I absolutely agree with you: Catholicism and eroticism should never ever be mixed. Not even as a terrific way to get to the top of Billboard's Hot 100 Singles Chart really, really fast!

"Confession #3: Father forgive me, for I have sinned. My performance at the first annual MTV Video Music Awards is still Number 11 on VH-1's *Greatest Moments That Rocked TV*, but that's not

127

because they showed me dishing out broth to poor kids in soup kitchens on Thanksgiving Day. I'm pretty sure that it had to do with the fact that I was writhing around onstage like a sleek feline in heat wearing nothing but a pair of lace stockings, garters, and combination bustier/wedding gown, singing—there I go again—sacrilegious love songs! And oh yes, I was also wearing my trademark 'Boy Toy' belt, which—on the positive side—eventually inspired more than a few of my boy fans to go out and become men in a hurry! At the time, I thought: How bad can that be? But now I know, contributing to the delinquency of minors is not the act of a Christian, which I mean to be if you make me your 7th disciple.

"Confession #4: Father forgive me, for I have sinned. In my glory days I also produced a book called, well, what else would you expect? 'SEX.' It was done without any taste—no taste whatsoever. I never thrived on taste, you know. I'm pictured doing some, well, lots of X-rated things. In my own defense I'd like to say that every one of those sex acts was just a simulation! No on-camera intercourse for me! So how could that have been anything but a very small, little sin, Christ? Answer me that.

"Confession #5: Father forgive me, for I have sinned. After that, I needed to do something to top it, so I produced a CD called 'Erotica,' which was me being, as usual, a showboating sex pistol, which I was and I suppose still am, but that I'll gladly—well, maybe not gladly—give up being, if only you'll sign me to your label—I mean, make me one of your disciples.

"Confession #6: Father forgive me, for I have sinned. After *Erotica* came the Girlie Show Tour, which, in retrospective, was a rare low point in my career because down in Puerto Rico I got dressed up on stage as a dominatrix and cracked a whip, surrounded by a bevy of beautiful bare-breasted dancers. That would have been okay—nothing too risqué in that—except for the last part. Somehow, I got it in my

128

head to rub a Puerto Rican flag between my legs. Well, it seemed like a good idea at the time. But you and I both know it was wrong. And especially wrong, wrong, wrong of me to do that in public, because as a result the Governor of Puerto Rico isn't likely to let me back into the Commonwealth any decade soon...

"So that's the worst of it. Of course there's more, always more, but if you can see your way to forgiving me those misdeeds, you'll have no problem with all the rest of them. So I think it's time to pop the question: Are you going sign me? If so, do I need my agent with me?"

Instead of answering, my stepbrother places His right hand on Madonna's nest of bleach-blonde hair, and says, "For if you will forgive men their offences, your heavenly Father will forgive you also your offences. But if you will not forgive men, neither will your Father forgive you your offences..."

Slowly comes the beautiful hue of recognition across Madonna's face.

"Oh, I get it," she says. "Sure, I can do that!" Then in a burst of forgiveness, she calls out to everyone and everything under the Heavens, "I HEREBY ABSOLVE EVERYONE OF EVERYTHING, INCLUDING SEAN PENN AND MY FIRST BOYFRIEND!!!"

She looks at Christ. "Is that what you had in mind?"

Satisfied with her performance, my crazy little stepbrother carves an invisible cross over her forehead, and says, "Ask and it will be given to you; seek and you will find; knock and the door will be opened to you. For every one that asketh, receiveth; and he that seeketh, findeth; and to him that knocketh, it shall be opened. Yes, Madonna, my daredevil rock star and most worthy confessor, you will be my seventh disciple..."

Then like a flower unfolding in a time-lapse movie, her face, her body, her soul even, appears to bloom. However does He do it? It drives

129

me absolutely nuts. He walks down the line of celebrities, with another convert notched in his belt.

I check my watch. Ready for nine-minute hack. It couldn't come a minute too soon.

Before Christ comes the Mind Behind U2: Yes, ladies and Gentlemen, it's the Great BONO Himself. Until you've actually seen him in person, believe me, no way you've seen cool. I mean, really, really cool. And it's not just an ordinary cool, it's a global cool. Because he is so very, very cool, I'll take a minute to describe him. Blue Italian shades frame his noble Irish fisherman's face. He's got that wild and rugged look, that rock climber look. Indomitable, yet friendly. His stone-washed jeans are slung casually around the lower half of his bod, topped like a neon sign by his signature 'END AIDS IN AFRICA' Tee shirt. Both of which make him look all the proletariat, even though we all know that he's actually a king, The King of Cool.

Bono embraces the King of Kings. King of Cool meets the King of Kings. It's an event, a happening, a Rather Grand Occasion. They pat each other on the back, like newly discovered brothers who've fought each other at last on the edge of the wilderness. It's very nearly touching. Why I can't quite say.

"Beautiful day, Jesus. This is a beautiful day.

"My name is…

"Bono," says Christ.

"And as you know I USED TO BE a rock star until my band turned me out in the rain like an old dirty dog. Why? Because as everyone knows, I spent too much time telling our fans to DO SOMETHING ABOUT ENDING AIDS IN AFRICA, and not enough time playing their favorite songs! So what else could they do? I had to go. It was strictly business. And my mission had become something close to Messianic.

It didn't start out that way though. It began with a little voice come slipping into my sleep, and calling out to me again and again, "Bono, Bono... End AIDS in Africa."

At first I thought I could ignore it, that I could wake up and forget about it. No way. Those four little words began to follow me into the day. They came when I was getting dressed and having cornflakes for breakfast: 'End AIDS in Africa,' that little voice said. Then they came to me in the strangest places, like in the dentist chair or when I was on the can: 'Bono: End AIDS in Africa.' Again and again, I heard those four little words. Pretty soon I heard them all the time. They were like the endless sound of traffic in downtown Manhattan. So finally I decided it was time to act because I concluded that YOU were the one who was sending me that message.

I acted all right. I acted so well, in fact, that my band got fed up with me and kicked me out for mouthing off about 'Ending AIDS in Africa' at all our concerts, like I said. But I didn't care. I was happy to give up my entourage, my limos, even my collector guitars for my cause. All I really cared about was finding a new band that would play my one and only song: 'Let's End AIDS in Africa.' And to play that song on the road until AIDS was, in fact, ended in Africa. I never did find that band.

"So I'm wondering, like wow, if I was one of your disciples, would you let me play my song in your band? It couldn't be more important that we raise public awareness. In your day, you had leprosy. In my day, we have AIDS. AIDS *is* the new leprosy! We're talkin' about the most ravaging health crisis in 600 years! And it's suffocating Africa, suffocating it right now! The Bubonic Plague has suddenly returned in a different guise. AIDS *is* the new Black Death! And we've got to defeat it, end it, bury it before it buries us! We have a moral obligation to do it and all those pharmaceutical companies out there need to cough up their pricey drugs to try to help the victims out: AZT, ddC, ddI, d4T, and

3TC! We need them all because worldwide there're 42 million people living with HIV! And 75 percent of them are dying in the sub-Sahara! Dying, man! Last year, AIDS took down 2.5 million Africans—that's 6,500 a day! So you can see that we've all got to do something—and do it fast. I've seen little black kids shoveling dirt on their parent's graves. I've seen brother burying sister and sister burying brother... It's too sad for words, man, too sad for words.

"Like I told President Bill Clinton and George W. and every other head of state I could pigeonhole behind closed doors, 'Each of us has a moral duty to DO SOMETHING ABOUT ENDING AIDS IN AFRICA TODAY!'

"So please Jesus, if you really want to do something big about AIDS, consider me for one of your disciples. I'm fine with playing backup lead, just so long as we get to play my one and only song that's worth a damn. But whatever you decide, I want to give you these—my shades and rosary beads. They're the exact same brand I gave to Pope John Paul II at the Vatican and these are the very same rosary beads Pope John Paul II gave to me in exchange. I want you to have them. They're not a bribe, not an inducement. They're only meant to thank you for calling out to me in the dark and asking me to help end AIDS in Africa... Thank you for changing my life."

Now everybody's weeping in the receiving line. It's embarrassing, but what can you do? This is Hollywood where charity work covers up a lot of sins and everybody likes to get dealt in to the love of the cause.

I can see a teardrop at the corner of my softhearted stepbrother's right eye. Naturally, He'd be the one to fall hardest for this kind of do-gooder crap. He raises His hand, marking the invisible sign of the cross over Bono's forehead. "Ask and it will be given to you; seek and you will find; knock and the door will be opened to you. For every one that asketh, receiveth; and he that seeketh, findeth; and to him that knocketh, it shall be opened. Yes, Bono, Hero of a Continent, Champion of Charity, you will be my eighth disciple... and together we will play your song in our new band, U12."

Bono thrusts a fist straight up in the air, like a band leader on stage at the end of his act, crying, "It really is a BEAUTIFUL DAY!!!"

Meanwhile, Christ adjusts his new pair of shades and steps down the receiving line.

Me, I'm left to ask an existential question at 37,000 feet. How fair can this be? How is it that my little stepbrother gets a pair of original Bono shades and not me?...

There's only one way to compensate: Ready for seven-minute hack.

Next up, my favorite: Da Austrian Oak, a.k.a. da Best Built Man in Europe, da Terminator, Conan da Republican, da Gropenator and da Governator. Wearing, well, next to nothing except a Conan da Barbarian plated snarling snake encrusted Bronze Age belt/ combination briefs; forearm leather shooting sleeve; furry, calf-high boots; and a three-prong, phallic Viking crown, laden with imitation precious stones, every inch as lethal as his glittering sword set point down between his parted legs and massive thighs, is da ex-Governator of da Great State of California, Arnold Schwarzenegger. With an Austrian accent denser than Hungarian oak and thicker than Nazi-sympathizer former Kurt Waldheim's, Arnold pitches da World's Premiere Forgivenator for his next new career move as one of "da Disciples."

"Dis is me, Arnold. I am Arnold Schwarzenegger. Dat's right, I am he. Trust me. If I'm not me, who da hell am I? No matter what dos Republicans call me des days because I left da stupid party, I'M NO-GIRLIE MAN!

"Now listen to me very carefully: I want to be one of da disciples. I have da energy, I have da intelligence, I have da know-how because I am da ex-Governator of California and I have nothing else to do and nowhere else to go. So I want to help you, and I swear I will kill no one: I only did dat in da movies…

"Together, we will do da people's work and we will take responsibility and be accountable to them. We will speak directly to da people 'cause da will of da people is sacred. We will stand for morally and fiscally responsible behavior—in and out of da government. I know dat and you know dat we have to bring back moral values and fiscal responsibility to da state of California. We can fix da mess widout hurting da public schools.

"I will be da people's disciple. Dogether, we will work honestly, and widout fear or favor. I'm running for one of da discipleships to help lead a movement for Change. My principles of discipleship are simple and plain: Progress over politics, bipartisanship always. I guarantee things will change, wid you and me in charge. I will go wherever you want and we will clean da state together. We will speak directly to da people. We need to send a message to Sacramento and beyond. And dat message is this: It doesn't matter if you're a Democrat or a Republican, if you're young or old, we will clean house. Just like I did. Nothing works if it's not thought out.

"This is my bio. You need to know dat. I was once da Pumping Iron Man. I was da seven-time Mr. Olympia, too. Den I was Conan da Barbarian in da movies and da Terminator, too, and den I got elected to da Governator of California. Den I became da two-Terminator Governator. I coulda been, shoulda been da three-Terminator Governator Running Man but da nurses, da teachers, da fire-fighters, and da trial lawyers, all voted against me because I said to them: 'You lack discipline!' 'Stop whining!' 'No deal!' 'Sue me, dickheads!'" Well, was da Governator! Who else was gonna say dat to dem? But dat lost me da election, so now I'm da Conan da Barbarian again. Dat is why I want to be one of da disciples. I don't like being Conan da Barbarian anymore, not after I was da 'Governator' and da only one in da state who pumped up Sacramento and told Governor Gray Davis: '*HASTA LA VISTA!*'

"Dink about it. And don't believe everyding you may have heard about me in da past. I have da utmost respect for women. Ask Maria. She will tell you. And I am not, nor have I ever been da 'Gropenator.' Not 'Herr Gröpenführer,' either. Gary Trudeau, you can go to hell for calling me dat, too! And there were only fifteen women—NOT sixteen! I only had fifteen! Let's not exaggerate. And I swear at your Daddy's knee, I have not been wid dat Gigi Goyette for decades!

"Thanks to Maria, I have more heart than muscles now, which is why I joined da Democratic Party. I told da Republican Party '*Hasta la vista,*' too, just like I told Gray Davis, and even though I liked what George Bush da Better called me, which was 'Conan da Republican.' Why did I leave da party? Because da Republican Party is nothin' but a bunch of GIRLIE MEN AND WOMEN! So now I'm proud to be wid da Democrats. Of course, it was da most difficult decision I ever made in my life, except da one when I decided to get a bikini wax.

"So please, Jesus, make me one of da disciples. I don't want to be remembered for my role as dat Det. John Kimble in *Kindergarten Cop.* I don't want to be remembered for askin' that stupid question in dat movie, 'Who is your daddy and what does he do?' I don't want to be remembered as Arnold, da Pumping Iron Man. I don't want to be remembered as Arnold, da seven-time Mr. Olympia. I don't want to be remembered as Arnold, da Terminator. I don't want to be remembered as Arnold, da two-Terminator Governator. And I definitely don't want to be remembered as Arnold, da Gropenator. I only want to be remembered as Arnold, da Disciple. Dat's all I really want.

"Make me one of da disciples and I will guarantee you, Jesus, we'll clean house dogether, and say, '*Hasta la vista*,' to all those GIRLIE MEN AND WOMEN IN DA REPUBLICAN PARTY OUT DERE!"

Only a Girlie Man would turn down Arnold's offer. And no way my stepbrother's one of dem Girlie Man. He carves an invisible cross over Arnold's forehead below his crown of Viking thorns without hesitation, and says, "Ask and it will be given to you; seek and you will find; knock and the door will be opened to you. For every one that asketh, receiveth; and he that seeketh, findeth; and to him that knocketh, it shall be opened. Yes, Arnold, you are no Girlie Man, and you will be my ninth disciple—da People's Disciple."

As Christ moves on, Arnold lets drop his sword, throwing open his arms wide in celebration. "*HASTA LA VISTA* Arnold, da Pumping Iron Man!" he cries. "*HASTA LA VISTA* Arnold, Conan da Barbarian!" he sings. "*HASTA LA VISTA* Arnold, da Det. John Kemble! ARNOLD'S BACK! BACK AS ARNOLD, DA DISCIPLE! NOW DOS REPUBLICANS WON'T CALL ME GIRLIE MAN AGAIN!"

Everyone up and down da line must think dat's pretty great, too, 'cause they clap him on da back and give him high fives. It seems that everybody loves Arnold, except dos Republicans.

And me. Likely because I love no one.

All I can say to da Terminator is dis: Enjoy your discipleship while you can.

Ready for 5-minute hack.

Martha Stewart, Grand Dame of Domesticity and Ornamental Triviality, appears next, cloaked in the same gray white Coming Home poncho that her fellow inmate crocheted for her at Camp Cupcake, a.k.a., the Alderson Federal Prison Center, while she was serving six-months for obstruction of justice and lying to federal prosecutors. I felt

136

bad for Martha, still do. They couldn't make their insider trading allegations stick, so they stuck her with some other manufactured charges. Which is why, if I were a politician—I'd run as a Republican. Hers is a classic case of government outa control. But not even the feds can keep a good woman down, especially if she's game. Just to show how game she is, she's brought along her declining little Chow Chows to demonstrate a united front. There's Zu-Zu, Paw-Paw, Chin Chin, and Empress Wu. They still look pretty game themselves, considering their ages. Dressed to the nines in tiaras and tutus, they nestle together in a big straw basket at Martha's feet. Naturally, hers is no mere straw basket. IT'S A MARTHA STEWART BASKET, lined in red satin, with green and white variegated ivy knitted into the slow curve of the high straw handle. A gorgeous silk white bow crowns the top, fluffed up perfectly. Milling about at Martha's feet are her nine half-blind Himalayan cats. She brought them, too—because Martha is nothing if not family minded. Today, everyone's turned out to welcome the King of King's to Mel's. There's Elektra, Vivaldi, Mozart, Verdi, Bartok, Berlioz, Polaris, and Teeny and Weeny. They make quite a show. Even though Martha would NEVER bring out her entire family to greet me, I still like her. To tell the truth, I have a little bit of a crush on her. And it's not because she got a raw deal from the feds and I feel sorry for her. It's because somewhere deep inside I've always admired the idea of having a family myself.

Martha comes to play, as always, in the big leagues.

"Oh, I just *love* your white linen suit, hat, and Bono Italian shades combo, Mr. Christ! I might also recommend a spot of seasonal chic: For your lapel, a corsage of tiny white sprays of rosebuds, set against a cluster of forest ferns, because the greens will bring out the soft pastel undertones of the pearly flowers, highlighting their pure

137

white hues and gently affecting their fragile fairness, as they rise to the surface, making so much more of their snowy blooms...

"But enough shop talk! My Chow Chows and Himalayans come bearing gifts! Gifts from Martha's Magi to Mel's Manger! Glory to the Newly Returned King! Here, this is for you, I made it myself! It's an embellished burlap tote bag, with twig handles, stamped with a decorative silhouette of your holy profile, set in a dusty red cake of soft, hushed colors, evocative of Roman frescos. Tote bags are indispensible part of modern living, especially for men. Besides, it's a Martha Stewart original, so you'll want to have it. I made them all the rage these days.

"And Number Two, I brought something for your breakfast table: my Collection of 'Dozen Shades of Table Setting Reds.' There's no easier way to add interest to your breakfast table settings than with these: A Fortuny-inspired burgundy linen tablecloth, reversible rose red placemats, cherry ceramic napkin rings, ruby red linen napkins hand-embroidered with wispy feathers tinted in crushed cranberry, crimson hand-drawn feather-edged place cards for all your disciples—including hopefully me—blood red pillar candles embellished with tall blades of hand-painted wine-red home-grown grass, a natural sago palms centerpiece dyed claret-red, optional hand-printed fire engine red sunset scenes fabric squares for your seat covers, and lastly, twelve elegant twig coasters dipped in a soft pink varnish, glazed with maroonish hand-blown sparkles, and dried by twelve virgins waving Japanese hand fans.

"But to be clear: Though I won't turn down an offer from you for your 10th disciple slot, if you happened to offer it, there's absolutely no insider trading going on here, and no attempt on my part, either expressed or implied, to peddle influence or manipulate stock anywhere in the world. There's also no requirement under the color of law that I register your gifts with the SEC. The feds don't have a thing on me.

"But if you decide to consider me, you won't be making a mistake. I have perfect taste, even though I have not always been perfect myself. Thanks to my time in prison, I'm a changed woman. I'm no longer contemptuous of the little people—and their imperfect taste. I no longer give people the Martha Stewart litmus test, such as, do they or don't they personalize their lampshades? I no longer judge them on whether they know the difference between Faux Bois and Faux Pas. I'm through criticizing them for not understanding how to change the style conversation about their bedroom pillows, or if they fail to hang seasonal satin ribbons on their powder room mirrors. And I'm done being judgmental about whether they understand the benefits of beautifying their kitchen walls with bulletin boards constructed of cut fabric and wooden molding painted in watercolors. Sure, it still bothers me some when good friends I know don't have my original grilled chocolate sandwiches and Chocolate Chip Meringue Kisses on hand when I come to call, but it's not like it used to be—it's not that I'm contemptuous of them for failing to have them on hand. I'm passed that now. Thanks to prison.

"Thanks to prison, I found spiritualism, which in turn helped me survive my temporary life without gracious living, without silk handmade scarves, without my favorite avocado salsa snack and my own Skylands® bed.

"Spiritualism lifted my spirits, gave me hope on those cold Alleghany Mountain days, when I was forced to do laundry detail. It pulled me through when the prison authorities wouldn't permit me to wash lettuce leaves in my imported Irish linen kitchen cloth, and when the prison guards rejected my application to hang swags of brightly colored fabrics from my cell window, and when the warden refused my request to clip the prison yard with a pair of tweezers to ensure the grass grew uniformly. And most importantly, it got me through that particularly rough spot when my petition to the warden to hang wreaths of variegated ivy from the prison gate was declined. I even appealed to the West Virginia governor on that one, but he heartlessly turned me down! I know Arnold would have been okay with that! Right, Arnold?"

"Right," says Arnold.

"So you may be wondering what I mean by spiritualism. From my perspective it's regardless of their sense of taste. It's all about tolerance and forbearance.

"Like, I learned to forgive those feds who persecuted me. I learned to forgive my yardman for trimming my hedge with clippers instead of the scissors. I learned to forgive my maid for moping my kitchen floor with Mop-n-Glo instead my of distilled rosewater and vinegar solution I requested. Admittedly, none of those examples were as extreme as my Italian cook forgetting to include pansies and nasturtiums in the luncheon salad for my guests, but I learned to forgive her, too, which is just more proof how spiritual a person I've really become since I was in prison.

"And nowadays I treat my employees with utmost courtesy and respect. I haven't humiliated my yardman in years! And my chauffer thinks I'm practically Father Christmas the way I shower him with unsolicited presents—which represent no attempt on my part, either expressed or implied, to peddle influence or manipulate stock anywhere in the world! Even my love life has improved because of my new spiritualism. I'm down to one boyfriend at a time. And Larry King and I are long done, though of course he was a lot of fun! Most importantly, I forgave my ex-husband Andy for walking out on me all those years ago. It was my fault that he did. I never should have forced him to hold up that gingerbread wall all by himself in the basement hour after hour while it set and dried. *Whatever was I thinking?* How thoughtless! I would have walked out on me, too!

"But spiritualism also means enduring sacrifices with equanimity. So when I wrote a book called *Jailhouse Living*, which became a surprise *New York Times'* bestseller, I was able to donate the proceeds to the Bedford New York Women's Rehabilitation League without losing it. And when I contributed the 25K I got from auctioning my ankle bracelet the judge in my obstruction of justice case made me wear for five months during my home confinement, it didn't hurt a bit when I wrote the check to charity. I was completely self-controlled, even after I dropped the check in the mail and couldn't get it back. And I owe it all to spiritualism, all because spiritualism brought me in touch with a higher, more magnanimous power, like you, Jesus, you.

"So, please, if you believe in my spiritualism, as I do, appoint me one of your disciples. I may still be somewhat of a perfectionist, but I'm a perfectionist just like you! And together, we'll make for the perfect partnership. You for the big picture ideas; me for the bothersome little details. We'll perfect the world together and beautify it, too, with soft, muted colors, evocative of Roman frescoes. We'll even put reversible rose red placemats and cherry ceramic napkin rings on every breakfast table, given time.

"So please, please, please, sweet Jesus, PERFECT ME!"

Who couldn't be moved by that pitch, I ask you? Martha's had a really tough life. Imagine having to live with all that perfection inside! So my stepbrother carves an invisible cross over her forehead, and says, "Ask and it will be given to you; seek and you will find; knock and the door will be opened to you. For every one that asketh, receiveth; and he that seeketh, findeth; and to him that knocketh, it shall be opened. Yes, Martha Stewart, you found spirituality in the Yard and learned to forgive your yardman, maid, even your cook... So you will be my tenth disciple."

Another disciple in his pocket, Christ ambles on. Martha, tears in her eyes, leans over to pat her Chow Chows in the basket, lingering over each to set their tiaras just right.

Yes, they look absolutely perfect now.

It's gonna be hard for me to take her out. It really is. Obviously, I do have more than a little crush on Martha. Shouldn't we all? If you ask me, the world needs more Marthas, not fewer. And I might even try out this perfection fetish of hers sometime; it just might do me good.

Ready for three-minute hack.

Yes, I must confess, I'm more than nervous. This is the biggest deal I've done since manipulating Pontius Pilate into crucifying Christ in 33 AD. That's right, Isaac Newton: My stepbrother's exact date of crucifixion *was* Friday, April 3, 33 AD, not April 23, 34 AD, as you theorized. I'm so glad I've had the opportunity to lay that misconception to rest. I feel better now, though I'm still nervous as hell. Taking out my stepbrother together with half of Hollywood's Hall of Fame celebrities with a single AGM-65 Maverick is not something I do everyday, you know.

The Diva of All Magnificent Behinds, Jennifer Lopez, a.k.a J.Lo, steps out from the receiving line to within a bird's breath of my stepbrother, leaving her Mount Rushmore-size behind partially back in line. I'm willing to bet her $3.5 million diamond engagement ring she copped from Ben Affleck, before all that fell apart, that she's out to snag one of the last two disciples spots. You don't need radar to see that. Not even a periscope.

Even though He's the Lord of Lords, and all that, she still comes onto Him. Ambition has no shame, no boundaries, no hesitation in Hollywood. Still, how is it my stepbrother attracts one of the sexiest old broads in Hollywood when he's supposed to be so celibate and above it? Not that I'd begrudge him a basic human impulse or two, if He were

142

inclined to go for it. But my opinion is she'd be better off investing her time skinning pelts off baby seals or manufacturing another line of killer J.Lo perfume. But that's just me.

J.Lo brings my stepbrother's hand to her lips, brushing it with a slow, lingering kiss, "Welcome to the glory of my bootie, Oh Jesus. I promise you, if you ask me to be your disciple, every inch of it will be yours. Anoint me with your oil, Jesus, and I can guarantee you, the word 'celibate' will be stricken from your vocabulary… Just ask Marc Anthony."

Christ looks taken aback, as well He should! *Whatever is J.Lo thinking?*

"Oh, I was ONLY TEASING YOU!" she says, registering His consternation.

"My parents wanted me to be a lawyer, but I decided against it, because I was afraid I'd end up singing in front of the jury and losing every case!

"Becoming a disciple though… that's different! If I lost control and broke out in song in front of the public, it might actually help you WIN your case! I have not an inconsiderable big fan base.

"I do however have a dark side that you should know about— before you sign me up. First, let me readily admit that I'm no Virgin Mary…but then again I'm no Madonna, either! No offense, Madonna!!!"

"None taken," she says.

"I've already publicly acknowledged that I spent many years sneaking out of bedroom windows, hopping off rooftops, and shinning down trees trunks so me and my first boyfriend, David Cruz, and could be together. Yes, I loved him very much. There has never been another David Cruz, even though, believe me, I've looked in more places than I've had hit records. The truth is I've never gotten over him! Until, well, now… Until I saw you… Now it's like, David *WHO?*

"No vetting process would be complete without my admission that I've struggled with the black dog, as Winston Churchill described our darker impulses. And I've lost more battles than I've won, and only drawn ties in the lesser scrimmages. You see, Jesus, I used to be a poster-child for animal cruelty. I regret to say that I was in bed with the fur trade. I was a profiteer, turning a buck on the slaughter of helpless furry, little creatures, building an empire by stripping animals for my Sweetface line designs.

"It was a sad, sorry chapter in my rise to fame. In my own defense, I can only liken my love for fur to an addiction, an addiction to heroin. All I could think about was fur, dawn to dusk. I counted sables on the way to the slaughterhouse while trying to get to sleep. I dreamed of rooms full of pelts, hanging down like chandeliers. I always insisted on making love on royal crown Russian sable coats—that's how obsessed I was.

"But then along came Heather Mills McCartney—my liberator. Anti-landmine crusader, animal rights nut job, and now Paul's McCartney's ex, she rescued me from the atrocities of my own insensitivity. For that I'll always be grateful. I could have kissed her for what she did—not that anyone should ever get the idea that I would *ever, ever* do to Heather what Madonna did to Britney! Yuck! That was gross! No offense, Madonna!"

"None taken."

"The day I began my journey over to the other side was the day that Heather showed up at my Sweetface office in Manhattan, pushing her poison pill DVD about the fur trade's cruelty to animals. Though I didn't actually watch her video and see all those Sweetface furry creatures slaughtered and skinned and hung up to dry, I read the report and my heart went out to them. And after the tabloids picked up the story of my security guards dislodging Heather's prosthetic leg in a

144

tussle, and her having to put it back on in a stairwell because they refused her permission to use the bathroom, I said, "Whoaooooo! Wait a minute! Something's wrong here!

"As a result, I sought counseling—animal sensitivity training to be exact, which was the smartest move I've except perhaps for not going to law school.

"I owe my redemption to Heather, Jesus! She should get the credit! She taught me to see those furry little things for what they really are—God's gift to nature—not instruments of exotic fashion, not stepping stones along the silk route to J.Lo's personal enrichment. Heather enlightened me. She opened my eyes and I saw that those sweet faces I had built an empire on were fellow custodians of the planet. Heather had led me to the Road to Damascus! And I was the she-Paul of Tarsus!

"So I ripped up the incorporation papers for my Sweetface fashion business, discharged my staff, sealed the doors, and wrote Heather an emotional thank you note on a bench in Central Park.

"All these years later, I'm still completely furless. I dream of fur no more! Still, it's not easy for me and I have to take it one day at a time because I am and always will be a recovering furcoholic, but I'm proud to say that I own more cats and dogs than Martha Stewart! Hear that, Martha?"

"For a hint of taste, try fitting them in tiaras and tutus!" Martha says.

"Sure thing, Martha!

"So on weekends, Jesus, I volunteer for the Humane Society, changing out cat cage linings and manning the phone banks on weekends looking for homes for abandoned animals. Did you know over 7 million cats and dogs are killed each year due to overpopulation? That's a form of genocide! And we must do something about it! I also contribute heavily to groups hoping to save the Red Wolf."

She leans in closer to Christ, if that's possible.

"It's been rumored—so you may have heard the rumor—that I've contributed to the Animal Liberation Movement—a pretty radical bunch whose name is self-explanatory. They're about freeing every caged mink from L.A. to Vladivostok. Their tactics are straight out of Malcolm X's playbook. That is, they intend to free the minks by any means necessary. That rumor you might have heard, I will neither confirm nor deny..."

She steps back; Christ seems somewhat relieved, actually.

"I see now that my entire life has been predicate for this very moment. I've moved step by step to this very day. I'm prepared to give up everything to serve you. My $15 million movie star salaries, like who cares—I mean, *really*! Get a life! Those next 50 million records I could sell? Well, what's that compared with saving the planet? I'd give up everything to walk with you, particularly if you'd consider endorsing my Adopt-A-Sweet-Body and Save the Canis Rufus campaigns—two campaigns dear to my heart. Your endorsement would mean... but of course it's not a pre-condition!

"About the only aspect of my other life I'd like to hold onto is my J.Lo Fragrance, which I'm very excited about. We just released the perfume 'Religiosity.' Good name, uh? And with your return to Earth, it's bound to be an overnight sensation. 'Course I'll donate all the proceeds to charity. But the rest, J.Lo Fashion, that's gone! Who's got time for silly old that? My Louis Vuitton Winter, Spring, Summer, Fall campaigns? In the ash heap of history already! I'm so glad I'm over that! And you see this ring? It's the original Ben Affleck engagement ring you've read about. Well, it's yours. Completely yours. Worth millions! Here, have it! And this, too—a complimentary bottle of my latest perfume."

146

She hands both her diamond Ben Affleck engagement ring and a sample bottle of Religiosity to my little stepbrother, who promptly pockets them.

"So please, Jesus, think about me. It certainly wouldn't hurt your standing with the ACLU to bring on a Latino. Hiring minorities is always the politically correct thing to do! Especially at Christmastime! I have only one condition: On weekends I'd like time off to return home to man the phone banks at the Humane Society. My week isn't complete without finding more homes for my sweet bodies.

"'Course, what I said about the glory of my bootie being yours still stands!"

Christ looks taken aback again, as well He should!

"I was ONLY TEASING YOU!" she says.

Which elicits a smile by Christ, as well it should.

He's heard enough. He marks the sign over the cross over J.Lo's forehead, and says, "Ask and it will be given to you; seek and you will find; knock and the door will be opened to you. For every one that asketh, receiveth; and he that seeketh, findeth; and to him that knocketh, it shall be opened. Yes, J.Lo... phone bank telephone operator at the Humane Society on weekends, supporter of the Save the Canis Rufus campaign, and maker of divine perfumes, you will be my eleventh disciple."

J.Lo shakes her bootie in glee as Christ steps down toward the very end of the receiving line.

Ready for one-minute hack.

At the end of the celebrity receiving line, the last applicant for the last discipleship bones up for his interview with the Lord of Hosts. The imposing Black Man stands alone, towering like a lighthouse, preparing for the speech of his life before an audience of one. He studies a fistful of notes through polished lenses of wire-rim glasses that

147

magnify the deep power and mystery of his shiny, black eyes, making them appear even larger than they actually are. His massive crop of hair, combed up straight with a tong comb, shines silver-white above his clerical collar. And his ring collar appears to float ethereally above his ethnic apparel, very nearly glowing like a communion wafer in the dark. Get up in a rainbow weave Dashiki, Zebra-striped slacks, and open-toed, Brown Sugar sandals, his imposing frame suggests that he actually used to be somebody, though I can't for the life of me place him.

As Christ approaches the last in line (the last shall be last), the Black Man removes his spectacles, pockets them in his Dashiki, and sets himself, preparing his welcome for the newly returned King. While I don't recognize him, my little stepbrother apparently does.

"The last shall be first and the first shall be last," He says, "For many be called, but few chosen."

"Matthew 20:16," the Black Man says.

"Blessed are the peacemakers, for they shall be called the children of God..."

"Matthew 5:9," the Black Man says.

"Blessed shall you be when men shall hate you, and when they shall separate you and reproach you and cast out your name as evil, for the Son of man's sake."

"Luke 6:22?" asks the Black Man hesitantly.

His answer causes Christ to smile. He calls out: "Jesse Jackson!"

Jackson replies, "Baby Jesus!"

They hug, giving each other a good back thumping.

Oh, now I remember that guy! Didn't he used to be somebody?

"I hope you don't mind me calling you 'Baby Jesus;' I certainly mean no disrespect, I only wish to connect. That's because ever since I was a little boy, I always pictured you lying in a manger, far from the grasp of danger."

148

My stepbrother doesn't appear to mind; Jesse Jackson carries on.

"'The first shall be last and the last shall be first;' if you disappoint me, Baby Jesus, and fail to appoint me as your twelfth disciple, it's a foregone conclusion that I'll burst! I hope you don't mind me being late; I had another date I couldn't break. You may have noticed that I've been at the end of the line for a very long time. I certainly hope you noticed that I made every effort to abstain from butting ahead of *anybody* in line, just because I used to be *somebody* all the time. And I hope you'll recall that I was once the hippest Black Man in da Hood, until Al Sharpton and Barack Obama reduced my life to a semi-comma. Still, I will forever be the King of Hope and Lord Against Dope in the African-American community. Not even Barack can take that honorary degree away from me!

"My qualifications for a discipleship with you are renown and abound. And, notwithstanding what you might have heard and read, *I WAS, I SAY, WAS,* standing on the balcony with Martin Luther King when he was shot, and *NOT* talking with Ben Branch down in the parking lot, as some of those trash talking fly-by-night websites have said and alleged. And yes, Baby Jesus, Dr. King really *DID* die in my arms, as the good Lord above delivered him from harm. That's, at least, the way *I* remember it going down, despite the fact that my recollection could be completely unsound.

"My soul is not rested, Baby Jesus, although it's been sorely tested. All I've ever really wanted to do is rainbow with you. So float my discipleship, Baby Jesus; lift up my boat. For if we are to achieve, then first we must believe, and then conceive. If we conceive, and then believe, then we will achieve. It's not the aptitude, but the attitude that finally determines the altitude. We can't lose, if you choose me, Baby Jesus. There'll be no opportunity to flop, if you put Jesus and Jessie at the top. Together, we'll put enough hope in their brains to remove the dope from their veins.

"But if you still don't believe that I'm the best, one good look at the book on the Master of Action, Jesse Jackson, should put your mind at rest.

"Number 1: I'm a supreme voter-getter; there're few any better. As two-time presidential candidate, I won over 10 million votes because I filled the people with hope, so they could cope, and come out to vote. I drew big crowds wherever I went; Lord knows they weren't Heaven sent. I prevailed in the primary debates, trampling my opponents in eleven states. I won 55% of Michigan's primary vote; not one automaker in Detroit called me a goat. I was a contender, not a pretender. I went from the outhouse to within spitting distance of the White House. My only regret was that my delegate count sank before I could knock Michael Dukakis off his tank.

"But, if you need a disciple to get the masses off their asses, you can rely—that ain't no lie—on your go-to, get-out-the-vote guy—the Reverend Jesse Jackson.

"And if you ever feel the need to spread your sacred creed with a little more deliberate speed, I'll intervene to make your powers even more supreme because deep down inside, I'm a blowtorch kind of guy—that cannot be denied.

"But if you don't believe that I can achieve, drop a dime to Anheuser-Busch and wait for the chime. When they answer, 'This Bud's for You," tell them you're a friend of Jesse's and then remain on line while things get messy, because they've seen the Master of the Corporate Shakedown in Action—the Reverend Jesse Jackson. They're aware I'm a blowtorch kind of guy; that they cannot deny.

"Because when their distributorship came under fire and earned Rainbow PUSH's ire for failing to promote, which is the same thing as demote, African-American employees, I conceived and then achieved the 'This Bud's a Dud' Budweiser beer boycott. We didn't defame, so they gave us a whole lot more than chump change. The Rainbow PUSHed Anheuser-Busch flat on its tuche. Because we redeemed them from their sin, it was a win-win situation.

"So if you ever need a disciple to help spread your creed with a little more deliberate speed, you can rely—and that ain't no lie—on your go-to, blowtorch guy—the Reverend Jesse Jackson.

"Please, Baby Jesus, give me a chance to be part of your great causes so that together we might enjoy the world's applauses. And know that I'm willing to do almost anything for you, just so long as it puts us on the *New York Times'* front pages for ages. And you have my word that if anyone tries to hold back your new tide or string you up on that damn wooden cross again, I'll give them a ride to where they'll most likely be fried because I'm a blowtorch kind of guy.

"But there's more because I'm no bore.

"So if you ever need a disciple to secure the release of anyone in prison caught by, let's say, the anti-Christ opposition, while on a sacred mission, you can rely—and that ain't no lie—on your go-to, Operation Rescue kind of guy—the Reverend Jesse Jackson. That's why they won't cry when I take the Red-Eye because I'm a trans-Atlantic savior unsurpassed, which is why the Legend of Jesse Jackson won't die.

"When Navy pilot Lt. Robert Goodman got shot down on a mission to bomb Syrian positions in Lebanon, I leapt in like Errol Flynn to meet with President Hafez al-Assad at his palace in Damascus. Al-Assad agreed that the pilot was a pawn of American brawn, and decreed that he should be freed. So Hafez acceded and I succeeded. First and last, I'm a trans-Atlantic savior unsurpassed.

"When twenty-two Americans were detained in Havana by that quixotic neurotic despotic, Fidel Castro, in a place, you can bet, that didn't offer the detainees the amenities of the Copacabana, he invited me to fly in to dine at his digs on the other side of the Bay of Pigs. So I did, armed only with my charms and just enough press to consider myself truly blessed, Castro and I found common ground over the sound of flamenco guitars and the sweet scent of cigars and any ill-will became nil and our goodwill became a thrill. So Fidel decreed the twenty-two should be freed. He acceded and I succeeded. First and last, I'm a trans-Atlantic savior unsurpassed.

"And when Bosnian armed forces captured three U.S. soldiers patrolling the Macedonian border on UN orders, I took the Red-Eye to meet with former-Yugoslav President Slobodan Milosevic in his new Bosnian Serb Republic to insist that he desist and free the three. And at first he was a little hard to read, and didn't seem to want to agree with my pacifist creed. But I appealed to his musical side and soon he and I were singing my tune, 'The Trans-Atlantic Red-Eye.' And faster than you could say, "Bosnia and Herzegovina," Milosevic concurred with my urge to free the three after reciting after me, 'We must conceive to believe before we can achieve...' He acceded, and I succeeded. First and last, I'm a trans-Atlantic savior unsurpassed.

"So if you ever need a disciple to secure the release of anyone in prison caught by, let's say, the anti-Christ opposition while on a sacred mission, you can rely—and that ain't no lie—on your go-to, Operation Rescue kind of guy—the Reverend Jesse Jackson.

"So please, Baby Jesus, the first shall be last and the last shall be first! Make me your last disciple!"

My stepbrother carves an invisible cross over Jesse's forehead, and says, "Ask and it will be given to you; seek and you will find; knock and the door will be open to you. For every one that asketh, receiveth; and he that seeketh, findeth; and to him that knocketh, it shall be opened. Yes, Jesse Jackson, you can rely—and that ain't no lie—on you

152

being my go-to, trans-Atlantic Red-Eye kind of guy, because, first and last, any friend of Martin's is a friend of mine."

That said, Christ turns to Mel with a pained expression, and says, "Now where's the men's room?" As Mel shows Him the way downstairs, Christ calls back to Jesse, who looks about as happy as the Man on the Moon, well, maybe more, "Oh yes—just so you know—I know exactly where you were standing when Martin Luther King was shot..."

That said, Christ slips downstairs to take a leak before eating breakfast as the go-to guy utters his last will and testament, "Now I really *AM* SOMEBODY again."

Ready for ten-second hack.

As the new age disciples mill about, congratulating each other like honors students, Mel anoints himself as the Class of 2019 President, issuing a full-throated endorsement of the Man in the Shithouse (Aussie for toilet), "I'm stoked, mates! In the words of Willie Horse Power Faunce, former president of Brown University and wearer of the cloth, 'No man can follow Christ and go astray!'"

I switch off the live feed. Can't stand that kind of sorority/fraternity crap anyway. I fly due east over Sunset Strip, home to the Roxy and the Dave Clark Studios Museum, banking my Flying Falcon. I dip down to get a better look at the neon shrine erected by Capitol Records in memory of Tower Records where Sunset meets La Brea. It's really quite a show, a revolving turntable playing "She Loves You," by the Beatles. I roar over a torrent of Mercedes, Bentleys, and Jaguars. The smog's as low and foul as it's ever been. But as I soar, the smog unexpectedly parts, and behold, I see something more beautiful than the aftermath of Chernobyl—the golden turnstile of Mel's rising out of the smog.

"Five-second hack ready."

I release my AGM-65 Maverick, and count three little sheep. Then, ah—

"Good Hack."

I fly over, bank south to circle back to gloat, leaving under me a new bonfire on Sunset, as bright and shiny as finger paints. It's a gratifying sight. Something to be proud of. Except that I'm feeling pilot's remorse over my collateral damage. I feel a rush of remorse about doing Martha in like that. 'Cause there'll never be another Martha. Who else on the planet would ever publicly insist that one should take the occasional Snickerdoodles detour? Who else on the planet would recommend that one should indulge her Gingerbread Snowflake distractions any time of year? That's right. Martha was the only one. And for reasons that were completely unrelated to her, I just roasted her, vaporized one of America's chief domestic assets. Then there's Oprah. What have I done? Why, Oprah was family! One of the TV Personality Greats. How are little schoolgirls in Africa gonna get educated now? Who's gonna replace her as CEO of OPRAH.COM? Collateral damage is the price of supremacy, I know, but still. In Martha's case and in Oprah's, too, it's a price too high.

Still, I don't suppose I should fret too much. There're always be re-runs of Oprah's old shows. They'll be playing those for a thousand years—maybe more. Then there's always Dr. Phil's show, which is quite good, considering he's no Oprah.

I come in too steep. Serves me right for thinking soft. My F-16 banks too steeply, reaching a tipping point: I try to get control, but my ailerons don't respond, and then my rudder freezes up, and finally my side stick controller becomes utterly useless. I lose airspeed, then altitude, even though, as Jesse says, attitude determines the altitude and my attitude appears to be pretty good. Nevertheless, I'm definitely losing altitude.

154

Mayday. Mayday. That's all I can say. It's not enough.

I eject as my F-16 plunges into Paramount's Bronson Gate. It's a fine mess. A compote of pandemonium. A stew of spilt combustible jet fuel. But don't blame me; it's not like I ever attended flight school.

I come down like a porcupine quill on Melrose Avenue, across the street from the volcanic front entrance to Paramount. No one seems to notice. No one seems to mind. My entrance is actually fairly discreet, other than the little matter of the explosion of my F-16.

Quick as cockroaches scampering across the kitchen floor at night, I roll up my chute, stuff it like a pair of old socks into the nearest storm sewer, and search out an empty alley behind Best Buy where I change out of my flight suit and speed jeans and into something, well, more fashionable.

I peel away my Air Force garb, revealing a virtual fashion billboard underneath. There I stand: An apocryphal James Bond in a handsome white tux, wrinkle-free, with a white rosebud pinned to my lapel, scented and appearing fresh as spring winds, principally because it's been sprinkled with Bombay Rum cologne and the rosebud nub is made of Chinese silk. Let's face it, I look great, while all around me Paramount burns.

In the display window at Best Buy there are a couple of dozen 100-inch TV monitors tuned into CNN's coverage of the attack on Mel's. For the latest in news, CNN is the obvious choice, who else? The caption below the melting images of Mel's says: "Terrorist Attack on Sunset Boulevard." What's nice is that I can watch what's going on at Mel's while viewing in the shiny reflection of Best Buy's gigantic window the holocaust across the street. How nice that is for me. How convenient. As Paramount becomes toast, I can watch Mel's roast.

Mel's appears eviscerated by the rather nice impact of my contact fuse AGM-65 Maverick. You've got to hand it to the boys at

155

Raytheon; they do big bang better than anybody else in the business. Bombs down, they're the best.

As CNN's cameras zoom in, out; pan left, pan right; tilt up, down, I think fondly of Sadie Sherwood, presently turning to ash, and how unfair it is that CNN scooped her on the biggest news story of all time—Christ's second crucifixion—when she was the first reporter on the scene. That certainly validates my stepbrother's homespun axiom: "The First shall be Last and the Last shall be first." Me, I've always believed that first is first and last is last and never the twain shall meet— nor should they, because hardly anyone is called and almost no one chosen. That's the way I look at it, anyway. Not that anyone cares particularly what I think about this.

Though I have no independent confirmation as yet, I'm pleased to report that no one could be left alive in Mel's. Cockroaches couldn't survive a strike like that. Typically, it's a mistake to be too optimistic about such things until all the facts are in, but I have every reason to hope. I toasted Mel's. That's fairly obvious. And if I'm right, this could be a real career-maker. Supremacy is everything, you know.

It's difficult to hold back stray tears, humiliating as that is. Understand: This day has been a long, long time in coming. You'd be emotional, too, if you were me. Getting a second bite at the apple—no pun intended, Adam—is not nothing. Something for my Wikipedia page, anyway.

Back on CNN, a parade of firemen in big black shiny boots, fire hats and yellow jackets make the rubble bounce with a battery of disgorging water canons. Obviously, it's hopeless, which makes me feel pretty good. If they want my recommendation, which they don't, they oughta let the fire die down on its own. It makes for nice entertainment. But I suppose they keep at it, not because there're any lives to be saved anymore, but for the sake of CNN's cameras. My only regret is that I

156

didn't bring my own digital camera to record these precious Kodak moments. I'd like to put up a few new snaps on my cavern walls, showing the bounty of my most recent progress.

My stepbrother's bones will rise no more. Of that I'm sure. This time there'll be no archangels rolling back the rock from His tomb door and handing Him a passport back to Heaven. He will not rise to return once more to settle old scores, like before. This time resurrection is NOT an option.

I start to get bored. Perhaps it's time for me to catch a ride back to Juarez. If I make the one o'clock flight from LAX, I could be there just about in time for dinner. Besides, it's not nice to gloat. What's won is won. I should get on with my life. I only wish I hadn't trashed my F-16. She was a beautiful flying machine.

The last I'll say about Christ is: May He rest forever. That's more than enough of a eulogy and demonstrates ample respect. Certainly, it's vastly more dignified than what I'd like to have said. He'll be no bother to anyone anymore—not even to Himself. Which will probably come as some sort of major relief. It must have been very difficult, even for Christ, being Christ. Think about it. Condemned to an eternity of do-gooderism. No room for negativity, no space for black marks. Where's the fun in that? Poor fellow. At least He's out of His misery. The King of Do-gooders is dead.

I gaze a final time into the television screen before departing, my eyes lingering over the Kodak moment, as a startling thought embraces me: Perhaps God *is* beneficent. Perhaps, after all, we could be reconciled.

But the instance of raw lunacy passes quickly as a most curious image appears on the Sony Trinitron screen in the display window of Best Buy. It's an image that inspires me to consider committing suicide.

157

At first I think, okay, it's got to be the jet fuel fumes I'm inhaling, or possibly the lasting effects of the pot I smoked at 37,000 feet this morning, or conceivably even the aftermath of the booze I was knocking back before dawn in my home cavern outside Juarez; but whatever it is, even if it's just the psychosomatic manifestation of my most dire fears being played out in my rather agile imagination, it gets my attention. Def. Walking across the bubbling estuaries of melted glass and steel, amidst the bouncing rubble and the steaming sprays of useless water cannon fodder, is the most remarkably serene person I've ever seen. I have only to study the lyrical gait, glimpse the stirring light in those fair and placid eyes to know, and know for sure, who it is, even at this smoky distance: It's the Supreme King of Resurrection, of course.

I try like hell to take it Like a Man, which is about as easy for me as pulling my own fingernails out one by one. In order to scoop CNN and show the world I can take a punch as well as Barack Obama, I'm prepared to confirm that the figure I see walking across the fiery pools of jet fuel is, in fact, my redoubtable stepbrother. The New Age Phoenix has risen indeed. The Dudie of Dudes is back—for the second time in one day. How many resurrections does He have in Him, anyway? You heard about it first here on KBEELZEBUB-TV.

All kidding aside, I scour my mind, searching, searching for a reason—any reason—why I, the Prince of the Bone Yard, of all people, should have this happen to me, repeatedly? You would think I could have gotten it right by now. But, oh no, even when I have the element of surprise on my side, I can't put a live dog down. One thing's for sure, I'm gonna fire off a blistering letter to Raytheon as soon as I can about the combat effectiveness of their AGM-65 Mavericks. I'm more than a little disappointed in them. They didn't get the job done.

Out of the pizza oven and onto Sunset Strip, He comes. Hello Hollywood Walk of Fame; good-bye Mel's. At curbside, a bunch of reporters hang out like stargazers waiting to get a glimpse of celebrities as they emerge from their Beverly Hills mansions. As Christ emerges from the ruins, they scribble notes furiously, as furious as flames chasing after smoke. Radio guys point their microphones at the miraculous man emerging; TV journalists take aim at the spectacle unfolding with handheld cameras, recording for perpetuity the miracle moment Christ steps from His jet fuel bath unscathed. Like Robert Redford in *The Candidate*, His every hair remains in place, despite the circus of commotion about Him and the rain of water cannons. Now that's a bona fide miracle!

Naturally, I'm impatient to listen to what He has to say to the press, so I go inside and punch up the volume on the 100-inch Sony in the window. Hike it almost all the way up, because I'm hard of hearing these days (Well, who isn't?)—too much loud rock music over a lifetime. When a Best Buy salesman insists I turn down the volume, I don't make a scene, as I usually would, or put a hex on him. No, I hand him one of my many stolen credit cards instead and just say, "Charge it," as if I was buying some cheap pair of J.C. Penny's pants with my Platinum Card.

That shuts him up faster than American Express approves my card.

Finally, after an exquisite entrance, my stepbrother's feet touch concrete. Yes, He emerges unscathed from the L.A. holocaust. I still can't get over His un-mussed attire, his perfectly groomed hair, but then, what would you expect: He's perfect. Always was. Always will be. Much as it galls me. So it's my problem and I better learn to handle it. Then on live TV—as national as national can be—He says without notes, "And every one that heareth these my words and doth them not, shall be like a foolish man that built his house upon the sand; and the rain fell, and the floods came, and the winds blew, and they beat upon that house, and it fell, and great was the fall thereof."

Clearly, my stepbrother requires urgent training in delivering nugget sound bites. That kind of verbose, metaphorical crap might have worked a couple of thousand years ago, but really now, these days it doesn't go down too well. That's what I think, anyway. But, as in all things Christ, His words work one way on me and another on others. In this case, they apparently have a salutary effect on the esteemed members of the Fourth Estate. They shut them up. Not one of them has the nerve to ask Him a question.

So being Christ, He continues, using similes a little too liberally for my taste, but all we know, there's no accounting for taste.

"But... every one that heareth these my words, and doth them, shall be likened to a wise man that built his house upon a rock. And the rain fell, and the floods came, and the winds blew, and they beat upon that house, and it fell not, for it was founded on a rock."

That line goes down easier than the first. By far, it's more digestible and everyone breathes easier—a real crowd pleaser.

Then because Christ always likes surprises, He turns his face away from His captive audience to face the burning lake. Something tells me that this is the moment I have NOT been waiting for. While everyone else is breathing easier, I'm about to gag. That's the affect Christ's always had on me. It's just one of those unavoidable things that happens. He turns like a swivel fan on slow speed, rotating to confront the hot grease of a frying pan on full flame. And as he looks upon the barbecue pit, roaring with the sizzling meat of His vanquished disciples, Christ lifts His outstretched arms, like some magnificent eagle borne of wings about to set off for the misty mountaintops. And in a voice clearer than Venetian sunshine, He says, His voice rising, rising, "To everyone I say: That thou art with me; and upon this rock I will build my church, **and the gates of hell shall not prevail against it!!!"**

Wow! He obviously means business! Like the sheriff's back in town! Sheriff Jesus. Lightening cracks the sky above, and CNN is the first to cover it. It looks like the scar on Harry Potter's forehead to me. But then I'm a Harry Potter fan, so it would. Thunder follows, sounding like freight trains rumbling past prairie towns hours before dawn. The smog overhead opens up, punctured by the gush of cold rain aimed at the frying pan on full flame below. It's pretty clear now that Christ's pulling rank on everyone. Which of course is exactly what I would do if I was him. And in, oh about thirty seconds or so, it souses the hallowed ground on which Mel's once stood, dousing the lava lot and pulverizing those poor flames.

Pathetically, they fizzle like spent sparklers dumped in a bucket of ice water. What's soon left of my beautiful bonfire is more sound than fury. There's the low hissing of dying coals lodged down deep at the bottom of charcoal craters. And the unimaginable stink of sulfur: Beelzebub's stink and, if Chavez was right, George W.'s, too.

"Your name, sir, is...?" asks a composed reporter from *People* magazine. All the rest are speechless. Well, you'd be, too, standing curbside. Hollywood hasn't been this gaga since Michael Jackson did the Moonwalk. But instead of answering, which would have been the courteous thing to do, Sheriff Jesus takes it over the top—and I do mean over the top—firing off His pair of verbal six guns concealed on His person. Violating any number of daytime noise level ordinances, I'm positive, He cries out, **"Rise, Mel's, rise oh Great of House of Christ! Be built upon a rock!"**

Instantly, as in a fast-speed cartoon movie, the smoldering lot becomes a hardhat zone. The rubble's bull-dozed and trucked out; cranes roll in and steel scaffolding goes up, followed by the walls and roof, windows and doors. The crowning touch: A new Mel's golden turnstile drops into place through the hole in the smog, landing where the other one once was. Inside lights flip on, infusing the gray smog about with yellow warm welcoming light. The firemen turn off their hoses; not a few reporters faint into lumps on the sidewalk; a L.A. Police Department captain mouths two pithy words, "H-O-L-Y S-H-I-T." And of course, wouldn't you know, this is all being beamed LIVE ON CNN. Christ has all the luck. Pardon my Latin, but why is it He, not me, gets to have the whole FUCKING world sitting ringside and watching His single Greatest Miracle? With a splash of sex on the edges, just the right packaging, and a hint of background music, it could even beat out Madonna's "Justify My Love" for the top spot on MTV's all-time music video charts. Now you can understand can't you why this is the kind of shit that drives my personality disorder, and has for a good part of my life? You can understand why it's been so hard on me, can't you?

So I ask you—anyone—anyone at all, and I'll pay top dollar, too: *Who will rid me of this man?*

Mel's doors bust open. Catastrophe just went seismic. Popping out like Mexican Jumping Beans come Jesus' baker's dozen: His Chosen Twelve, His newborn litter, who act like cute little puppies. They greet Jesus as their Savior, which I suppose He is. It must be great being a Savior, not that I'll ever know. Obviously, for me, this is more than embarrassing. Christ snatches awesome victory from annihilation; I snatch hyper-humiliation from victory. Not only has Christ made his second comeback today—but Mel's is back, too. Yes, Mel's is so very back.

162

Outside, on Sunset Strip, it's one big party now. And everyone's invited, except for me. Understandably.

Madonna slathers Christ with what look suspiciously like real kisses. Proof positive Christ gets all the girls even when He's supposed to be so celibate and above it. Mel hops up and down like a roo hyped on methamphetamines. "Oh, you beautiful bastard you!" he croons. Nancy Pelosi maneuvers Christ away from Madonna—(a feat worthy of a great politician) and has a not-so-private word with Him, picked up by CNN's roving microphones. "Mighten you consider, Lord of Lords, running for office as a Democrat in your spare time?"

Wake me when this Rocky Horror Picture Show is over! Take me back to my warm, safe bed in Juarez! I can't take it anymore. This is catastrophe of seismic proportions. I leave Best Buy, revolted by what I've seen and heard. It's a mental health thing for me actually, like avoiding cruel, inhuman and degrading punishment. I step outside again to glory in the spectacle of Paramount Studios back lots burning to a crisp before heading to LAX to hop a standby flight home.

I hadn't anticipated the back lots flaring up like this. They burn like a barn full of straw, which gives me a lift. Proof positive that my trip hasn't been a total loss. I dig out a joint from my pocket. Exactly what I need to take the edge off, my old favorite, Acapulco Gold. I light it up to the sweet sounds of police sirens and fire truck engines swooshing to a halt too late to save the burning back lots. Win one for Beelzebub! In Hollywood, it's about show, and so they put on a brave show, especially since so much Hollywood history's at stake, but it's more show than performance.

After two tokes, I get a buzz on, which makes me feel disturbingly cheery, practically nice, even. Pot does that to me; that's the real health hazard of smoking weed for me. Taking the edge off puts me in the danger zone.

I float along in my jolly misery, until the words of Clement of Alexandria get into my head, making me nuts: "He changed sunset into sunrise..." Clement spoke of the Supreme Do-Gooder Himself, of course. My best accolades are likely to be different. Like "He changed clover into weeds." Napoleon Bonaparte's own praise for Christ's ways invades, sullying my merry state of mind: "Alexander, Caesar, Charlemagne, and I have founded empires. But on what did we rest the creations of our genius? Upon force. Jesus Christ founded his empire upon love; and at this hour millions of men would die for him."

I turn uncharacteristically introspective, and inquire of myself, knowing full well that my honest answer will be even more characteristically bleak: Who would die for me? Who will weep over my silent body? In a pothead haze, I give voice to a revolutionary thought, as quietly as I can and in the furthest frontiers of my mind, so that no one else can possibly hear, especially CNN's roving microphones: Could Christ be right?

Not only does pot induce me to merry extremes, but it also makes me weak in the knees. I snuff out my joint. I swear, I'm off pot for good. That last thought's really, really dangerous and as unhealthy as sniffing glue...

Firemen heroes and do-gooder passersby wade into the wreckage and the back lot conflagration to save as many victims as they can. They seem to love their danger. I don't get it, obviously. The fire spreads like lightening fires through Malibu Canyon. Paramount's white water tower is a tangle of flames. The Blue Sky wall burns like sunset at the edge of the world. The mock brownstones, where some of my favorites were made, burn like Watts during race riots. The backdrops for *The Untouchables* and *I Love Lucy* give way to the inferno. At Sound Stage 4, the flight deck of the Starship Enterprise collapses, as though hit by meteor showers. All in all, it's a pretty nice back lot holocaust, if I do say so myself. And I did it all without the aid of special effects. Who needs Linwood Dunn when I have my own F-16? Maybe it's not quite up to Christ's caliber of extravaganza, but it's no campfire of smoky twigs and damp logs, either.

The media arrives—or what passes for it. By the look of the modest pack, it's mainly local press, with a print reporter from the *Santa Monica Boulevard Gazette*, and a radio gal from a NPR affiliate. I can always tell when they're from a NPR affiliate: Fresh out of grad school, they are, always clutching their digi-recorders to their breasts, like the devout grasping their crucifixes. So NPR affiliate is good because there's always some chance that NPR national will pick up their story. Naturally there's no sign of CNN, ABC, CBS, NBC, or MSNBC! No *L.A. Times, New York Times,* or *Washington Post,* either. Nevertheless, I'm grateful for any kind of press attention for my stories. Some is better than none.

Still, even though I'm architect of this cataclysmic event, none of the reporters are choosing to interview me. In fact, they do interviews with everyone on the scene but me, notwithstanding the fact I'm the only one wearing a nice white tux with a rosebud cluster pinned to my lapel! At least Martha will appreciate the touch!

Then it hits me. Could it be that my beard and hair are off-putting to mainstream media? If so, I consider their oversight discriminatory. Media should learn tolerance. We can't all be telegenic. I just want to be me.

The words of W.E. Orchard come rushing back. "They gave him a manger for a cradle, a carpenter's bench for a pulpit, thorns for a crown, and a cross for a throne. He took them and made them the very glory of his career."

Maybe it's because I'm high or because I haven't eaten since sunrise, but suddenly I think I get it.

I swipe a shaving kit from the cosmetic aisle at CVS, lock myself in the men's room, and with Gillette razor and a can of Schick shaving cream, I do what needs to be done. I cut away, bit by bit, at my beard in the name of media recognition. Of course, for me, it's more than a little emotional. It's positively traumatic. So many centuries of history tied up in that beard. All those years of deliberate mischief, planned agony, and pursuit of misery, all of that and more, being hacked away and falling to the bathroom floor. But before I know it, it's over. And suddenly, miraculously, my new face stands before me reflected in the men's room mirror, glowing pink and fresh under the harsh fluorescents. My God, I look like a saint! It's a face even my mother could love. News flash: I look wholly human.

But the big item is—and the one that makes my radical operation worthwhile—is that miracle of miracles—my face looks like the face of Christ. Yes, that's right, I could be His double, His very twin. After all these centuries under that barbarous beard, I'd forgotten that we had more than a passing facial resemblance. We look as though we could be perfect carbon copies of each other. Surprisingly, it's an uplifting feeling, which is reinforced by a sudden, extraordinary sense of solidarity with the likes of my stepbrother. Yes, actually, I feel, well, born again, actually. Yes, born again. That's exactly how I feel.

So now I get why people make such a fuss over baptisms and now I get the attraction of good grooming!

I emerge from the men's room, my hair combed and nicely parted straight down the middle. I smell of Schick shaving cream, and am proud of it. There's no other way to describe me: I look, well, respectable. Yes, that's spelled, r-e-s-p-e-c-t-a-b-l-e. But the really good thing is, emotionally, I'm over it! As in, what beard? Like Jesse, I'll do anything to attract media attention. Because I'm a sentimental fool, I save a knot of it as a memento, and put it in my pocket. I'd like to remember it in my old age.

I hike back up to Paramount Studios. Since I left, two more local reporters have come on, adding a little more heft to the media mix, and making it look, well, more respectable. It's a happening morning for respectability here on Melrose Avenue. The reporters come from the *City Paper* and *Hollywood Bulletin*, and I'm delighted to see them. They ask me to do interviews, proof positive that those other reporters are intolerant and discriminatory. As I answer the reporters' questions, and describe the horror of the impact at the Bronson Gate, a tear rolls down my freshly-shaven cheek. It's pure Hollywood, but that one tear touches the reporters deeply. They get teary-eyed, too. We're a pretty teary lot, but my baby tear isn't manufactured. It's as genuine as my affection for the most bombastic of Ludwig Van Beethoven. That's because my tear rolls down in beautiful memory of my fallen F-16. May she rest in peace.

Just then a CNN satellite broadcast truck draws up at the curb, blocking the local reporters' view of the burning Bronson Gate. They pitch a fit, but I couldn't be more delighted. My deepest wish, my sweetest desire has, at last, true: I got CNN.

The driver recognizes me as he steps from the truck...

"Say, aren't you...?"

"Yes," I answer.

"But I thought—"

"You thought wrong."

That pretty much ends our conversation right there.

When CNN's all setup, I step in to do my thing.

I walk out into the middle of Melrose, center stage for CNN's camera. I raise my arms to the smog banks of the L.A. sky. It feels so good to stretch! Then in tone and with gravity consistent with my stepbrother's, I unloose the necessary words to create my own holiday

167

season miracle, *Miracle on Melrose Avenue*, which I admittedly crib from you-know-who, but that hardly matters. A miracle's a miracle, no matter how many there are, right? Anyway, I always say, if you can't do miracles as well as the next guy, why not plagiarize?

So beginning quiet as a whisper, just as Christ, I take the world stage, my voice rising in crescendo: "To everyone I say: That thou art with me; and upon this rock I will build my church, and the gates of hell shall not prevail against it!!!

"RISE, PARAMOUNT, RISE! BE BUILT UPON MY ROCK! For I am the true Son of God come back to claim Dominion, and to lay low my impersonator!!!"

I feel better about myself having said that. Give then an inch, they take it all.

Now, for me, it's all about performance, and performing the Miracle of Miracles: Miracle II. We've had a couple of comebacks today, so why not a couple of miracles, too?

So I lift my arms higher toward the very roof of the L.A. sky, so high in fact that it tears my arms' sockets, but I'm still having fun and feeling good, so who cares? All the while, CNN's camera turns. My sole thought, aside from wondering whether I remembered to pack the Ben-Gay, is: This had better work.

As my arms reach high above my head, lightening strikes, pretty much on cue, cutting an authentic Harry Potter-like scar in the smoggy forehead of the low sky. Thunder follows, again sounding like freight trains rumbling past prairie towns hours before dawn. And then, because I plagiarize so well, the smog above opens up, punctured by the great gush of cold rain aimed at the frying pan of Paramount's back lots

168

and the Bronson Gate directly below. And in, oh about thirty seconds or so, just like at Mel's, it souses the historic movie studio grounds, dousing the lot and tamping out the flames.

But the best is yet to come!

With comical animation, as in high-speed, time-lapse photography, the destruction is left undone. Bronson gate pops back into place; construction cranes roll in raising back lot facades and sound stage roofs. Even the Blue Sky wall miraculously reconfigures itself, with a fresh coat of sky blue paint. Paramount's signature water tower climbs back up into the low sky, rising above Melrose. The cub reporter from the *City Paper* faints. Well, I would hope so! Somebody should! Even the imitation New York City brownstones used for the *Seinfeld* series return, looking superior to the originals. And at Sound Stage 4, the bridge of the Starship Enterprise has returned from where only one man has gone before—my tardy stepbrother. The only thing missing is my F-16. That I edit out for obvious reasons.

It's really quite a miracle by really quite a guy, even though it was plagiarized.

And it's all been carried on a live feed by CNN—worldwide. They got me with my arms up; they got the lightening strike and the low rumbling of things happening; they got the rains coming down and the Blue Sky wall re-materializing. In other words, they got the whole thing, the new news, which is what we've all come to expect from CNN. God bless, Ted Turner.

I really don't require a whole lot more convincing: There truly *is* a merciful God. The proof is in the news. I got CNN worldwide press coverage!

I turn toward CNN's camera and, like the good Jesus Christ I'm not, I proclaim: "I am the Lord Jesus Christ—there is no other Jesus but me. Those who have come before me and claim to be me are charlatans,

169

as low as snakes, for I am the King of Kings and the Lord of Lords and the Dudie of Dudes and have come again to judge both the quick and the dead."

Okay, so I plagiarize my stepbrother's lines, not just His miracles. The only commandment I observe is this one: "Thou Shalt Always Win!"

A crowd of on-lookers gathers around me. Well, I should hope so! But it does make me feel like a Boston cream puff. Everyone, it appears, wants a piece of me. I kid you not: I haven't generated this much frenzy since my days in Darfur. Oh, those were the days, stirring up all sorts of tribal strife and even the odd day of genocide, well, on my best days. I throw them another hunk of plagiarized meat to boost my divinity credentials. You can never have too much of them. And I suppose I also do it just to show them that I can get away with absolutely anything.

"Live in me, and let me live in you, says the Lord. Remain in me, and I will remain in you. No branch can bear fruit by itself; it must remain in the vine. Neither can you bear fruit unless you remain in me."

"Tell it, Jesus!" a studio techie sounds.

"You go, Jesus, you go!" another one chimes.

Then the entire ditzy throng weighs in, chanting the same kind of encouragements. "Tell it, Jesus!" "Oh, Jesus, sweet Jesus, say it!" Even though they've got the wrong guy, it's still flattering. It must be nice to be Christ sometimes.

For the first time ever, I can appreciate why Christ must occasionally get a kick out of being, well, Christ. I finally understand: It's the adulation, stupid. It's the glory, stupid. It's the miracles, stupid. It's life after death, dummy. Those are all very attractive rewards. So, like any self-respecting drug addict, I decide to get myself some more. I go at a second round of plagiarism to raise the ante. "If you bring forth what is within you," I intone, "what you bring forth will save you. If you do not bring forth what is within you, what you do not bring forth will destroy you..."

Then, momentarily, I struggle to come up with the right punch line. I want to nail it, if for no other reason than I'm on CNN. It seems to take a thousand years to conjure it, but then I remember one of His pithiest lines: "For we walk by faith, not by sight."

A hundred oooaahs and aaaoohs ooze from my cluster of supporters. That went down well. Yes, my Sermon on Melrose Avenue went down like Moet champagne. Clearly, I'm the King of Sham and the Lord of Subterfuge. And pretty soon the real Christ is gonna to be crying to His Old Man.

My fans egg me on.

"He turned fire into water!"

"Raised the Bronson Gate!"

"Brought the dead back to life!"

"He's a Miracle Maker!"

"He's the real Christ!"

"The Greatest Miracle Worker this side of Sunset!"

But they've only begun to get worked up.

"Put Christ in the White House!"

"Yes, he should be America's next president!"

"Open up the gates at 1600 Pennsylvania Avenue!"

"We want Christ!"

Then—shall we call it Miracle III—my Bronson gate groupies begin chanting, quietly first, then rising:

"Run, Jesus, run..."

"Run, Jesus, run!"

"RUN, JESUS, RUN!"

"RUN, JESUS, RUN!"
"RUN, JESUS, RUN!"

I do believe they're serious. Yes, they actually want ME to run for PRESIDENT. Well, why not? After all, if someone like George W. can land the job, why not me? I couldn't do much worse and perhaps, depending on your point of view, I could do a bit better.

So... and then I begin to daydream, such is the influence of my fans. I suppose I could run at the top of the Republican ticket. That's a natural fit. Who better to advocate for a kick-the-shit-out-of-all-terrorists-foreign-policy platform than me? After all, it takes a terrorist to know one. And who would be better, now I ask you, to promote torture and renditions for terrorist suspects? And who better to shrink big government? I detest government intervention, especially when it comes to me. Of course, I'm a fan of the top 2% of the population holding 98% of the wealth. In my opinion I think the top 1% of the population should just about get it all. There's room for improvement there. And naturally I support massive capital gains relief and am all for taxing the middle class and the poor. How else are we Republicans going to sustain our monetary primacy? We'll gloss over the family and moral values side of the platform; but it's no problem, I can always fake my allegiance to those. That's no problem. So I may not agree with every little part of the national platform—what Republican does?—but I won't be the first Republican to have to swallow something undesirable. Lying, pretending, never hurt anyone. Anyway, in politics, that's the way it's done. Believe me, I've watched the lies go round for a long, long time.

It's what all politicians do. So I should be good at it, too.

"Run, Jesus, run!"

They really are getting rather insistent.

Of course, I'll need to consider the financial side of this transaction. I'm fairly confident that the boys at the Business Roundtable down in Big D. will offer me assistance. After all, they already think that Christ's a Republican and that God is on their side, so I imagine that I'm a perfect fit. And naturally when I dangle the odd incentive to major contributors, like guaranteeing them screwing privileges in the Lincoln bedroom or weekend passes to Camp David, good for a night or two of debauchery underneath the presidential seal, I'll rake it in. I may even be able to put some aside for those rainy days. One thing's for absolute sure: I'll never forget my backers. I'll take care of them, if they take care of me. It may be true that you can't live with them; but you sure as hell can't live without them, too. The art is to find a way to get along. Which is one of the first rules of being a Washington insider. Get on getting along. Give to get and get to give. That's a philosophy that will take some getting used to. But I'll get there. I'll learn to get over myself, and soon. The prize of the White House is enough to make a mad man sane.

"RUN, JESUS, RUN!"

Their will is sucking me in. Such is my luck. When I got up this morning, who'd have thought? Still, nothing is for nothing. You and I both know that there'll be hell to be pay. Like starting now, if I accept, I'll have to learn to hold my nose and pretend to be a do-gooder. That'll be my single greatest challenge. Once I hit the campaign trail, I'll be all about giving. Not about getting. For me that's far more than a stretch. That's an Eval Kenival hurdle over the Grand Canyon on a motorbike!

So how did this happen to me? It's a total mystery.

Perhaps, just perhaps, we're talking divine intervention. We're talking God's own hand. That's the beauty of politics. God's hand can be seen everywhere, especially in the Republican Party.

It just goes to show: The more you know, the more you know how little you know, no matter how much you actually know. It's a great system God worked out. Couldn't He have made the world a little less complex for us?

Being shrewd, I play it cool, neither confirming nor denying my interest in their proposition. Not since James Dean played Jet Rink in *Giant* has anyone in L.A. played it so damn cool. I plagiarize James Dean, too. I pass the flat of my hand slowly in front of my belly, like a slow-motion wave... It's a sign that my Hollywood supporters can truly appreciate. Everyone knows the moves of James Dean. Still louder, the cry goes up:

"RUN, JESUS, RUN!"

That's when they sign me up, whether I want it or not. I'm their guy in 2020. It's all about seizing the moment—the right moment, and this, evidently, is it. And somehow it all makes sense to me. Indeed, I can say that I've waited my whole lifetime for something so wacky, so outrageous, to happen to me, to come my way. And it's finally happening, here today, on Melrose, across the street in Hollywood. Who says you need to go to Schwab's to be discovered? I owe a debt of gratitude to my stepbrother, too. After all, if not for Him coming back—a little late, that's for damn certain—I would have been down in my hole in Juarez, instead of considering running for president as a Republican. Yes, I see the Hand of God everywhere. He works in very mysterious ways, that's for sure. But the Religious Right was right all along. God really does steer political candidacies. Most importantly, He's

174

on the side of those politicians who stand on the right of history. Politicians like me.

So as John Lennon once said when introducing Paul McCartney and his newly written song, "Yesterday," "Opportunity knocks." If Paul can be a walrus, I can be the president. You better believe it, good news has arrived: My ship's finally come in.

It's gonna be beautiful. Once I'm president, I'll be in position to take on my stepbrother. Compromise his credibility, sabotage His do-gooderism, undermine His base. Do the stuff I usually do, only with the entire U.S. Government behind me. Like the IRS. Like the CIA. Like the NSA. Like the DOD. I won't let things get out of hand, like last time. Back then I gave Him a free run of Palestine. Such a fool I was. I won't make that mistake twice. I remember the wise words of Chinese President Zhang Zemin at the peak of his power: "Nip the opposition in the bud." That's the strategy I intend to follow.

"RUN, JESUS, RUN!"

All right already. They aren't going to take no for an answer. It appears as though I have only two real choices: Either 1) to accept their request, or 2) to give in to their demand. So what's it going to be? Oh, that's a hard one. It's like choosing between making love and having sex.

And in truth, I have no choice, if survival is my object, if I am to bring the Voice of God to the White House. Consider this: Should the San Francisco Democrats get their mitts on the Oval Office and win a majority in Congress, I'll be more screwed than the drywall in the world's tallest skyscraper.

If that happens, no doubt they'll invite the genuine Jesus Christ to the White House and invite Him to participate in important policy discussions. That of course will inevitably lead to higher taxes on the rich and bigger government and a weaker national defense, which will in turn give the terrorists an upper hand. With the Dems hand on the nuclear trigger and terrorists abounding, they'll be no safe place on earth for me to hide, not even down in Juarez. Either the Dems or the terrorists will hunt me down, probably with overhead drones and bunker-busting bombs—whatever. It won't be like waiting for Santa on Christmas Eve. And the terrorists will be glad to come after me, too, because, as we know, I'm their competition. This earth can only hold so many terrorists at one time.

So from my perspective, running for president is an imperative. More than jealously, more than ambition, more than anything else it's about self-preservation, in addition, of course, to fulfilling the will of God.

So that's it. My mind's made up. I intend to run for president—as a Republican, under the banner of my natural party affiliation: The Grand Old Republican Party. It's perfectly understandable. I could never align myself with a party that has as its symbol a jackass.

Of course, I won't let on to my supporters that I intend to accept their proposition immediately. I play it *cooler* than James Dean. For James Dean and me, cool is everything.

About then a boy, age nine, and of distinctively Latino origin, fishes through my throngs of supporters with a dead dog laid across his outstretched arms. He would have to be crying, I mean really balling. It's just got to be the family dog, hit by a car. So he stands before me, holding out that damn dead dog, expecting me to do something! "Please, Mr. Jesus," he says, "Bring my doggie back to life."

Naturally, my first impulse is to tell the kid to stop his sniveling, and to get a grip. But I hold my tongue because I'm a politician now and the last thing I want to do is to let people know what I'm actually thinking.

And then it occurs to me that opportunity may have come a-knocking for a second time today. I take the damn dog and for the first and only time in my life, I close my eyes and pretend to pray. It makes for a perfect photo opportunity. But the thing is, I pray and pray until that damn dog comes back to life!

Well, why not, let's give the kid a break.

The kid grabs the yapping damn dog and hugs it to within an inch of its life. It's quite touching, actually. Me. I'm somewhat flabbergasted by what I've wrought. It seems that there's to be no end of miracles for me today. Understandably, all my Hollywood fans go nuts, or Chiquita bananas, since we're down here near the border. They think this is just great. Just great. Even the kid turns his affection on me. He hugs me as though I was his poppa or something. It's all a little too emotional for me. I'm more than uncomfortable. In fact, I feel an outbreak of the hives coming on.

No good deed goes unpunished.

Still, as a politician, I'm not unaware of the beneficial impact that my second miracle will have on the viewing public as seen via CNN. That's got to be very good for me. Re-constructing a burning studio is one thing; bringing a boy's dead dog back to life is another, and quite a bit better. I know I should be grateful. But for the hives I would be.

The press peppers me with questions.

"If you're the real Christ, who's that fella over on Sunset Boulevard?"

"He's the Father of Scoundrels, the Lord of Lies. He's my stepbrother, Beelzebub."

"Isn't it more than a little strange that you both showed up on the same day?"

"'Tis' the season of miracles."

"So will you run for president?"

177

"First, I will establish an exploratory committee."

"But when will you announce?"

"Stay tuned to CNN tomorrow. Now if you'll excuse me, I really must be on my way. I'd like to buy this kid an ice cream cone and get a bone for his dog. They both look hungry! And as everyone knows who knows anything, the real Christ feeds His sheep and tends to them."

I wave goodbye to all of my adoring fans and supporters and escort the kid and his damn dog down Melrose until we turn the corner, out of sight from the press. Then naturally I ditch the kid and his dog and hop a cab to LAX. As is my custom, I stiff the cabbie for his tip, too.

In the Southwest Airlines VIP lounge, I watch CNN's coverage of my escapades on Melrose. I couldn't be more impressed with myself. It's pure drama, the stuff of legends; it even has the makings of a Hollywood hit movie. There's the gratuitous violence, the dichotomy of good and evil, the story of righteous redemption, a dead dog and a weepy kid. Add to that a happy ending, and all I can say is: Where's my agent? That last bit with the dog was extraordinarily good.

But wouldn't you know, just when everything was going perfectly, my flight gets delayed, because of mechanical difficulties. So I have all the time in the world to watch more of CNN's coverage of my attack on Mel's. They repeat it interminably. Christ fire-walking. Christ resurrecting Mel's. Christ bringing back disciples to life. He's got talent, I'll say that much for Him.

Then for the surprise, which is what you'd expect coming right after I actually say something nice about my stepbrother. There on camera, Nancy Pelosi invites Christ to run for president as a born-again Democrat. In front of the whole damn world even! Though He doesn't say yes, He doesn't rule it out, either. That doesn't make me feel particularly comfortable: It makes me feel like ice.

Then they announce my flight over the loudspeakers, so I get in line at the security checkpoint. That doesn't make me very happy because as a general policy, I don't do lines. Except coke lines. But then the nice TSA officer recognizes me from today's CNN performance, and he gives me a pass. No security, no screening, no nothing. "This way, please, Mr. Presidential Candidate, hopefully," he says.

That one last simple courtesy is all I need. I mount the skies and ride, on my way to the U.S. presidency, and the feeling I get is far, far nicer than flying even my own F-16.

CHAPTER FIVE

"**M**y name is Jesus Christ and I'm running for president. Why? Because the real Christ is a liberal Democrat, not some conservative Republican."

"Cut! Cut! Cut!"

However righteous the sentiment, Mel, my director, informs me that I'm putting a little too much emphasis on the word "name", and not giving quite enough punch to my own name—Jesus Christ.

Right, thanks, Mel.

So we try it again. Take six.

"My name is *Jesus Christ* and *I'm* running for president. Why? Because the real Christ is a liberal Democrat, not some conservative Republican."

"Cut! No, no, no," says Mel, climbing out of his director's chair and approaching me at the podium. Evidently, I'm not accentuating the word "real", so we have to do it over again.

Take Seven.

Take Eight.

Take Nine through Sixteen.

Then joy of joys, Mel likes Take Seventeen. At least better than Takes 1 through Sixteen. However, Take Seventeen could still be more perfect, according to Mel, so we're onto Take Eighteen. This is to be expected, I'm told. A-list Hollywood directors insist on perfect deliveries every time. They want their actors to shine, shine like smiling golden Buddhas in sunshine. Disciple Pelosi, the true author of my words, makes similar demands. She's sitting in an assistant director's chair opposite me on Sound Stage A at Universal Studios listening intently for the truth in my delivery. Truth be told, it's odd for me to be parroting other people's lines, but then whoever said that politics was anything but a bit strange? The situations I get myself into!

I do Take Eighteen. "My name is *Jesus Christ* and I'm running for president... Why? Because the *real* Christ is a liberal Democrat, not a conservative Republican." Eighteen's the one, evidently. Even to my untrained ear it sounds mighty righteous. Well, fairly okay. It sounds as though I could possibly know what I'm talkin' about. Now I get why Mel's *The Passion* went into boffo box office orbit, considering it was only a film about me. He certainly knows what he's doing, all right. Mel's spot-on direction, coupled with Pelosi's no-nonsense speechwriting, and after considerable direction, my not entirely inept delivery, give me the occasion to hope that together—somehow, someway—we can beat my stepbrother through the presidential chute.

"CUT! PRINT! THAT'S A WRAP! She'll be apples, all right!" Mel exclaims, exuberant to the point of stupor, relishing his own new role as disciple director. "Break out the communion wine! Chalices all around!"

I'm relieved and pleased. Considering I've never attended a single actor's workshop or even taken one lousy speechmaking class, I'm psyched—definitely psyched—by my maiden performance. It should be a good speech and even better TV spot.

"He's the fair dinkum Christ, all right!" Mel spouts out, as he cracks open a bottle of communion wine and toasts me before chugging it down. I take a swig, too. As I said, politics is no easy work. We've been at this since around 2:30 this morning, after AP released a wire service story about my stepbrother's presidential announcement down in Dallas at noon today. So naturally we must respond, with out own announcement. Disciple Pelosi recommended we stage it in Watts and I agreed. It'll set the right tone and image. In politics, according to Nancy, image is everything. Image is king. Thus spake Disciple Pelosi. Thus agreed Candidate Christ.

I've made my share of concessions to image already. Take my wardrobe. Take my tie. I put on a barbershop pole colored tie to strike the right patriotic note. In politics nationalism is in. And I must say, it goes nicely with my white suit. I did, however, dump the Panama hat, but kept my long and greasy and always messy locks. Striking the long hair would have definitely undermined my sacred image at the very time I need it the most. But I did shave. Stubble plays badly in the exotic realm of high political ambition. If you harbor any doubts, invoke the ghost of Dick Nixon. He'll tell you a thing or two about five o'clock shadow. The truth is I had wanted to grow out my beard again, after having had it closely cropped for centuries because the Old Man has a thing about the absence of facial hair and good grooming up in Heaven. But down here Disciple Pelosi put her foot down, too, and said forget about it! So okay, okay, okay, I said. Whatever Nancy says goes. Just ask any Democrat; she knows exactly what she's doing.

Which is why I said yes when she said we should announce down in Watts today. The meek shall inherit the earth and all that. You can bet there'll be plenty of unassuming, self-effacing meek and lowly milling around looking for a savior political champion. And I'm the one. I'm hooking my political wagon to Nancy's star. There's no question about it: Nancy's the Queen of Gambits. That's why, as I said, when Nancy speaks, I listen. When Nancy says do it, I do it. Besides, I'm proud to be led, in part, by a *real* San Francisco Liberal. They don't make liberals any better than that. Of course, in the firmament of San Francisco liberals, I'm a mere disciple, unworthy of washing their feet. But we all have to start somewhere.

I chug down more communion wine. I don't mind it one little bit. At this ungodly hour of the morning, anything goes. My other disciples are joining in. A good time is being had by all. What Disciple Madonna is wearing I'll never tell!

The truth is, even though perhaps I should, I have no regrets about taking up politics. Oh, I know, of course, what you're thinking. You're thinking that perhaps I've gone over the edge, that I've taken this challenge from my stepbrother quantum leaps too far too soon. But have a look from my perspective. I do what I do to *stop* my lunatic stepbrother from ever dominating the pinnacles of power. And don't think he won't do it, given half a chance. First he steals *my* identity, then he muscles in on my territory, and come twelve noon today he'll launch a vast conspiracy to win the White House in the name of the Republican Party. Not bad for a day's work. What galls me is this: He's doing his levelheaded best to transform himself into something nature never intended him to be: Something more than a frustrated, distant relative stomping around back streets with a vast inferiority complex. Believe me, that's all he's ever been and ever will be. And if he thinks that I'm going to let him subvert the sweet intentions of my perfectly good

182

religion while he's at it—painstakingly built up, brick by brick, stone by stone, over the centuries through the trials and tribulations of others—that is, do what bin Laden did to the good name of Islam—he can think again. No way he's going to use Christianity as a club to wage his own special brand of barbarism against others. And one more thing: He can forget trying to advance, at least superficially, Republican social and economic policies in order to camouflage his real world domination intentions. Tax cuts for the millionaires? Oh no, I don't think so. Space weapons? No way, Jose. That's got to be the worst idea since cop killer bullets.

I knock back still more communion wine. No question about it: I could use some shut-eye. I'm a little red-eye. Well, a lot red-eye.

But there's no rest for the good! It's pathetic, really pathetic, when you stop to think about it. I mean, I finally get back to Earth, only to be forced by my stepbrother's brilliant opportunism to turn all my good intentions and attentions to opposing him. One individual instead of billions. Go figure. But what can I do? This is the hand I've been dealt. So I hereby resolve to go at him—very, very hard. The last thing I'm going to allow him to do is to portray Christ as a Republican. The real Christ—that's me—is a card-carrying liberal, from dawn to dusk, that's for sure. He's all about tax cuts for the poor, naturally, and shutting down the industrial military complex and transferring all that wealth to good causes. You bet your sweet life! So when all is said and written by all the pundits and scholars and your average citizens, they'll confirm—boy will they ever—that the *real* Christ—that's me—was as *liberal* a Democrat as Senator Edward Kennedy! And mighty proud of it! They'll record that I carried a torch of hope for liberalism, yea, even down into the chilly lowlands of American politics because, like Barack Obama, I'm your more than YES WE CAN AND YES WE WILL kind of candidate! I'm the Hope of Barack and the King of the Ages! Got

183

hope? You bet your sweet life I do. It follows me everywhere I go. Hope and me were born on the same star. Where it would go, I would go.

I take another swig. Okay, so four's my limit.

I'm so glad the spot's finally in the can and that my speech prep is over. Ever since AP flashed its wire service story we've been playing catch-up. I hate that. Pro-active is my middle name. To think that the Prince of Smog, my stepbrother, has anything over on me is about more than I can take. You can imagine how much he has us worried though. It's self-evident that he'll receive the endorsement of the Business Roundtable and all that campaign money. And the oil industry is a shoe-in. To say nothing of Halliburton. Talk about Daddy War Bucks. And it's not even an open question about who'll get the Religious Right. That's a no-brainer. According to the wire service story, he's all ready positioned himself to the right of Attila the Hun. It's clear my coddled days in Heaven are way over. I'm faced with a formidable adversary who'll spare no lie to do a world-full of harm: Like nothing is beyond the realm of comprehension. It'll be like having bin Laden times ten in the Oval Office. And George Bush times one hundred. Invade Denmark? Entirely conceivable. Bomb London? Count on it. Rain down shock and awe all over Baghdad again? Naturally! The day after his inauguration! Oh, the possibilities! On the home front, his impact might be more subtle—a variation on neutron bomb tactics, if you will. Eviscerate the Department of Health and Human Services? First thing! Shutter H.U.D.? Second thing! Pull the plug on Social Security? Third thing! Invite NSA into every boardroom and bedroom? Fourth thing! Dump habeas corpus? Fifth thing! Welcome in torture on a whim? Fifth thing! Define U.S. citizens as enemy combatants? Sixth thing? Rename America, Guantanamo Bay? Now we're back to first thing again!

So let's be perfectly clear here, if my stepbrother ever gets into the White House, it'll make the George W. Bush presidency look like Camelot.

Which is just another way of saying that the Democratic Party needs me—truly and sincerely needs me. I take another swig as Madonna swirls by dancing like she did on her Girlie Show Tour. That puts a pause in my stream of consciousness. 'Course, I could do worse than be the de facto head of the Donkey Party. I've always had a natural affinity for them, having ridden more than a few. Especially down the back alleys of Jerusalem. My only reservation—okay, let's use the f-word—fear—is that the Old Man will be watching when I announce. Count on Him going ballistic if He does. He won't take kindly to me mixing *His* religion—let's underscore that—and democratic politics, to be sure. It's always about religion and morality and spirituality with Him. It's *never ever* about politics, a word alien to His vocabulary. But then I'm the one assigned to this task, not Him. The truth is He doesn't exactly live in the real world anymore. I, on the other hand, if I want to be relevant, have to keep up with the times, with the changes. As Bobbie Dylan once said, "The times are a-changing." And change they have. Especially compared to where I last left off. Not that everything's completely different, mind you. There are some similarities. Like we can all still count on the fact that Lucy's going to take away Charlie Brown's football every time! Okay, a touch of humor never hurt.

I take another gulp. Feeling ever wider and wider awake! And fortified by the courage of my convictions! Or is it the wine? Whatever it is, I believe that my candidacy, given half a chance, can do more good than harm. Brave words, I know, but dangerous times require them, along with an ample supply of communion wine.

Plenty tipsy, but by no means certifiably drunk, we check into the Comfort Inn Motel on Santa Monica Boulevard. Naturally, I'll cover all my disciple's expenses because it's my Second Coming. I put the room charges on my MasterCard. I intend to pay for my own campaign every step of the way. I intend to take no pact money whatsoever, not even grassroots, Internet contributions of a $100 or less. For obvious reasons, I can't afford even a hint of political influence. So let the word go forth: I intend be beholden to NO SPECIAL INTEREST GROUP should I win the Oval Office. None. My allegiance is to the People and to the People only. My campaign will be financed strictly with Celestial Dollars minted in the Treasury of the Divine, and nowhere else. I have always been and always will be my own God—man. Alone, I stand. That's an eternal given.

I sign the credit card receipt in the name of Jesus Christ, which gives the Jew in spectacles behind the counter pause, for sure; but in light of the fact that my credit card's stamped with my name and my face matches my California state-issued photo I.D. and the $1500 room charges go through quicker than ruby red lasers slice through lemon pudding, he seeks no further explanation. Smart fellow. But you can bet he'll be on the phone to his Rabbi asking him what's up with this before my head hits the rubber pillow.

We're all taking naps in order to sober up before meeting back in my motel room to watch my stepbrother's press conference live at noon. A few hours shut-eye will do us all a world of good—me in particular. It's been a day and a half—multiplied by the Power of Ten. First, there was my descent through the lavender fields of Heaven; second, my rather rough ride across the Golden Age of Genocide; third, my resurrection act at Mel's; and fourth, my impromptu decision to run for president of the United States—not a decision to be taken lightly, even for a man in my position—and necessitated of course by my stepbrother's uncharacteristically brilliant tactics that threw me on the defensive. He's no dummy, that one. So it's fairly understandable why a little shut-eye is about the limit of my ambition right about now. I seriously need to reclaim my sobriety and reestablish my sense of objectivity.

So to sleep and to dream on my spongy bed in a relatively hygienic but wholly characterless motel room. (That drafty old Bethlehem barn had infinitely more character than this and I'd trade in this for that in a snap!) Straight away I slide into the most draining dreams: There's my cranky stepbrother chasing after me in his F-16, firing AGM-65 Mavericks about my head and shoulders as I scramble across dusty sands. Then there's me, huffing and puffing, rowing across the broad and bubbling River Styx, in hopeless pursuit of my renegade stepbrother, who's far, far ahead, and moving further beyond with each stroke. Let me tell you, I'm wiped out, even before I wake up.

Rest assured—there's no rest for the good. The only let up we ever get is the rest of our final reward—and then, at least for me, it was something like a dollar short and three days late.

At noon my disciples and I are huddled before a flat screen TV in my motel room, with CNN switched on. Everyone's there and Schwarzenegger baits Oprah into a pillow fight, warning her that he's the original Pillownator. Oprah takes the bait and whacks him with a pillow. The Pillownator smacks back. The room's soon consumed with eddies of swirling feathers and it's every disciple for themselves. Even I can't resist a lusty pillow fight. Never could. I abstain for ten whole seconds before diving in.

Martha's victorious, of course. In the end, we're all begging for mercy. Thankfully, Martha's magnanimous in victory. And happily, to the conquered go gifts. Martha promises each of us—the vanquished—a pair of matching pillowcases hand-embroidered with her Omnimedia logo and stamped with potato-cut renderings of the face of the Baby Jesus, traced in feathery brushstrokes of soft sky-blue oils, each sweet face glazed with hand-blown sparkles made from crushed robin's eggs and sand dredged from the Dead Sea and ground fine in New England apothecary mortar and pestle.

My stepbrother's frame flashes on the screen, snagged from yesterday's CNN's coverage. His mug gets plastered across the world—just like that. When I was struggling back in Jerusalem getting any sort of publicity—accept for the wrong kind of publicity—was practically hopeless. But in the Age of CNN, my stepbrother makes it look painless, easy, especially since he's plagiarizing me.

Frankly, it's disturbing that he looks more like me than me. His old, familiar Fidel Castro look is gone for good, I'm afraid to report. All dolled up in a Ralph Lauren tux, his grisly beard stricken from the rugged landscape of his brutal face, he looks, well, out-and-out respectable. Still, I liked him much better when he could easily be mistaken for Fidel's stepbrother. He had that special dictator's sense of style about him, right down to his smoky Havana cigar stub.

"Day 2 of Jesus the Republican's Return" a glowing caption reads below his CNN mug shot. Lou Dobbs anchors the coverage.

"Welcome to CNN's live coverage of Jesus Christ the Republican's news conference at which he's expected to announce his bid for his party's nomination for president. CNN's own Sam, a little bit of ham, Donaldson reports live from Dallas, Texas on this historic announcement."

CNN shows clips of his motorcade slithering through the soupy wetlands of waste and smog. First, the chain of limos peel off North Central Expressway; second, the caravan rolls past the Skyway Towers, First City Center and Bank One with their smog lights on, before finally plunging onto Elm Street and sliding to a choreographed stop at the base of Thanksgiving Tower, which rises hulk-like into a cobweb sky, and then disappearing stealth-like into an upside down cauldron of charcoal clouds. A velvet glove, pearl gray, grasps the rear right door handle. Jesus the Republican steps forth. Tony Lama boot heels strike sidewalk.

Sam, a little bit of ham, reports, his big baritone voice booming like a megaphone.

"Thanks, Lou. That's right. There always was a little bit of ham in me. And there're plenty of people who say there's a lot of ham in me. I suppose I owe it all to my mother who gave me a push. If I hadn't had her, maybe I wouldn't have had the push. If I hadn't gone to military school, maybe I wouldn't have decided to get with the program. Maybe I'd be running a bulldozer, rather than going on and doing something more because as you know, Lou, I was a typical farm boy. I liked the farm. I enjoyed the things that you do on a farm, go down to the drainage ditch and fish, and look at the crawfish and pick a little cotton. And all I ever wanted since college was to be in this business, and once I got into the business I knew I enjoyed it, and I liked it, and I wanted to continue, but I never had a five year plan. The two things I've learned in my years as a reporter are these: Questions don't do damage. Only the answers do. And new conferences are the only chance the American public has to see the candidate use his mind. Which is why I'm here, standing in the shadow of Thanksgiving Tower as Jesus the Republican mounts the granite steps to make his announcement. As you can hear, this crowd is behind their man—their God!"

"Jesus, Jesus, Jesus! Elect the Baby Jesus!"

"Believe me, folks, I haven't heard or seen enthusiasm, nay, delirium, like this since the early days of Barack Obama's campaign!"

Watching him, I can empathize. I know how awkward he must feel. Having abandoned his traditional beard and traded in his Castro fatigues for a Ralph Lauren penguin suit, he must not be feeling like himself anymore. Gone are all the visible hallmarks of an extraordinarily dangerous man.

The Plagiarizer of All Plagiarizers climbs Mount Pronouncement. He opens his arms, waving them to and fro, like Mick Jagger embracing his overwrought fans on stage. I wonder: Can I do that? Can I emote like Mick?—I mean, Beelzebub? This is my challenge, for sure. Do I really have what it takes to be an American politician? My stepbrother does, absolutely. He's got it deep down in his bones. When it comes to prevaricating before the masses, he's a born natural. Me, I've got work to do. I was born to tell the truth.

Suspended behind is a silver cross, made of polished steel. It looms large and is very great. On the ashy face of the smoggy sky, it seems to shine out like streetlights reflected in a soaking rain, lit by a bank of floodlights from below. I have to hand it my stepbrother's handlers, it's a fine piece of showmanship, worthy of the late great master of political theater himself, Michael Deaver. Deaver was the genius behind Ronald Reagan's presidential image. In setting after setting, he plopped Reagan down in front of such backdrops and made him appear as noble as any face on Mt. Rushmore on television screens across America. Come to think of it, I could use a Michael Deaver, too. Nancy? How 'bout it?

"How these Texans love their candidate," Sam, a little bit of ham, interjects. "Listen to this 'Hallelujah Chorus'—Texas style!"

"Run, Jesus, run! You're our King of Kings! Run, Jesus, run! You're our Lord of Everything! Run, Jesus, run! You're Just Our Kind of Republican!"

190

Like Sam says, these Texans love their candidate. In a twisted, contorted way, I suppose I should be vaguely flattered, because they— misguided as they are—are demonstrating a real affection for me—their Lord of Everything. That's one thing I get about democracy right away: It's not only about winning a majority of the vote—as helpful as that can be. No, it's also about the unconditional right of the majority to be 100% wrong. Like when they back a catastrophic man. Or woman! (ALMOST FORGOT!) Like Terrible George in 2004—not to dredge up too many distant, unhappy memories or anything. Now there's a prime example of the unconditional right of the majority to be dead wrong, with calamitous consequences!

Placards bob and weave above a drifting sea of cowboy hats. "THERE IS NO JESUS BUT OUR JESUS!" "JESUS IS JUST ALRIGHT WITH ME!" "JESUS'S THE GODFATHER OF REPUBLICANISM!" Under the circumstances, pretty much what you'd expect from Republicans, right?

CNN's attention zeroes in on my stepbrother's newly falsified face. I can almost smell his reeking Noxzema shaving cream on this side of the screen. And his old eyes look SO benign. However does he do it? They smile a thousand smiles. He was born to play this role. You can just tell. What's the cliché? He's playing the role of a lifetime? It's right about now that I fully comprehend just how royally screwed I really am. There's no other way to cut it. I'm out-flanked, out of my league, and just plain out of it. I can't do THAT! MY MOMMA DIDN'T BREED NO POLITICIAN!

To begin with, I don't smile. Has anyone ever seen a picture of me smiling? I don't think so. I don't do smiles. I'm far too serious a guy for that, and smiling is about as essential to successful politicians as shaking hands. Now shaking hands, even I do. I'm good with that. But

191

smiling while trolling votes is bound to be a train wreck for me. Not that I won't try. I will. But I don't expect my rate of success to be that great.

All of this is to say that even before my stepbrother opens his trap on stage, I'm fairly convinced that by virtue of my inability to crack the obligatory smile I've pretty much already handed him the keys to 1600 Pennsylvania Avenue.

Sam, a little bit of ham, distracts me from my own groundswell of pessimism with his singular form of infectious, wide-open Texas skies gregariousness and irrepressible optimism. It must be the big sky country in him that does that for him. "Folks, this promises to be really something today! In just over twenty-fours hours, America has witnessed the reappearance of not just one, but two men claiming to be Christ. Yesterday both established their—how shall I say it?—miracle-making bono fides, but only time will tell which of them is, well, let's not beat around the bush—Beelzebub Himself. Not even my good buddy George Will has been able to figure out yet who's who and he went to Oxford! In any event, this match-up of Holy Twin against Unholy Twin promises to make for one of the most exciting elections since John McCain took on Barack Obama! (Let's just hope we're not faced with another $700 Wall Street bailout in the middle of it! That would make it a little TOO EXCITING!)

"Yes siree, folks, be it Republican or Democrat, stay tuned to see if the *real* Christ will win!"

This is why Sam's still so basically adorable after all these years. He exudes ounce for ounce more pure Barack Obama optimism than even Barack Obama! And that—ladies and gentlemen—is really saying something!

Sam's sanguinity persists. "I, for one, believe that if there's any justice left under the eyes of Heaven, the real Christ will prevail!"

Well, that's all very well and good, but I, for one, believe that if there had ever been any real justice in the world, I wouldn't have been strung up on that damn cross the way I was; but I guess that's a grievance to be aired on another day with other parties, right? Not even I can completely get over that.

Meanwhile, Sam's running commentary runs on.

"We'll have to wait to see what Christ the Republican's economic platform will be, but as a Republican, it's a pretty safe bet that he'll have to come up with some kind of ingenious thinking to reconcile keeping his supporters wealthy and one day getting them into the Kingdom of Heaven! Remember, Christ the Republican—if he is the genuine Christ—is on record as saying, "'Tis easier for a camel to pass through the eye of the needle than for a rich man to get into Heaven.' How he'll get around that, I'll never know! But this is why I LOVE politics!"

At the pulpit—the podium, I mean—my stepbrother raises his arms in a disingenuous effort to silence the crowd. But it's perfectly obvious to me that he's eating it right up. Think about it. How long has it been since he's had approbation like this? Like never. That much is for sure. So there's no chance—none whatsoever—that he'll stop it before it dies a natural death. He basks in the beauty of the noise. He soaks it in like ultra-violet light in a tanning salon.

But finally, it does die down of its own accord, and Beelzebub, doing a damn fine imitation of me, bows his head, escorting the crowd by hand into the land of prayer, speaking into the hunk of microphones clustered on the podium standing in front of him.

"Let us pray…" he says.

I almost fall for that line, but catch myself before I close my eyes!

"For victory…"

"For victory…" he supporters reiterate in a low, respectful murmur.

This is probably only about the second time he's ever prayed for anything in his whole miserable life. The first, no doubt, was in gratitude for my crucifixion, that sweet day of my death. You can just bet he was down on his knees, head bowed, fingers knit together like interlacing cobwebs, in rapt thanksgiving.

"My name is Jesus Christ and I'm running for president!" he booms, cracking the silent mood of prayer. "Why?" he asks. "Because the real Christ is a conservative Republican, not some liberal Democrat!" His diction is faultless, his modulation is flawless, as he pilfers my opening line, delivering it in ideological reverse far better than I ever could even under the direction of Mel Gibson.

Jesus! Not only has he purloined my name, made off with my corporal identity, he's stolen my opening line! It's a classic case of Beelzebub larceny, which of course he'll get away with it. Just you watch. He gets away with everything, always has.

The Texas cowboys and cowgirls cheer, oh do they ever. My disciples jeer, but not quite at the same, sustained level. Madonna does her very best to throw out more swear words in a row at the television than there are letters in the alphabet. God bless her. In this case, even I don't mind.

"What shall it profit a man if he gains the whole world but loses his soul?" he continues.

Jesus! Why doesn't he just re-title all my best lines "Beelzebub's Sermon on the Mount"? Is there nothing of mine he won't happily swipe?

"I am the Lord Jesus Christ and your fellow venture capitalist and as your president I will be your dream investment banker and the US Treasury will be your dream bank. If elected, I'll make the 2008 sub-prime mortgage government bail-out of Fannie Mae, Freddie Mac and Wall Street look like Scrooge's best offer at Christmas. With me in charge, we'll print all of the investment capital you can spend, if you meet the requirements of being in the top 2% of wealth-owners in America! How's that for a deserving act of charity? How's that for the Christmas spirit of giving? Give unto those who truly deserve! Under a Christ the Republican Administration, there will be one new theory economics called Trickle-Down Charity or Jesuseconomics, for short! Why do I intend to give so much to the wealthy? Because, as every Republican knows, without wealth in the hands of the rich, there can be no alms for the poor. That's why!

"Wealth for the wealthy must come first!"

There isn't a dry eye in the whole crowd. His supporters are moved, so very moved by his position. Finally, they have a candidate who truly understands them.

I shake my head in astonishment. Oprah blows raspberries. Then in a fit of Christian generosity, she pledges to contribute ALL of her fabulous wealth to the pockets of the middle-class and to all those families of five or less with incomes below the poverty line, if it turns out that cad on screen ever gets elected. Wow, I'm thinking. That could really help. Her wealth alone could solve the trade deficit. Oprah, well, she's just a miracle all unto herself. God love her. The most generous of the generous. She gets an angel's star for that statement, to be sure.

"Nominate me for president you will be able to gain the whole world without even losing your soul! The whole world and the Kingdom of Heaven can be yours!"

Now that's an offer very few will be able to refuse.

"Gain the whole world without losing our soul! Gain the whole world without losing our soul!" his supporters chant over and over.

"But if a Democrat gets into the White House, be forewarned, there'll be no Trickle-Down Charity to assuage your conscience and save your soul. There'll only be bailouts for the middle-class and the poor. They'll go hat in hand to the U.S. Treasury, expecting it to pay off their bad debt, and worse, pony up for their socialized health insurance! He'll make America just like FRANCE! And you'll all be eating Brie for breakfast instead of pork sausage."

The Texans jeer. My disciples cheer.

"There'll be no more Gucci's, no more Maseratis, no more McMansions. There will only be row houses from sea to shining sea. NO MORE SUBURBS. DID YOU HEAR THAT? NO MORE SUBURBS! CAN YOU MAGINE THAT?"

An audible groaning and gasping floods Thanksgiving Tower plaza. No way these Republicans will take that lying down.

"So I say this day—Go Jesuseconomics! Go Guilt-free! Gain the whole world and save your soul! With the U.S. Treasury at your beck and call, Trickle-Down Charity will work!"

His pocketbook platform seems to work the magic. Everyone's hugging each other, their hearts full of irrational exuberance.

Sam isn't sold so fast. He presses my stepbrother with the key question. "But can you demonstrate—right here, right now—how Trickle Down-Charity will actually work? Otherwise—let's be Sam Donaldson frank—"

"Which is a pretty scary thing—I'm all talk and no action. So glad you asked that, Sam. For just this purpose, I've prepared a little demonstration."

Putting his face up to the low slate skies, spreading his arms wide, looking like a human (or sub-human) crucifix—which burns me, believe me—he summons up the exquisite powers of Trickle-Down

196

Charity, based on ideas plagiarized in part from the Ronald Reagan era. Naturally, my stepbrother avoids giving full and proper credit.

"Lord above," he roars. "Reveal the bounty of Trickle-Down Charity to the biased Liberal Press!!!"

Then, inconveniently, very inconveniently, nothing much happens. The smoggy skies stand still; the Westerlies don't blow; the moon doesn't cover the face of the sun. At the foot of Thanksgiving Tower, there's an abundance of partisan disbelief. Everyone's wondering: How could such a thing have happened, especially to the party of Michael Deaver? Wasn't this rehearsed?

"It's a dud!" sneers Dago.

"Lord of the Frauds!" Bono thunders.

Jesse Jackson interjects, "He who invokes, eventually croaks…"

I, however, know enough to reserve judgment. I'm a seasoned Beelzebub-watcher. I recognize that it's very dangerous to underestimate him. I've made that mistake before and don't intend on repeating it. He sicced Pontius Pilate on me, remember? He could do it in one form or manner again. And probably will.

"Permit me try again," he says, back on the road to redemption. He clears his throat, shouting to the rooftops, closeted in smog, "Neo-Neo Cons above, reveal the bounty of Trickle-Down Charity to the biased Liberal Press!!!"

Instantly, there's the sound of a thousand slots machines hitting the jackpot.

CNN cameras pan up. Squalls of silver dollars raining down, down, down, tumbling out of a dry, gray sky. That Beelzebub—I told you it was far too soon to get cocky. Neo-Neo Cons like him are just too smart.

"There's your proof, Mr. Donaldson! Put that in your left-wing conspiracy, biased liberal press autobiography and give your readers something to stay up about!"

Sam starts, momentarily at a loss to say anything too terribly abrasive. "Well, I never." He stares into the camera. "This is a Texas sky-size miracle, folks! Sky-size! Jesuseconomics put into practice! Oh my! Miracle of loaves and fishes move over!"

A silver dollar beams him, but good. That's gotta hurt! Donaldson rubs his dented forehead.

"Ladies and gents, if there's one thing Jesus the Republican has demonstrated today it's this: He's the best damn showman this country's seen since P.T. Barnum!"

Sam dodges a second silver dollar. "Moreover, it's clear that Trickle-Down Charity is an economic theory that will work! Here's a candidate who can finally deliver, folks! This is Sam Donaldson reporting live from—Ouch—Hey, that hurt!"

Sparrow pushes the remote. Sam, a little bit of ham, goes black. Sitting on the garish shag carpet of my motel room, we're all thinking what's painfully obvious: It's going to be mighty tough to top that.

My L.A. Twelve and I hop de Blue Line down to Watts. As de Metro doors part at Imperial/Wilmin'ton/Rosa Parks station, OG Killa is dere to greet me on de platform.

"Yo, like duuuude!" he says, "We wanna be in de Zone wit u!"

"And u need to git mor' juice wit ME, duuuude!" I answer, gratified by my gracious welcome.

"Check it out, cuzz, I'm de king of de Crips, de PJ Watts Crips, de best gangbangers in Watts. OG Killa, I am—de head of de gangbangers, and we cum to welcum u, Mr. JC Luva! We been waiting fo' de real King of de Hood—de one and only Baby Jesus—for a long, long time. U de best gangbanger dere ever was.

"Tank u," I replies, deeply touched.

"U r de Man, JC Luva. And we appreciate u cumin' down to git wit us in de Hood! We won't forgit this, cuzz. Not if we live fo'eva!"

"You will."

"Dat's right, we will! Long as we stick wit u, right, cuzz?"

"Dat's right."

"Welcum to r vida loca, Mr. Luva! Welcum to de Projects!"

De head gangbanger slaps me wit a high-five.

"Tanks again," I answers again, feelin' right at home now.

"Dog!" he says, "u de King of de Hood and cuz u r we gotta protect u from dem Grape Street Bloods. Dem Bloods, they'll kill ya, now that ur wit us." Showin' off his old knife scar, he hikes up his shirtsleeve. "Dey did dis to me."

Below de scar, on his forearm, above de wrist, is de tattoo, "Smile Now, Cry Later." It's de Crips' tattoo. Not exactly my kind of motto. I pull up my sleeve, just above de wrist and show him my tattoo: "I am with you always, until de very end of time."

"Cuzz—u de coolest," de Killa says, "de coolest."

Dat's de good news. De Killa thinks I'm de coolest. Da bad news is dis!

"We heard dem Bloods r gonna try to smoke u on our turf," he continues, unnervin' me. (Well, what'd u expect?) "But no worries, Mr. Luva. We don't care nothin' about no 187 California Penal Code... We'll light 'em up. We got our gats."

Hikin' up his sloppy Pirates baseball shirt, Killa exposes his snub-nose .38 jammed into de waistband of his 501 jeans. "Bang 'em first—den ask questions. Dat's our way, cuzz. De King of de Hood's safety cums first."

199

Dat makes me feel better. Dey can always count on Mr. Luva gettin' down wit dem in de Hood den.

He turns to de other Crips on de platform, who have about dem a certain sense of nitroglycerin, and den makes de introductions.

"Meet mi vato locos!" he says.

Each of 'em flips me de Crips hand sign.

I feel special.

De Crips, dey fly deir tribal colors. Dey look like 21st century pirates 'cause dey got Pittsburg Pirate baseball caps flipped on sideways, backwards; bandanas wrapped about deir foreheads stained navy-blue; baggy jeans, jean jackets never washed; Fruit-of-the-Loom t-shirts boiled bluish-black in de kitchens at de Projects on late summer nights. Dey look dodgy, voguish, dangerous. But dat's okay—dey're my guys.

I flip dem de peace sign, and says, "I'm peace-n."

"Follow us, King of de Hood, u in de jungles now, cuzz!"

Dees are exactly de kinds of alliances I'm supposed to make, so I feel good. To tell u de truth, I don't mind bein' called de King of de Hood, not in the least.

De Killa and me bone out, guarded on de right and de left by Crips security, and followed by an iridescent trail of celebrity disciples and a bubblin' tide of North Hollywood politicos and left wing evangelists come to egg me on, hundreds of whom just stepped off idlin' Metro cars at Imperial/Wilmin'ton/Rosa Parks station. Lookin' back, my first impression is that my campaign's taking off, even before it officially begins, if I do say so myself.

Down de gritty platform stairs we go—on de march—headed for de exit signs. Rising up on either side of de station's walls are ceramic clouds of chalky tile black-washed in complex tapestries of interlacin' graffiti, classic gangbanger art makin' a darkly mood. Quite lovely, if you're sensitive to street angst, which, of course, I am. De acronym "V.I.P." appears pretty much everywhere, high and low and right in de middle, too. OG is my modern museum street art guide. "V.I.P.," he says, is de sign dat bloodshed is on its way. Which makes sense, since dis is de Hood. Along de lower level corridors, a ribbon of graffiti, consumes de public space, wit de phrase "CRIPS 187 SLOBS". De letter B on de word SLOBS is all X-ed out, like someone was tryin' to cover up a stupid spellin' mistake over and over again. De Killa tells me what it's about. He says dat de word SLOBS refers to dem Bloods gang and dat de X-ing out of de letter B is meant to disrespect dem. Which, if you're a Crips, is what u live fo'— Disrespectin' dem Bloods. It's de way it is wit dem Crips. U get a violation, if u don't and dat's not good. And—just so u know—de number 187 refers to de California Penal Code—de California Penal Code fo' homicide. Not de one fo' litterin' de sidewalk. Dis is de way it is in de Hood. De Crips try to kill de Bloods.

Clearly, I've got a whole lot of work to do down in Watts.

"Dems de projects," OG Killa informs, pointin' through the frame of black iron metro station gates etched in imaginative graffiti to a low row of cheerless concrete whitewashed houses, framed like an open garden gate etched in fine graffiti. Dey stand buried in driftin' cobwebs of smog across de concrete swamp of de Imperial Highway castin' about deir rovin' eyes in search of a savior, I have no doubt. Yes: Dere are de Projects—de Imperial Courts—in de flesh. Dey don't bring me any happiness. Dey are de homes of de lowly and de meek. Worse, dey amount to a supreme low point in modern L.A. architecture—which is really saying somethin'. Where are all the Frank Lloyd Wrights I've heard so much talk about, anyway?

We wade across de highway, causin' a bottleneck of urban commuters in dusty metal bugs, with deir yellow smog lights shinin'. Once all dose drivers find out why dey're jammed up, I can forget about deir votes. This is gonna cost me—big. But den dat's politics. Votes, dey come and dey go! Isn't dat de beauty of democratic politics? Sometimes dey're wit u; sometimes dey aren't.

"WATTS FOR CHRIST!" "IMPERIAL COURTS WANT JESUS!" "JP CRIPS LOVE DE KING OF DE HOOD!" "CHRIST DE DEMOCRAT FO' PRESIDENT!" All de good folks of de Projects are dere, waitin' fo' me. And dey look so very happy to see me. I'm happy to see dem, too. As I've always said: It's nice to be loved. I see bloggers by de dozens, too, crouched at de foot of de stage typing furiously on deir laptops, reportin' in, providin' live coverage of de main event—my presidential announcement. I'm also cloaked in security, a wedge of live ammo, courtesy of de Crips. Dey march me to de stage, constructed of stockade fence lifted from someone's backyard not too long ago, and mounted on broken cinderblocks. Though it be so humble, dis is de site on which I'll launch my drive to change de world.

Knots of frustrated TV, radio, and print reporters vie fo' space up close to de stage, but de bloggers in front of dem won't let dem in. Dem bloggers, dey have a lock on de whole media world dees days. Dey are de mainstream now and don't give dose others anything. I won't step in to arbitrate just yet, 'cause media wars aren't up dere at de top of my list of priorities. De bloggers give way fo' de gangbangers as dey swoop in to surround de stage. De Crips open up a gap between a block of bloggers for me and I get up on my stockade soapbox. Den dey line up side-to-side, in front of de bloggers, like a pack of playing cards. Dey are my first line of defense against dem Bloods and dat makes me feel safe. Should dey Bloods decide to try to smoke me—fo' whatever unlikely reason—even if it's just 'cause dey are jealous dat I'm wit de Crips and not wit dem, des Crips will lay down deir lives fo' me. Pure and simple. Even de thought of it brings tears to my eyes. Why? 'Cause I know what it's like to lay down my life fo' others. Been there, done dat. Dat anyone would do dat fo' me makes me want to cry.

Patriotic buntin', bright American flags, hangin' limp on the smog, line de back alley behind de stage. Dere is not a crucifix in sight. I told my advance team to can it. If my Old Man ever saw me mixin' His religion wit my politics, I'd be spendin' a week or two in de woodshed. Besides, my stepbrother already played dat hand. If we want de Old Man to be mad at anyone, we want Him to be mad at him. Besides, humble is as humble does. De more humble de more righteous. Dat's what I always say, anyway.

My name is Jesus Christ—candidate fo' president—and I approved dose stage decorations.

I step to de podium. You'd think I'd be nervous, but I'm not. Until I see Dan Rather. Now I'm stressed. Really anxious. Why? 'Cause Dan's a living CBS News legend, dat's why. Especially since de CBS News Division dumped him years ago fo' botchin' his George W. military reserve story during de 2004 elections. But u can't keep a good newsman down—not one as good as Dan. De truth is, CBS treated him like a dog in a cage at de pound in da rain. I feel sorry fo' him. So I make up my mind to invite him to ask de first question when I open de flo'. I know dem bloggers won't be happy wit me, but—right or wrong—Dan's my man.

I look around. De whole place looks like a prison yard, poverty incarnate. Which is why de issue of poverty is so high up on my agenda. Lookin' at de concrete shacks, de shabby lawns, de bars on de windows, de rag clothes on de clotheslines, gets my blood pressure up. It shouldn't be like dis! Poverty is de pits! I take a long, deep breath, reignin' in my anger, and then deliver my openin' line, de way it should be delivered down in Watts: My name is Jesus Christ de Democrat—de King of de Hood—and I'm runnin' fo' President.

I took de liberty of changin' Nancy's openin' line out of respect fo' de Crips, but I deliver it de way Mel wanted me to, wit de right emphasis in all de proper places. After I say dat, der is jubilation. In fact, de Watts I see is pretty much delirious. No kiddin'. Now dey really know dat I'm one wit de po'. Dey're my first cousins, in fact, so I feel perfectly at home wit dem, 'cause I was born in ta poverty and went out de same way.

I get on wit my Sermon on de Stockade Fence.

If I'm deir party's nominee, I tell 'em straight, I'm gonna be de best moral values candidate dey ever had. Dat sounds indecorous of me, I know, but dis is no place fo' false modesty. Presidential candidates don't become president by bein' immodest—dat's what Nancy always says, anyway. And whatever Nancy says...

Den I tell my Imperial Court po' people dat I intend to move de country in a new direction—dat dis is an election about Change—real Change—change in Washington, D.C., change across de country, change in de hearts and mind of Americans, especially, and dat if dey elect me and after we get done changin' everything, as I just said, dere won't be any difference between Watts and Heaven. Dat gets a mighty big rise outa everyone. "De Heavens will come to Watts!" I say again and again. It sounds like cathedral bells ringin'.

Again, I make up dat "De Heavens will come to Watts!" line myself witout any permission from Nancy and witout even message testin' it, which I know is a cardinal political sin, but sometimes you've just got to go wit your gut when you become a real politician—no matter what Nancy says!

I wade into de particulars of my domestic programs—in general terms, of course—first. Even wit ex-Governator Schwarzenegger in charge of dat, dere's been no time to tap out all de specifics of every program, so I speak in broad generalities, which is pretty much what you'd expect from a politician anyway, isn't it?

Equal housing opportunities? Why, dey're still millions of sub-prime homes available from da days of da 2008 financial meltdown. Dey're all across California, Arizona, New Mexico, and Florida, wit deir windows boarded up like de hurricanes were comin'. So I promise u, as president I'll make HUD take off dem boards and open dem houses up to de poo' on a Christian first-come first-serve basis. I'll give 'em out to de Christians in de Projects and de Main Streeters across America—not dem Wall Streeters.

Good payin' jobs? I know for sure dat de Old Man's lookin' to recruit untold millions more—from Spokane to Key Largo—into His Church, of course. Well, what would u expect? He's got a lot tied up in de Church already, at least emotionally. And more is always best wit Him. So I propose a federal three-year clerical apprenticeship program in de Christian Church of deir Choice—any denomination, anyone at all, will do—to anybody willin' to sign on da dotted line and take on de job of doing good works in da name of His Church. Like Kennedy's Peace Corps, only even more spiritual and concentratin' on America's fifty-one states. I call it da Divinity Corps.

Education? Dey gonna get all de education dey can take. And then some mo'. Catholic schools are some of de best. Dere will be no child left behind—no adult either—
so long as dey enroll and keep up wit deir homework and pass de exams. De pope will make some hefty financial contributions to build bigger, better parochial schools in America, from Watts to Washington, D.C. He won't like it, but dat's de way it is. I'm gonna use deir Vatican fortune fo' somethin'. Dat way de U.S. taxpayers will be off de hook. Even de Republicans—God love 'em—will go fo' it.

Universal health insurance? I tell 'em dat everyone can count on equal access to health care under a Christ Administration. Where we'll get de money I'm still not sure, but maybe we can clump all de Christians together, and get some super discount rates from carriers which will help subside America's uninsured. If dat doesn't work, I volunteer in my spare time to dish health care out myself: Heal de sick on de sidewalk one by one on Saturdays and Sundays, if I have to. Dey cheer me wit alleluia after alleluia when dey hear dat. De amazin' thing is, it's not even Easter Sunday.

Poverty? Well, as I said, there'll be my Divinity Corps to ensure good payin' jobs fo' everyone, if dey don't already have dem. Those who won't go in fo' dat can enlist in my Transcend Poverty program. Dat's right, de rest will transcend de old fashion way. Dis is how it works. I tell dem: "Do not be worried 'bout ur life, as to what u will eat or what u will drink. Nor fo' ur body, as to what u will put on. Is not life more dan food, and da body more dan clothin'?" You get de idea. Poverdie can also be a state ta mind. My program is designed to help dos who will help themselves overcome dat.

So long as da Crips don't have to give up deir Pittsburg Pirates baseball caps put on backwards and deir bandannas and jean jackets, de like that idea. Dey cheer me wit another round of alleluias. De rest of de folks at de Projects aren't quite so sure. So I try another tact. I tell dem: "Look at da birds of da air, dat they do not sow, nor reap nor gather into barns, and yet ur heavenly Father feeds dem. Are you not worth much more dan they? And who of u by being worried can add a single hour to his life?"

Dey don't buy it. So I try again. "Why are u worried 'bout clothin'? Observe how de lilies of de field grow; they do not toil nor do they spin, yet I say to u dat not even Solomon in all his glory clothed himself like one of these. But if God so clothes de grass of de field,

206

which is alive today and tomorrow is thrown into de furnace, will He not much more clothe u? U of little faith! Pray and it shall be given!"

Dat gets 'em. De Crips and de folks of de Projects start chantin': "HAVE FAITH AND YE SHALL BE CLOTHED!" Dey go on like dat fo' quite some time. When things quiet down again, I tell 'em what I'm goin' to do to get green back in de planet. Fo' sure. I'm no Rep. James Inhofe (R-OK)! Dat I swear! I'm friend to de poplar bear. I'm protector of de Koala bear. Most of all, I'm de enemy of Big Oil.

I say dat loud enough so dat de CEOs at Exxon, Chevron, and Mobil can hear me in deir boardrooms: "Da Republican's gave u government by big oil, of big oil, fo' big oil! Under my administration, I'll give u government by green technology, of green technology, and fo' green technology!" Dat lights up de sky above my head wit de light of GE Energy Smart fluorescent bulbs, fo' sho'.

Den I tell 'em dat dere is about to be a change in de Ten Commandments. Dat de Old Man has authorized me to add No. 11. Which is to say: "Thou Shalt Create Green Technology and Conserve Energy."

I also float my carbon-tradin' scheme, dreamed up by de Governator, Nancy and me. It works dis way: By shrinkin' ur carbon footprint, u earn extra credit fo' gettin' into Heaven. It's an experimental notion, granted, and we don't have all de plan's glitches worked out quite yet—but I think de Old Man will be open to it, especially considerin' its in His interests not to preside over de liquefyin' of de planet. Dis is His sentimental favorite, after all.

Anyway, de Crips and de folks at de Projects seem to like de scheme okay. After I float it, dey cheer, "Shrinkin' Carbon Footprints is de Key to Eve'lastin' Life!" It has a decent ring to it, doesn't it?

Dat's it fo' domestic policy. Onto foreign affairs.

207

I get de biggest threat to national security out of de way first. I pledge my support fo' a constitutional amendment makin' it impossible fo' Jeb Bush, or any other descendant of George W.'s, to run fo' president fo' de next one hundred and fifty years or so. Why? We all know why. Dere is no greater moral imperative in foreign policy dan keepin' Jeb out of de White House. Dat's all dis country needs: Iraq War III.

Next, I tell 'em dat I support a 400% increase in foreign aid. I remind everyone dat sum represents only 1% of de U.S.'s GNP, even when calculated as a percent of gross national income. Even then, de U.S. will remain on de world's most miserly major country donor list. (After de election, I'll push Congress to cough up another 3% to get serious 'bout some real foreign aid. I can't imagine dey'll refuse me. In de end, I'm deir ticket to deir salvation, am I not?)

I promise dat America's defense will be second to none. Like, I intend to scrap de next crop of F/B-24 Raptor stealth jet fighters and de new batch of Iowa class battleships and dat daffy space-based missile defense system, codenamed R.R.D.S.—short fo' de Ronald Reagan Defense System. And in deir place I'll push fo' globally enforceable internationally recognized human rights and revamping de U.N. Security Council, makin' it more representatives of de family of nations on Earth. Wit a seat fo' de kids. Dey should have a vote, too.

I also pledge to keep dem nukes out of de hands of de Iranians and North Koreans and dose guys in Afghanistan. Dere wouldn't be a whole lot of peace on earth and good will towards anyone wit dose guys pullin' de nuclear trigger now and again. I'd go after de nukes on de black market, too, and call fo' global denuclearization. Dat means de U.S., too. De Crips shake deir heads like dey aren't at all sure 'bout dat, but den what would u expect dem to do? Dey're Crips and Crips grew up wit weapons, so getting' rid of weapons seems unnatural to dem. But u can bet, I'll teach 'em to turn deir gats into plowshares, just like dat.

I also commit to take on de terrorists and take police actions against dem. Dey won't be able to count on my lovie dovie nature for a pass. I'll be tough on dem, u beta, though naturally so-called harsh interrogation tactics—a.k.a. torture—are a thing of de Bush Administration, not mine.

I hit China pretty hard on human rights and announce dat I'm not a big fan of de One-China policy on Taiwan. (I can almost hear dose guys at State on de China desk fainting and droppin' to de flo'.) But aiming 10,000 missiles at poo' Taiwan is not my idea of a reconciliation policy. More like a policy of intimidation. Only I get to do intimidation tactics, not China.

Of course, I chastise Russia fo' its on-going war in Chechnya and fo' its illegal incursion into Ukraine. Dose po' people! Subjugated once again! Will it never end?

I also slam de new dictatorship in Mauritania and de continin' slave traffic in de Congo and de nasty civil war in de Yucatan, and promise everyone dat a Christ Administration will change all dat. Democracy, freedom and peace will be deirs!

Den I focus on de issue dearest to my heart: De Palestinian-Israeli conflict. I pledge to bring peace to de whole of de Middle East. How? Well, one ting I'll do is build a new homeland fo' de Palestinian Diaspora right dere in de middle of de Mediterranean Sea. Dat idea sure gets everyone's attention. Okay, I'll admit, it makes me sound like I've been hittin' de juice heavy and hard, but den as RFK once said, "Dere are dose who look at things the way dey are, and ask why I dream of dings dat never were, and ask why not?"

Finally, 'cause I love Bono and believe in his good cause, I vow dat together Bono and I will END AIDS IN AFRICA!

He drops down on his knees hearing dat. "Oh, sweet Lord Jesus!" he sings, "Thank you!"

"Not a problem," I answer him back.

And on dat last note of hope, I do what Nancy told me to do—and what every good politician knows to do if dey ever want to win. I ask everyone fo' everyone's vote.

"A VOTE FO' ME IS A VOTE FO' GETTING' INTO DE DIVINITY CORPS! A VOTE FO' ME IS A VOTE FO' UNIVERSAL HEALTH CARE! A VOTE FO' ME IS A VOTE FO' DE HEAVENS TO COME DOWN TO WATTS!"

I know, I know, I'm pandering to pocket book issues here, but dat's what Nancy says works. Look how pocketbook issues helped Obama in 2008! De folks of de Projects, dey listen to my every word at de base of Mount Stockade Fence and den dey break out into a lusty round of alleluias. Who can blame 'em? It wasn't such a bad speech, danks to Nancy. And considering it was my first policy speech—and I'm no policy wonk to be sure—I think it went really rather well.

Dan flags me down wit de first question. Dose bloggers don't stand a chance. Dan gets his chance.

"Yes, Dan."

"Mr. Christ, welcome to America's warm shores, at last. For sure, this race is going to be hotter than a Times Square Rolex—hotter than the Devil's anvil—hotter than a New York elevator in August—even hotter than a Laredo parking lot! The heat will be enough to peel the house paint. I'm Dan—'Never at a loss for a simile or metaphor'—Rather reporting for WAMU public radio in Washington, D.C.

"It's a privilege, Jesus, to be covering this fast-breaking story, though what I say or do here doesn't matter much, nor should it. Nevertheless, it's destined to be the Greatest News Story ever told and I intend to be here every step of the way, even though it's going to make my fingernails sweat and from time to time be hotter than a sauna where all you can do is wait and sweat. It's certainly promises to be the most consequential presidential race I've ever covered in my career as a reporter and it will likely be closer than Lassie and Timmy—tighter than the pages in a book—tighter even than a too-small bathing suit on a too-long ride home from the beach. Still tighter than the rusted lug nuts on a '55 Ford. That's right, Spandex tight. But that's great because this campaign will be crackling like hickory fire from now until election day, and will sweep across this nation as furious than a tornado through a trailer park, even though from time to time the candidates backs will be against the wall and their shirttails on fire. That's why I'm happy to be here. This election promises to be the whole deal, the real deal, the big deal.

"And I swear that if it is within my power, I'll try to keep my mouth shut, and let you, Mr. Christ, answer my questions in your own words rather than in mine. I'm more interested in your story than in mine because what I say or do here doesn't matter much, nor should it. I want to know what you think and how you feel, what you hope for and what you believe in, putting aside for the moment whether or not you are in fact the true Son of God, though I personally think that it would be likelier for a hippopotamus to run through Watts than for Christ the Republican to turn out to be the real Christ, but…"

"Your question, please, Dan."

"Oh right. I'm all too well aware that my real purpose here today, as a reporter, is to throw open a window on the real Christ for the American people—so they can see you through your words, your work and your dreams—because as a reporter all I can do is walk beside you, not with you. All I can do is listen to you, neither agreeing with you nor disagreeing with you. All I can do is question you, neither confirming what you say, nor denying what you say. And that's exactly what I intend

211

to do today—and every day of the campaign. I think it's fair to say that we really don't know whether to wind the watch or to bark at the moon. I certainly don't want to live by the crystal ball and eat so much broken glass that we end up in critical condition, know what I mean?

"Still, let me say this: As a human being and an American—and not as a reporter—I know standing at the foot of Mount Stockade Fence here today that I'm witnessing something special and that when I go back to my hotel room this evening, or when I head home at the end of this particular assignment, I know I won't be the same person. The world won't look exactly the same way because I will have seen a Great Man intervene in world events. It wouldn't surprise me if all Americans weren't doing back flips, either. Though I wouldn't bet the trailer money yet."

"Dan?"

"Right—almost done. 'Course it wasn't too long ago in the life of this country that I heard another great man use only the power of his language and the sound of his voice to defeat injustice and tyranny. That man, of course, was Martin Luther King, Jr. One of my personal heroes and one of America's giants! He stood four-square against the menace of racial discrimination, and won, even though his opponents tried to beat him like a rented mule. Dr. King walked through a furnace in a gasoline suit! His only mistake was that he taunted the alligator when he hadn't finished crossing the bridge. I hope you don't make that same mistake, too, or rather—again.

"And while I'm on the topic of great Americans, in the intervening years since Dr. King fell victim to an assassin's bullet in 1968, I have only come to see even more clearly how special Dr. King truly was. He was such an inspired leader. I'm proud to say that like me he was never anyone's lapdog. If his opponents had been a bottle of aspirin, he would have given them a headache! As a reporter and as an

212

American, I miss the timbre of his voice, and all the great and powerful things he said with that voice. I miss the music of his ideas. I miss sound of the choir of voices that sang the anthem of justice along with him. Dr. King made music where others made prose. He was a leader, not a soloist, just like you, I believe. My only piece of advice for you is this: Never eat spinach just before going on T.V.

"Dan? Your question—please?"

"Right. Just about getting to that. The fact is I haven't heard another voice quite like his until right now. This minute. Not until I heard you speak. Until you made music out of prose, like I said. For all these years, I've traveled around the U.S. listening for another voice like Dr. King's. But it was not until today that I have found it. Not until today that I heard again the music of Dr. King's choir—the choir that sang the song of equality, singing not with its original choirmaster, but with its new one. Sure, over the years, I've heard a phrase here and there from the same beautiful song—a mellifluous moment, a euphonious bar, but never Dr. King's magnificent choir. Not until right now here on Mount Stockade."

"Dan—!"

"Okay, okay... Almost done. Promise. As I said earlier, I'm determined to keep my mouth shut and let you do the answering because I'm much less interested in what reporters like me have to say and think and much more interested in you and your story and what you have to say and think.

"However, I'm sure you've heard about the shabby way CBS News treated me over the Rathergate affair after I erroneously reported during the 2004 presidential election campaign on President Bush's undistinguished Texas National Guard performance. God's truth, it wasn't my fault! My story was based on official documents gleaned from the files of the late Lieutenant Colonel Jerry B. Killian, George W.'s

213

Guard commander, but which, it later turned out, had been falsified by Lt. Col. Bill Burkett, who evidently had it in for George, like so many others. In any event, my story proved to be wrong and got me in more trouble than a frog dropped in boiling water. Again, it goes to show that you shouldn't taunt an alligator until after you've crossed the creek. Still, it didn't entitled CBS management to treat me like a mug wamp. The tough lesson here is that not everybody wishes you well.

"But I know you do, Mr. Christ, and I want to take this opportunity to thank you for permitting me to stand once again on the warm, sunny beaches of mainstream national media. As a veteran presidential campaign watcher, I'd also like to offer you some unsolicited advice, realizing of course that what I say or do here won't matter much, nor should it. My advice is always simple and always the same: Only votes talk—everything else walks!"

"D-A-N!!!"

"All right, all right, all right. Give a guy a chance to speak, will ya?!"

Because I'm the King of Kings of Tolerance, I ease up on him.

"Now begins the part where I keep my mouth shut. Still, I wouldn't bet the doublewide on that completely just yet, because if history has taught us anything about Dan Rather, it's that his word on holding his tongue is shakier than cafeteria Jell-O. However, now I'm about ready to take that momentous step. I'm prepared to step off history's center stage so that my colleagues in the media will also have the opportunity to ask their questions and, like me, bear witness to and report on, but not participate in, one of history's most important news stories. So my question is..."

Finally! The Old Man's still a merciful God...

"Will you be performing a Democratic miracle to match your opponent's?"

214

"Miracles fo' miracles' sake don't turn me on, Dan. As a miracle-maker, I must perform my miracles responsibly. It's never about showmanship, as you know."

"With all due respect, Mr. Christ, it's cardiac-arrest time for your presidential campaign unless you walk the miracle walk. You can be sure that after your stepbrother's trickle-down spectacle today, your lead's going be thinner than turnip soup—or is it November ice? Whatever! My advice—as a veteran campaigner watcher—is that you strut your miracle stuff or else you can count on Slim leaving town. Remember, once the herd starts moving in one direction, it's very hard to turn it, even slightly…"

"But now would not be de time, Dan."

Dat's when we hear de sounds of de herd of elephants comin' up de Imperial Highway, headin' towards de Projects. Everything stops; everyone listens. But de more we listen de more we know fo' sure dat it's not de sound of elephants dat we hear. No, it's de sound of de drumbeats of dozens of subwoofers, comin' nearer and nearer.

Fo' sure, somethin' big is about to happen at de Projects.

Dey emerge from de smog, lookin' like an army of dusty metallic bugs crawlin' across dirty concrete lawns. It's no herd of elephants, now we know dat fo' sure. No, dey're a huge horde of ghettoized Honda Civics, rollin' and creepin', creepin' and rollin', toward us from out of de L.A. smog. And dey come and dey come and dey come—low riders, all of dem, deir windows down, deir subwoofers pumpin' out nothin' but rap. Dey come rumblin' into de Projects lookin' dangerous—very, very dangerous. I don't need OG Killa to tell me it's dem Bloods, come to 187 me—Mr. Luva—and de Crips!

Dey stop at de Imperial Court Gates and we just stand dere lookin' at dem rumblin'. Dem paint jobs put on quite a nice show. Dat much I know. Dey look spooky, like underground rainbows. A pipe head named Shameel probably sprayed dem in his backyard garage. Dem Bloods probably paid him wit sum soda. Dat's de way it works in de Hood. De ear-splittin' beat of de rap music coughed up by de subwoofers make de concrete move below deir platinum rim tires. It feels like dere is a volcano below and it's about to blow...

Dose dudes inside dose Honda Civics make even OG Killa look like a first-year choirboy. And I'm thinkin' dose bulges inside deir pants ain't no cool cucumbers. It's dis press conference dat's about to blow! Dis could be a pretty good time to perform one of dem miracles, just like Dan suggested.

But before I can act de Honda Civic doors split open. Out spill dem Bloods. From de front seats. From de back seats. And none of dem are smilin'. Dey race to deir trunks, flip 'em up, and lean in to get somethin'. I'm expectin' dey're gonna get deir weapons. Automatic weapons. And aim dem at me and de Crips. I recite a high-speed prayer, envisagin' tomorrow's *L.A. Times* headlines: "CHRIST GUNNED DOWN IN DE HOOD!" It's never too late to slip one in under de wire. But then somethin' miraculous happens. De head banger steps away from de Honda wearin'—what?— not de Bloods' customary purple attire—but white painter's pants. Yes, and he yanks out a Monarch Paints painter's cap from his back pocket, dustin' it off by slappin' it on his kneecap. His voice soaring over dos 500-watt subwoofers: "Hey, ese Vatos! We come to paint ur houses! Fix up ur roofs and plumbin'! We swear—no more pedo! No more gettin' down wit u! We love u! Da Bloods be peace-n, cuzz, 'cause we wanna get wit de Christ!!! We seen de light!!! We want to be wit de Christ! Be one wit de Christ, like u!"

Now de rest of dem Bloods step away from deir Honda Civics, armed wit nothin' but paint brushes and buckets, hammers and saws, cardboard boxes of drywall screws and roofin' nails, stepladders and

216

roofin' tiles, and tons of plumbin' supplies. De thing is dey're not here to rumble; dey're here to renovate. For sure. Dey wade through de crowd and get up on stage. Dey hold up their tools and supplies in solidarity. "We love de Christ! We love de Crips! We love everybody in de Projects!"

I'm just so pleased. So thrilled to be alive. Delighted to be witness to such a gesture of reconciliation. Den layin' aside deir gats, 'cause OG Killa gives dem de nod, all de Crips get up on stage, too, and everyone—de Crips and dem Bloods—joins hands. Together we look like a picture from de Home Page of de Habitat fo' Humanity's website. Everyone hugs. Everybody cheers. I'm tellin' u—it's a bloody miracle. A Watts miracle. De Bloods' head banger, Lil Loc, says it like dis: "We all in de same gang now, cuzzes—it's de Gang of Christ! Dere'll be no more por vida between de Crips and de Bloods, 'cause we're wit de Christ!"

I look down at Dan at de base of Mount Stockade Fence. And I can't help but smile. Why? Because de thing is, de truly miraculous thing is, America's witness to history, as a reporter and as an American, is utterly and absolutely speechless.

THE AFTERNOON AFTER

McClellan always liked Dan Rather, purple prose, metaphor king, lord of ego, and all. He was *so* American, with a personality bigger than the Amarillo skyline. And of course he had no trouble imagining that he was a real Dem—one of Them, unlike the Brit Humeses and Chris Wallaces of Washington, who positively reeked like week-old salmon from being bloodline Republican. However did they face their mommas?

McClellan stretched his legs, wiggling his toes beneath his red, white and blue hand-knitted socks that his momma knitted for him last Christmas. He'd worn them for Election Day, as good luck, but so much for that. He hadn't seen too much of it lately, though he was always on the lookout. In politics, luck, like timing, was everything. Now his toes itched. He wiggled them again, which helped itch the itch. That felt better, but not completely. Itches were ticklish. Sometimes itching itches begat more itches, without solving the problem. But McClellan was on the job. He was in charge. Placing his read facedown over his kneecap, he reached all the way down to scratch. Nothing quite like it. He was master again. His itch disappeared as fast as it came—only to be replaced by an inexplicable urge to light up a joint. Itches and urges. They went and they came. Who could blame him if he felt the need? Certainly he wasn't about to blame himself. Ms. Worthington might have something strenuous to say about it downstairs, but she'd never know, would she? He'd crack the window and smoke it out the window headfirst, like he used to in his college dorm. He could almost smell it, the edgy scent of locoweed. It drifted like sweet incense into the bright rooms of his aging memory. Those college days of joints and roses, when the way to bliss was paved with a trip to Rock Creek Park with his long-hair, left-wing pals in a Volkswagen bus and a couple of hand-rolled joints smoked back-to-back beneath the cool green understory of forest trees.

Rapture like that vanished in his last puff of a Purple Haze joint on the night he graduated from law school. Ever since he'd been straight as Mother Teresa and look where it got him. He'd left his blood on the tracks and nobody loved him for it. They would have loved him if Kerry

218

had won the White House. They would have revered him for at least four years and his name would have been all over the Internet. Reward enough in some parts. But Kerry would not be the agent of deep Change. And he would not be the shadow of the agent of deep Change. Their fortunes had been changed by the Great Change: George W. Bush. And now the affairs of the nation would be unalterably changed by George W. Bush. Well, good luck, America. You have no idea how bad it's going to get. That's what the political barometer in his head said. At least he—he and Kerry—had fought to prevent it: The Bushing of America. His conscience was okay about that. Decision 2004 was on America's head. The right to be wrong was so democratic. He couldn't get past that. It was a fundamental right to be wrong. A core democratic value. He only hoped the republic would survive its error.

What he wouldn't give for a joint.

He pictured himself firing up a dovetail joint of devastating Mexican weed with the manly flick of a silver antique lighter his college girlfriend gave him for his 21st birthday before she slept with his roommate when he wasn't looking. (She said it was her—not him. Which came as no large consolation.) He saw himself taking a toke at the open window of his college dorm room, anticipating the very moment his carpet ride would arrive and fly him through canyons of cumulous clouds to the skies of enlightenment, or what passed for enlightenment in college. Well, at least it was the perception of momentary enlightenment... Which was second best.

Enlightenment. Hmmm. Real enlightenment. Now there was a personal agenda worth the consequences of defeat, if in pursuing it it ended in failure. He paused to consider what seemed like the politically absurd. If only Kerry's campaign had been about pursuing the politics of enlightenment. Come to think of it, if only Kerry had been Christ, and Christ had been his candidate. If Christ had been America's agent of

Change, not Kerry and not Bush, like the book said. Half in jest, he wondered: Where was Christ when the DNC really needed Him?

Okay, time for McClellan to climb down off of Cloud Nine. That book was messing with his mind. The good thing was, it was legal this time.

He got up out of his big comfortable chair, slid up the old second-story window. The autumnal afternoon air swept in on the heels of sunshine. Smiling sunlight painted the peeling window ledge with a fresh coat of hilarity. Beyond it showered down like rainwater, passing through the swaying rafters of the trees, mingling with the burnished rainbows of tapestries of turning leaves. Above the crown of trees was a new Georgetown sky, as wide as Dan Rather's personality. It, too, shone through the unwashed window, filling the narrow room with a certain sky blue look, rinsing every spine of every book for the moment. The skylight was joyous blue, the color, McClellan decided, of enlightenment.

The sound of laughter of little children down P St. snapped the library silence of the quiet room. They had found their own paths to enlightenment—their magic carpet rides through the clouds—riding on trolley tracks on dirt bikes, their joy of life awoken. If only politics could be that way again, he mused, rather than the pain of politics broken.

McClellan was onto something. The idea of searching for and achieving enlightenment, for no other purpose than living the life of a person seeking a New Life Order and experiencing the challenge of trying to get there, was as good a career path as any other, for sure. In fact, after his political slaughter, what could be better than shedding his damaged coil and taking for the spiritual skies? Even if it ended in disappointment or at best momentary enlightenment, or a short-lived burst of equilibrium, measured in moments rather than years, even after spending a decade or more getting there, it struck him as not an unintelligent thing to do. After all, politics was never intended to save

220

souls. It was more about bread and butter practicality. Functionality. Not the functionality of his soul.

Enlightenment. Just thinking the word made him feel as though he had set off on the road, trekking pole in hand. But what would Margaret think? He considered language. "Honey, I'm breaking out of the box. I'm going down the stony road to Enlightenment."

"Oh, are we?" he heard her say, as she washed potato skins at the sink, her back turned away from him. "Does Enlightenment come with health care coverage, or are enlightened people automatically eligible for HMOs? Just asking…"

McClellan cushioned his forehead on his forearm as he leaned his head against the windowpane of rippling 18th century glass and started down at the cobblestones in the street, dissected by trolley tracks, and covered in loose, curling leaves blown by an invisible wind to nowhere in particular. He closed his eyes. Today seemed suddenly distant. Today become yesterday and soon yesterday transformed into last week and last month and then last year and then the year before and soon McClellan was borne back into the ancient past, into his impulses of his youth where instant enlightenment, or what passed for it, was just a joint or two away.

There they were again, the tumbling leaves blown by an invisible wind, rolling down M St., scrambling as if to find a branch to pin themselves back onto; and there he was, riding, riding, riding down M Street, riding, riding, riding up to the old inn door of Nathan's Bar & Grill, riding, riding, riding bareback on a great silver stallion, riding, riding, riding on Halloween night through Georgetown, riding, riding, riding as the Lone Ranger, white cowboy hat, black mask, pearl-handle six-shooter, belt of silver bullets and all, calling out, well, what would you expect? Hi-yo Silver away!

"Who was that masked man?" a bystander asked as he flew past, faster than the execution of swift and certain justice.

Jerry McClellan—that's who. Masked rider against injustice, for justice, or so he imagined as he had put on his political mask every day, readying himself for his next ride to raise money to elect fellow riders on behalf of justice and against injustice. He'd ridden down ten thousands trails since then in a world where true justice riders were few and getting fewer. He'd ridden as the masked man into all those disappeared years and where, he wanted to know, did it get him? Now it was time to lose the mask, time to follow a different path. Seek a spiritual awakening for the sake of living life without a mask.

Enlightenment. Sky blue consciousness. A nice addition to his resume, if there ever was one.

Suddenly, McClellan became conscious that he was Dunkin Donuts famished. A glazed sugar craving had taken over, compromising his thoughts about arriving at destination Enlightenment. Sky blue consciousness could wait. But a sugarcoated donut—or better yet a hefty lunch—plus a cup of black coffee couldn't. Not any longer. He put the open novel facedown on the arm of the chair, and went downstairs. He stepped over the chain at the bottom step, and told the Grand Dame of Bryn Mawr that he was stepping out for lunch.

"Please keep my place," he said.

"Don't worry, I'll keep out the great unwashed."

"Republicans?"

"And Ralph Nader should he happen along while you're gone."

"You've got dogs, right?"

"German Shepherds."

"Just in case."

"Just in case. Now go and enjoy your lunch, Mr. McClellan. There're no worries."

McClellan flew free as a trick-or-treater on Halloween down 32nd Street. He kept his head down just in case someone happened along who would turn him into the DNC police. At Prospect Street, he dipped into Booeymonger delicatessen, rather than go onto Paolo's Ristorante. He was in no mood to be recognized, for obvious reasons. He was traveling incognito. Nor was he of a mind to splurge. He bought a Pita Pan sandwich. Fresh spinach, alfalfa sprouts, muenster cheese, tomato, mushrooms, fresh spinach, salad veggies, avocado and house dressing slapped together in whole wheat pita bread, all for $5.95. He also ordered a side of homemade potato salad, jazzing it up with white chunks of feta cheese for extra protein. He hesitated in good faith before tacking on a couple of cheesecake brownies and a lemon bar to his order. Technically, if you're counting each and every calorie, he should have gone for a double scoop of Moxley© Sorbet instead, but misery loves calories, so he got the tastier high calorie fare, vowing blessed monastic silence should anyone—Margaret in particular—ask him what he'd had for lunch today.

After, he downed two shots of lukewarm espresso served in a meager paper cup. Not exactly Paris, but it wasn't Pittsburg, either had worse. Leaving behind a monstrous tip—$6.74 on a $13.26 order—because he wanted someone somewhere to feel good about the day—he shot out of there like he'd just received an emergency call from the Office of Communications at the White House offering him the job of writing George W.'s resignation speech. He was not above hoping—praying even—that sooner or later Justice would in fact hand down an indictment against Bush and/or Cheney charging them with voter suppression in Ohio as well as operating a highly illegal screw-the-Dems-outa-their-votes black bag ops from the VP's office. That would be one way to contest the election results. One could always hope.

McClellan soon found himself back upstairs on the second floor of Bryn Mawr sitting in his big chair, staring out the window and watching burnished leaves blow in no particular direction along the obsolete trolley car tracks of P Street. Life was measurably more tolerable and enchanting, especially on jet fuel espresso.

The path-to-enlightenment career option he'd been considering earlier seemed even more tantalizing now. And his self-directed message that he should take any road, make any detour, to steer away from catastrophes of politics, even if he never quite made it to full-blown enlightenment—whatever that was—the change in direction away from the microscopic, explosive matters of men and women bent on fulfilling agendas would do him a shocking amount of good. Think cosmic, he told himself. Think salvation. Hey, even if his pursuit of enlightenment fell flat, there were still other life options available other than politics, right? Like writing his memoirs. He knew things. Like going back to his twelve-string guitar and writing rock 'n roll music, á la the Byrds. Why, it could even live the dream of dreams, go Dead Head and follow the Grateful Dead from gig to gig—it wasn't too late. Not yet anyway. He could simply unload all human ambition other than walking the streets of Venice and Paris. Or simply spoil his grandchildren every chance he got. All he knew was that the sooner he distanced himself from his former self, the better. He wasn't too big on enduring humiliation. And standing at the epicenter of a crushing national election defeat definitely constituted the mother lode of all public humiliations for him. Or was it more like a public execution? Maybe that's why he'd felt that he'd been hung from the gallows in the public square of Middle America this morning. Enlightenment would be his way back to anonymity again, right? Taking the road to enlightenment would be, by its nature, a thoroughly private affair. The public-at- large wouldn't give a damn whether he succeeded or failed. No chance AP and Reuters would ever report it. No special news coverage on Fox Channel 5 News, either. No, he'd be left alone, enlightened or not. It would be a personal thing.

McClellan heard squirrels scampering across the roof, sounding like children rushing from fun to fun in the summer of delight. The very concept baffled him. Politics. Politics was The Fun. Had been the Fun, the Only Fun. It had been the Alpha and Omega of his fine living; the substance over style; the cause than won the even greater Transcendental Cause. The trouble was, he never reached it. Once he'd harbored a silent belief that the day would come with the election of enough in Washington that a wondrous new era of enlightenment would reign over the nation. Now he'd die waiting. Certainly Bill Clinton had been no Buddha, nor was Jimmy Carter Christ. Even the Religious Right couldn't get its transcendent politics right, although it considered Bush to be an agent of Christ, no doubt.

Still, McClellan was a rider—riding, riding, riding—always riding. He couldn't—hadn't—wouldn't—give up hope entirely. But with Bush back in the White House for four more years and no transcendent Democratic figure in sight for 2008—hope was just another four-letter word. Perhaps the surest route that America now had to reach a new era of consciousness was for there to be a resurgence of the 1960s mentality—for the age of love and peace and potheads to come roaring back—with the Grateful Dead and their faithful Dead Heads leading the holy charge—followed on by compliant Republicans, Democrats and Independents lighting up hand-rolled joints in every corner of America. Well, why not? Nothing else had much worked.

It was the espresso speaking, McClellan knew that. One shot really was his limit.

Downstairs, he heard the Grand Dame's laughter breaking the stuffy silence, and rising up like a grand surprise through the floorboards. She was evidently whooping it up on the telephone, sharing a literary anecdote or some such thing with a good friend. Yes, having fun. However did she do it, especially because it likely had nothing to do with politics? With an attitude like that, McClellan needed psychiatric attention, for sure; but at least now he could admit it, now that his days in politics were almost over. Still, he worried. How could he ever have fun again in a world beyond politics?

Her burst of laughter rattled the floorboards. There it was— proof positive. She'd found fun. It could happen to anyone. She'd found it in a house full of books, in corridors packed with paperbacks, in a wall-to-wall library stuffed with dusty hardbacks. That's what he wanted, too, in a parallel universe: The end of politics, enlightenment, bliss. It could happen. What he really needed right now was something less than that. Total distraction. Separation. Isolation. So he turned to his novel, which lay facedown on the arm of the big chair next to the sunny window. He flipped it over, faced the open pages.

The chapter heading on the left-hand side read: Chapter 6

Of *My Name is...* Jerry McClellan and I Need a New Life *and* Enlightenment.

CHAPTER SIX

"**G**ood morning, sir, the name's Jesus Christ and I'm running for president as a Ronald Reagan Republican..."

"Drop dead."

"But, I can do a lot for you."

"Like what?"

"Lower your taxes, shrink the size of federal government..."

"Just like Bush?"

"No! *Not* like Bush! Like Ronald Reagan!"

"Not likely."

"Deregulate everything, too."

"Just like Bush?"

"No! *Not* like Bush! Like Ronald Reagan!"

"Not likely."

"Can, too."

"Cannot."

"Can, too."

"Cannot."

"Can, too."

"Look, buddy, I haven't voted Republican since George Bush led us into another Depression!"

"But—"

Farmer Joe leans into the wind, nudging past. He lumbers up the steps to Princess Café and Sweet Shop, fists bolted to the bottoms of his cozy red plaid pockets, head lowered into the rim of the fleece white collar of his olive green field jacket, leaving me behind, depressed and disappointed, marooned on a thick slab of black ice in the Iowa arctic cold, waiting—not because I want to but because I must—for my next voter victim to try to slip past, so I can put the arm on them before they get away and find refuge over a piping hot cup of morning coffee.

The truth is, the day isn't going terribly well so far. Nor yesterday, either. But Faith in Victory is my middle name. I do not doubt. My hope reaches down into the lower regions of the lowest parts of old earth.

One thing I've learned for sure these past couple of days: President George W. Bush really screwed my party—the Grand Old Party, the Republican Party, way back when he was in office and America was great. I should have run as a Democrat. It would have been a piece of cake. My stepbrother was right to run as a Democrat. Regardless, we've heard that my primary Republican opponent will be dropping out today. That was prescient of him. I would have had to have had him killed otherwise. I don't take competition nicely. I'm not a good sport. Winning is more or less my religion.

'Course I would save myself a measure of treasure and trouble by knocking off my stepbrother—as of now. But in a quaint kind of way, I kind of like the idea of beating Him fair and square. For a change. No doubt it's the distance of time and space that's made me bust out with such confidence—and my recent run at the tables. Maybe I just feel sorry for the guy. He's had quite a time, when you bother to stop long enough to think about it, which normally, of course, I don't.

It's 5:00 a.m., and dawn is still hanging out, out of sight. The last time I was up and out this early was back in 1861, I think, although maybe there was a morning at the start of the Bolshevik Revolution, too—I really can't remember. All the centuries are beginning to seem like one. Anyhow, I got up before daybreak in April 1861 so that I'd be able to watch hostilities break out in the War Between the States. I'd applied a lot of extra elbow grease to get that one going, so I wasn't going to miss it—not for anything. And as it turned out, it was totally worth it, giving me years of unfettered jollification. Not unprecedented in its grotesque atrocities, mind you—not by any means—but really good stuff, artful warfare in fact, nothing to be embarrassed about. Not at all. Civil wars are the most labor intensive to ignite, for sure—backbreaking even, but once they blow they tend to roast the most. Take my word. Been there, done that, plenty of times. And am looking forward to doing it all over again, too—just as soon as I get myself elected.

I only mention the above because rising early is not what I do best. No apologies, really, just fact.

As I said, it's dark and seems to be getting darker rather than lighter. Maybe it's just my eyes. I had no clue that slumming for votes could be so humiliating. People don't have to treat you nice. They don't have to bow down to you or anything. It's not what I'm used to. Not at all. Slumming for votes is not exactly an enlightening experience. But this is what my advisers said I had to do to win. So be it. It's put up or shut up time. Assume the proper attitude time. Suck it up, big time. I now know how Vladimir Putin must have felt his first day out campaigning for president of the former Evil Empire. I can totally relate. It's all about conning votes. Which is why I shouldn't be having so much trouble. This should come naturally to me. Unfortunately, I wasn't born to supplicate. I wasn't raised to do democracy. Not that I won't admit that it's a rather inventive and imaginative system, which is saying something coming from a guy in love with brute force. I've found that it does have its points, like offering me the opportunity to hit on beautiful girls going by under the pretext of asking for their votes. Not that my qualified endorsement of the process on the record should be taken too hugely seriously. Remember, I'm only using it to abuse it.

Another Iowa Falls farmer boy goes by, head buried in his turned up fleece collar. Clearly, he's not too interested in me. Me! I like that! I'll pull his farm subsidies. It'll be the first thing I do when I get into office. I'll teach him to snub me... Then I collect myself. I need to park my temper at the limousine door, parked out back, cheerfully idling, just waiting for my return, stocked with Bombay Rum, and warm as my mother's womb.

The next one I confront, putting out my hand, forcing a smile, one of my first in many centuries. They feel about as elastic as saltwater taffy. He's not interested. Votes Democrat. At least he listened. At least he was polite. We commiserated over the downward spiral of soybeans and the prospects of weak corn future prices. At least he didn't leave with me wanting to execute him. He actually seemed like an okay kind of guy. Said he'd return after breakfast with a mug of hot coffee for me. Guys like that give life a good name. Come to think of it, charitable acts such as that could go a ways towards making me a much more likeable guy—and perhaps most importantly, improving my favorable ratings, which could use a boost or two. I got a look at them this morning. And they didn't look good. But then I'm still relatively unknown in my new role. Untrusted, yes. Untested, absolutely. Unnerving, well, maybe. But they'll see. The people will come to love me. They always do. Give to get, that's my motto. Giving helps the getting. Getting the three Gs: Greed, Gluttony, and above all else, Glory.

"Good morning, sir, the name's Jesus Christ and I'm running for president as a Ronald Reagan Republican."

Farmer John sniggers.

"Christ or not, any man running for president under the party name of George W. Bush gets no vote from me. He bankrupted my 401(k)!"

Punctuating his point, he blows pipe smoke in my face, before dipping into the Princess Café and Sweet Shop for a plate of steak and eggs. I just knew I shouldn't have screwed with those Palm Beach County chads in 2000! The sins of my many generations have come home to roost. That George W. will be the death of not only the Republican Party, but me, too.

I hike up the collar of my Harrod's long black woolen coat, cutting quite a picturesque figure in the early snow. The cowpokes at the Business Round Table are sparing no expense on quality threads for me. Sarah Palin's $150,000 campaign wardrobe had nothing on me. I'm beyond three hundred grand and counting. And that's before the nomination! They've turned me into a clotheshorse, but I don't mind. I marvel—really I do—on how far I've come since my Castro army field jacket days. I wore that thing for decades. And now look at me. I could pose for *GQ*.

Fine white snowy powder sprinkles down, adding to the soft web of morning snowfall collecting on the ground. If only it was cocaine. Then this would be fun. I rub my hands together, blow hot breath into the cradle of my palms. My arthritis's acting up again because age spares no man, not even me. It's not what I would call a grand presidential posture—like I'd hate to have that profile chiseled into the face of Mt. Rushmore—but then I'm only a wannabe now, so I suppose it doesn't count. Besides, nobody notices because there's no one nutty enough to be out here but the somnambulist farmers. You can bet the legions of press aren't camped out yet. They're much too smart for that. They wait until at least the sun comes up to warm the snowy skies. They like it as cozy as possible, right up until the last possible moment. But that's why people like me—the few, the brave, the proud, and the presidential—get to be president. We'll gladly suffer in the name of Glory; the press toil in the name of scratching out relative obscurity, at best, the poor dogs. There. I've convinced myself that all this is worth it. It amazes me I can trick myself as well as the public, just like that.

A vote—I mean a sleepy-headed farmer—emerges out of the frosted dark, making for his morning watering hole. I put out my hand, like a gentlemen vote-getter—just like I was taught by my political consultants. It's a man's handshake—at the very least, reassuring but firm. But he looks at me as though I was a nobody, and walks on, breathing back over his shoulder these words with quiet disdain:

"Where's Ron Paul when we really need him?"

'Course I let it go. Libertarians. They come and they go. And I don't need to prove everything to everyone. I *am* somebody. Me and Jesse Jackson. Well, me more than Jesse, but that's another point. What's important is that I learn to take the snubs gracefully. Part of the job description. As the libertarian in a checkered red and black hunter's cap sinks into the rosy recesses of the Princess Café and Sweet Shop, my thoughts wander back home—to Juarez. Sometimes out here on the campaign trail, I feel like a freshman college kid absent from home. I miss it that much. Like when I'm in one of my moods, I pine away for my flat screen TV. More than I can say I long to knock back a Miller Bud Lite early in the morning. I'm absolutely nostalgic about sitting in my very own stolen REI chair again—with no hands to clasp, no political pitter-patter talk to make. Just me under the stalactites. And all the other little things, like being in my own bed and those occasional hot nights down in Juarez with my girl.

These are just a few of the stark sacrifices I've had to accommodate in order to compete in the country's biggest con. *Now* I finally get what all those previous presidential candidates got so worked up about every few years. Who wouldn't make great and small sacrifices to vie for this kind of ante? A treasure trove of nuclear weaponry I can call my own. It doesn't get any better than that. I should know. I've never been able to afford them.

I blow on my hands again. Feels good. I look up at the great white sky above. It seems small; I feel big. Snowflakes tumble down, like millions of tiny ballerinas in sparkling white dancing about. Nice. I'm all wide-eyed, a child wandering in a wonderland again. I'm reminded of a fragment from a Robert Frost poem, the titled of which I can't quite remember. The Lord above really went creative when He thought up snow. Very soothing. Quite calming. Maybe it's meant to be a gift 'cause I've been on such good behavior lately. Not that I have much of a choice. The press is almost always everywhere, hanging over me like a Sword of Damocles! So maybe I'm boosting my good karma these days, thinking more positively, saying things that sound—at least superficially—hopeful, full of promise. I'll say anything to win the presidency. Just like most of those other presidential candidates who preceded me. But I must be careful. Karma giveth and karma taketh away. Right now, anyway, despite the hour and the Siberian cold, I'm enjoying the sparkling ballerinas dancing in the sky above, and my rare moment of sheer positivity.

At last, it's finally getting light. I shake another hand. Farmer Bob says he'll support me. That it's always been obvious to him that if the real Christ returned he'd be a Republican. Now that He has, He is. A registered voter who'll vote for me... How awesome is that? I don't need no sun washing my back to make me feel toasty because I'm basking in Farmer Bob's adulation. I had no idea that the practice of democracy could make me feel so, well, *different*. Sure, this could spell a particularly dangerous and destructive chapter in my life, like perhaps I could start to lose my satanic edge from acting like a real politician, but I'm nowhere near that catastrophic point of yet. I'm still all about Giving to Get, my campaign code of ethics. I must always, always remember that, no matter how all this running for president drags me down and makes me empathize with ordinary people's problems. I am faking my new earnestness. I do possess only a counterfeit conscience. Way down inside I couldn't care less about promoting social welfare, let alone lifting up the downtrodden, the homeless, and the disenfranchised through Trickle Down Charity. That's all to get myself elected—I assure you. I still harbor the darkest of motives. Let your imaginations run wild and you'd be right. Anything you hear me say or claim that I'd do on bringing a new day to the American people will be just so much hogwash. Debris down a storm sewer. Lift up the poor on a rising tide? I hardly think so. Will you hear me saying that on radio and television? You bet you will. But it won't be the real me—the storm sewer me. It'll be the better angels of my twilight shadow mouthing off, stumbling drunk crossing the cornfields of democracy.

Add to this psychodrama the schizophrenic mindset of having to pretend to be my stepbrother—day-in, day-out—a horrendous challenge, believe me, while holding onto the crumbling fragments of my own conflicted personality and you can understand why I might be alarmed by the possible unintended consequences of my plan. I'm in new territory here. I'm flying blind in a cloud upside down looking for the horizon.

And it gets worse.

I'm also forced by the very nature of my ambition to chat with likely caucus voters—the jobless lost in the wilderness of unemployment, retirees trying to live on pensions decimated by careless Republican fiscal policies, mom and pops scraping funds together to send their kids through college, first-time voters enchanted with democracy, disgruntled farmers looking for more farm subsidies—all armed with what I'd call trivial grievances of no consequence to anyone except them, over weak coffee of non-Starbucks variety—totally beneath me—and glazed donut holes, not the donuts themselves, mind you, in the Flamingo Room of the Holiday Inn in Mason City, a city put down in the middle of nowhere for no apparent reason other than to make me go to it in January when I'd rather be snug and warm in Juarez. But happily, I think they'll all vote for me because my opponent never showed up. He met with a rather unfortunate accident along the way. Imagine that. I, on the other hand, had a trouble-free experience chilling out in a white stretch limo fitted with Las Vegas running lights, disco floor, disco ceiling, and alligator upholstery, sipping Bombay Rum, and watching frozen cornfields flow by under the white, wooly eyes of a blizzard, escorted by Iowa Highway Patrol cars and U.S. Secret Service vans in a thespian display of emergency lights that colored the passing snowy columns of cornstalks all shades of shining psychedelic. I can take the punishment of the Flamingo Room so long as the reward is great and all about the end result—self-aggrandizement and the Axis of Power, which converges, first and last, at the center of me, me, me.

The punishment knows no bounds, but the reward grows by leaps and bounds.

In Marshalltown, my staff has me eating Chicken McNuggets at a former Maytag factory with erstwhile Maytag employees, who also lost their life pensions in the Economic Meltdown of 2008. They cry a lot and then naturally we cry a lot because I'm the one running for president. But I tell them it was Bill Clinton's fault. His fetish for NAFTA had their jobs going overseas. Clinton had a fetish here and a fetish there, but NAFTA was one of his worst. I also blame the demise of their pensions on my opponent, a candidate who had significant ties to the Bush II Administration, I note. It's all over but the voting after I say that. Easy as spelling "W."

We spend the rest of our time rapping about front-loading washers, top-loading washers, and washer-dryer combos, not to mention the host of glossy finishes available in a multiplicity of tantalizing colors: Crimson, evergreen, slate blue, ultimate silver metallic, silver metallic with white, white with chrome Black, and black with chrome. I myself am pretty much enamored with the thought of owning a silver metallic one with white trim, but that's just me, caught up in the moment. I'm having a Maytag Moment.

And still, it gets worse.

I'm encouraged—ordered, actually, by my campaign staff—to hang out with construction and blue-collar workers at Ike's Job Site in Marathon, west of Marshalltown, and drink beer. Lots of beer. Theoretically, I should have had a pretty good time, out with the guys, and all, but for reasons passing all understanding strippers and lap dancing are strictly prohibited and the beer itself didn't do it for me, so it was about as much fun as going to a six-year-old's birthday party and being told that I wasn't allowed on the pony ride. Still, the guys get drunker than a room full of Irish at the wake of a drinking buddy. And when they do, they accept me as one of their own, like I actually used my hands for a living, which is a laugh, because I don't do manual labor of any kind. Never have. They sing to me, buy me beers, which are not technically campaign contributions, and tell me that they love me. It's nice to hear them say that. It makes me feel, well, rather friendly to them, not so condescending of their working class status. I admit to being a huge fan of Joe the Plumber as well as Joe Six-Pack. I even confess in a moment of uncustomary weakness that one of my Brobdingnagian regrets as a recent recruit to the Republican Party with an historical overview is that John McCain and Sarah Palin never made it to the White House. They order another round all around after I say that. So next I do a John McCain. I promise not to raise their taxes. I know and they know they want to own their own businesses someday, and make more than $250,000 a year without getting stuck with an Obama-size tax hike, just like Joe the Plumber back in 2008. The thing is they accept me for who I am, even though I'm no Joe Six-Pack or Joe-the-Plumber. As a newcomer to politics, I have to appreciate their latitude, particularly in light of the fact that I don't get soused on beer like ordinary guys and have never unclogged a single drain with a plumbing snake in my entire life. I mean, there're worse things other than an Iowan Republican I could claim to be, especially considering you and I both know where I'm coming from... Next morning I wake up on a couch in my room at the Holiday Inn in Marshalltown with a doozie of a headache, but do I care? Not even close. It was worth it because those were totally solid votes I signed up yesterday. They knew I could out best the best of them. Exactly what a candidate must do to win the nomination. So, I'm proud to say, the first election returns are in: At Ike's Job Site bar, at least. Joe-the- Plumber and Joe Six-Pack, it's fair to say, appreciate a drinking man—one with centuries of hops-guzzling experience—though I'll admit, this body of mine can't take the beatings the way it used to. Those days are long gone, sorry to say. I mean, totally gone, GONE, G-O-N-E...

I'll say this for my little stepbrother, he's shrewder than I gave him credit for. He's got me coming and going, mostly going, and doing and saying relatively reasonable things, being generally open to and even vulnerable to the needs of others. And it's all because democracy works that way. It gets you in its grip and won't let go because you need it as much as it needs you. It makes you into a democratic clone, pandering for the votes of others. Worse, it spawns engagement, communication and, dare I say it, even caring? But I can do this. I can fake it till I make it. It's only for nine months, not a life sentence. Until I hit the campaign trail, I never entertained a kind and considerate thought in my life. Today, I've had one or two. Perhaps three. It's unavoidable, actually. You can't look into the eyes of an eighty-two-year-old famer who's lost his life's pension in addition to his farm and not empathize. I tried—believe me—I tried to avoid any kind of sympathy, but there was just something about his circumstances that seemed, well, really rather touching. I know that doesn't exactly sound like me. Of course, I know it. And I wish I could get over it, seek counseling or something and get rid of these feelings as fast as they came, but I don't know, the feelings are simply too strong and there's just too much at stake to be able to put them aside. I have to do what I have to do to get myself to the White House because, yes, I was born to do this. If George W. can do it, why not me?   Yes I can. And if I have to pay the price of emotional connection to accomplish it, well, so be it. So what? I just do it. Associating below my pay grade is a minor price to pay for the exigencies of obtaining new powers. Even if—and yes, I'll admit that this will be very, very hard—I have to schmooze with more people like the Ramseys from Black Hawk County, angling, always angling, for their vote by using methods of verbal persuasion rather than resorting to what I'd normally do to get consent—initiating "enhanced" interrogation techniques, following the path forged by the Bush White House, or lobbying May Wagner, the chairwoman of Scott County Republicans, all afternoon over watercress salad and weak Lipton tea and getting nowhere, absolutely nowhere with her or, worse, being subjected to the unfettered ravings of Chris Barnes, one Iowa farmer with a screw loose, who was convinced he spotted a UFO fly over his farmhouse last New Years' Eve that landed in his corn patch out back, before a troop of galactic heavies armed with Star Trek phasers marched into his house, invaded his sleeping wife's body, and then carted her off into a pint-size spaceship before disappearing into the cozy embrace of an extrasolar constellation out in deep nowhere.

But do I say anything? Do I even question him? Do I raise one incredulous eyebrow? No way, José. I simply listen, nod, and then permit myself to ask him for his vote. Which is what any politician worth a vote would do. He's says that I've got it, too, all because I listened to his loony story about the body snatchers. It's all in the listening. I'm finding that more and more. Ask Barack Obama—the Master Listener Vote-Getter.

I know, I know. I've turned round the bend of no return by prostrating myself for the American Way: More votes, more power. Fast, very, very fast it's becoming an unnatural way of life. But given the delicious spoils awaiting me, like a young bride on my wedding night, should I get it right, it's a price I have no problem paying, even if by doing so, I'm becoming step by step a kinder, gentler person, newly endowed by fate and circumstance with a thousand points of light invading my cerebrum, like there was daylight upstairs.

****

My Hope First Campaign 1998 Chevrolet Blue Bird School Bus, complete with broadside banner declaring it so, has broken down with a flat tire on the shoulder of Interstate 35 somewhere south of Des Moines. Dago, bless his little Mel's Angel heart, is cracking the lug nuts while the rest of us stand shivering next to the off-ramp bundled in horse blankets, donated by an Angus cattleman from Waldridge Farms, who said he won't necessarily vote for me because I was probably too damn liberal for him, but was being generous because he thought it smart to hedge his bets, since I really could turn out to be the real Christ and might even win the election—even with my liberal policies. My beautiful yellow school bus was, in fact, generously donated by Boy Scout Troop 42 from Cedar Rapids to my campaign (in full compliance with the Federal Election Campaign Act of 2016, I hasten to add) following a thumping speech I gave at their annual Hawkeye Area Council meeting week before last. For starters, I praised them for their tireless flood relief efforts during the Flood of 2019, when the Des Moines River overflowed its banks down near Fort Dodge, rising up about 5 feet high and causing widespread damage—not unlike what my stepbrother, Mr. B., likes to do. Then, because I was finally beginning to get the hang of campaigning, after some rather embarrassing moments early on, like when I suddenly launched into an entire speech in Aramaic instead of English, I asked the lads and their families to embrace my message of hope for real change in America—Hope First—a slogan by amalgamation coped from Barrack Obama's and John McCain's 2008 campaign by Pelosi, evidently, before beseeching everyone still listening

239

to sign up for Iowa Caucus Day to help turn out the vote. Naturally, I've learned—and learned fast—that it's all about the numbers, and not the number of my good deeds I perform on the trail, which pretty much limits me to grubbing for votes, just like every other politician in history. Can't say that I like it. Definitely can't say that I do, but I got myself into this and collecting votes is the only way I'll be able to get myself out of it—so there it is. So they say, do-gooders finish last, a place I can't afford to be, don't want to be. I constantly have to remind myself of that. (Pelosi tutors me about the fact of politics in the back of the bus while traveling from town to town, city to city. At least she does when it's not broken down next to a cornfield that looks like it's been painted with Tom Sawyer's brush.)

Even though they all knew that I'm basically begging for votes, like the future of springs depends on it, they seemed to like me anyway, and it helped, of course, that I remembered to speak in English rather than Aramaic. "Hope First! Hope First!" I rang out, finishing up. They did seem pretty wild about my message of Hope and applauded me as I'd saluted them. And to demonstrate their solidarity, they presented me with the keys to the Blue Bird school bus, which made me want to cry because I was just so touched. As a gesture of my profound gratitude, I pinned "It's about Hope, Stupid" buttons on each of their uniforms—next to their Tender Foot and Palms merit badges. For me it's all about mutual respect. Boy scouts—you go! Now GET-OUT-THE-VOTE!

We should have been at Lynx Wind Turbine warehouse by now where I'm to give my standard stump speech about retooling state industry in support of transition to 50% wind farming by the year 2024 because cellulosic ethanol production takes too much eatable corn out of the mouths of hungry people in Third World countries; but then this thing happened and so we're running behind. But as they say in Iowa, flats happen.

Nevertheless, everything looks positive. Yesterday's tracking polls had me up by only two percentage points over my opponent. What makes him real competition is that his name just happens to be Ralph Nader. He's running as a moderate Democrat while selling solar panels and home wind turbines along the campaign trail in order to raise money to finance his campaign without tainting it with corporate contributions. He rides around in a big old school bus, just like me, but painted forest green. A banner hangs on the side that says, "GREEN MACHINE: SAFE AT ANY SPEED". Of course, he retrofitted each seat to have multiple seatbelts and the dash has backup airbags. He had a similar chassis crash-tested too many times to recall. When it comes to auto safety, Ralph's at his best and right where he belongs. For the campaign he's crowned himself, The Good Shepherd of the Environment. The truth is we have few environmental policy differences. So you can understand why Ralph spells potential heartache. Against him, my name carries only so much water. Why, Ralph's practically revered as God down here, even though he screwed the Dems in 2000 by running against Gore. But the good thing for him is that practically nobody remembers anything in politics for much longer than a couple of years, and also because Americans are a fairly generous lot when it comes to getting over transgressions made by politicians, though it's fair to say that one against Gore, which gave the world W., was a whopper. Still, unlike the Old Man who never forgets, let alone forgives, anyone for anything (He never did learn how to chill.), U.S. voters are generally willing to forgive and forget. It's all very Christian of them and I give them enormous credit for it.

I also have to assign credit to Ralph, too. Like Saul on the Road to Damascus, he came to see the light, making the jump to the Democratic Party in order to prevent another run for the presidency as a Green Party candidacy from contributing to the defeat of another

241

Democratic challenger going up against an opponent from the George W. Axis of Incompetence Party. He saw the light, all right. I give him points for that and certainly don't take his bid as an insult. He genuinely believes he's better on the environment than me. And maybe he is. Besides, his book, *Unsafe at Any Speed* saved thousands and thousands of lives, which is more than I can say I've been doing over the past six decades…and a whole lot more.

At last, we get there: The Hope First bus, its tires full of air. And like a farm boy late for dinner at twilight skating across a frozen pond, I make for Lynks Wind Turbine warehouse, where I observe a Secret Service agent whispering my code name into his wrist radio as I near, with golden shafts of light spilling out onto the parking lot ice through the open door. "Golden Halo floating south," he says. Then—and this is the fun part—I hear the sweetest sound any politician will ever hear: Their name being repeated over and over.

"Jesus, Jesus, Jesus!"

Thousands anticipate my entrance, like an alien people from another galaxy deprived of sunshine for far too long and now expecting its return. What's nice to know is that they want me as much as I must have them! But will I break my all-time speaking attendance record? I grip my wind turbine policy speech, rolled up like a Masters Degree, as though it was the key to my Iowa caucus victory. Which maybe it is. Naturally, the Dean of Public Policy and Speechmaking, Disciple Pelosi herself, handed it to me, tied up like a diploma with a piece of blue ribbon, as I shot away from the bus at breakneck speed.

I can feel it deep down in the marrow of my bones that my self-confidence is at an all-time high: Yes, that's right, I think I've learned how to be a pretty good imitation of an American politician. No time too soon, either, since Iowa Caucus Day is the day after tomorrow, and today's tracking polls have me up by only 5 points, with a sampling error of +/- 3 or 4%. Still, I sense my first victory. I can beat Ralph, I can.

Lord only knows what the Old Man thinks of me. Undoubtedly, He's been looking down from His seat in Heaven, judging my every move as though I was a teenager slumped behind the wheel of the family car. I can just feel that penetrating stare of His. Of course, He's seen me begging for votes every which way, schmoozing one-on-one with prospective voters on the windy streets of Waterloo, Ames and Sioux City; standing before gatherings of 50 or less at house parties in Ida Grove, scoffing down Roadfood with diners at the Maid-Rite restaurant in Newton, glad-handing at the VFW Post 5240 in Dakota City, doing a meet-and-greet for 300 at the Des Moines Public Library, speaking before over 500 at Beaverdale Park in a swirling snowstorm, delivering wonkish speeches to a 1,000 at the Convention Center, to over 1,500 at the Jefferson Jackson banquet, to 5,000 at Vets Auditorium, and yes, thanks to Oprah Winfrey and her Oprah Angels Network, to a record 20,000 at Hy-Vee Hall! I bested Barrack Obama totals by over 2,000 there! A new record!

No question about it. My campaign's gaining traction, which was inevitable after I had the good sense to appoint Disciple Madonna as my press secretary. She's the Grand Goddess of Press Manipulation, she is. She knows how to make it happen. She's especially apt at drowning out the Green Geezer's Green Machine publicity machine. Green Geezer's the name she gave to my opponent and the one she uses to identify him in all her press releases: The Green Geezer—Unsafe at Any Speed. It's shameful, I know. All negative advertising is, but there it is. This is politics, baby, and if nothing else, politics is a body blow sport.

I hear again the sweetest sound any politician will ever hear: Their name being repeated over and over:

"Jesus, Jesus... Jesus!"

Ergo...

It may be that I really have become an American politician.

Which is saying something since just a few weeks ago politics was about as alien a subject to me as, well, the Church of Scientology... (No offense, Tom.) Lord only knows, the Old Man's probably suffered a heart attack from looking down. But a savior's got to do what a savior's got to do.

As of now, my allegiance is to Hope First, Humanity Second, and the Old Man Third.

I give the speech, I receive their applause, and most importantly, I think I get the votes of the Iowa Wind Farmers Association because I'm all for government subsidies for their turbines. They also seem pretty much taken with me personally, like I was their wind god, or something, an American Aeolus. At the end of my speech, I lead the farmers in a very special wind prayer, based on the Lord's Prayer, the 1928 version.

It goes a bit like this:

"Our Wind, which art in heaven,
Hallowed be thy Name.
Thy winds will come.
Thy winds will be done,
On earth as it is in heaven.
Give us this day our daily wind.
And forgive us our windlessness,
As we forgive those who are windless.
And lead us not into the valley of calmness,
But deliver us from stillness.

For thine is the Kingdom of the Wind,
And the power, and the glory, for ever and ever.
Amen.”

Before long my twelve disciples and I are barreling back down Interstate 380 toward Iowa City in plenty of time for my debate tomorrow night with the Green Geezer. Along the way we sing old Beatles tunes. In particular, "All You Need is Love." Lennon & McCartney—I've got to hand it to them; they knew a thing or two about capitalizing on my line of work. So we've made that song the anthem for my campaign. It gets us up and going every time.

My stepbrother? He picked "Sympathy for the Devil" by what's-their-name? The Rolling Stones. Which just goes to show, if I do say so myself, the real Christ has much better taste in 60's rock music than his lowdown impersonator stepbrother. That should give the voters a clue come November about who they should cast their votes for—that is if they want really good music flowing through the halls of the White House and rockin' a Christ Administration.

As for the Green Geezer? He selected "Big Yellow Taxi." Put up a parking lot and all that. That'll get him some votes, for sure, but it's still no match for a song about love.

Or so I better hope.

CHAPTER SEVEN

Three days before I'm destined by all that's right and wrong to rack up a second major victory in as many weeks—this time in New Hampshire's First-in-the-nation Primary or Die, as I barrel down Interstate 2020 on my way to winning the Republican nomination, just two weeks after pulverizing my "I-want-to-spend-more-time-with-my-family" dropout opponent in Iowa, and thirteen minutes into my private flight to speak to a room full of loaded pistols at the Gun Owners Club in Concord on a private CL-600 Bombardier Challenger jet out of Nashua in a freezing drizzle, now soaring at 40,000 feet through clear blue skies at 529 mph in a machine weighing 40,000 lbs., I feel as light as an angel dancing on the head of a sewing pin. I had no idea running for prez could be such an unmitigated blast. If I'd known that pressing the flesh and making speeches with poetic rhetorical flourishes like Peggy Noonan inserts at even the most mundane of speaking engagements could be so entertaining, I'd have entered American politics back in 1776. (And to think I missed my chance to shape the debate over the drafting of the U.S. Constitution! If I'd only gotten in with the revolutionary brat pack crowd—sometimes referred to the Founding Fathers—think what I could have done to make it *my* kind of constitution. Could have even outdone George Bush! The Bill of Rights? *I don't think so...* Oversights like that make me nuts!)

The flight captain extinguishes the seatbelt sign ten minutes in—like I really needed his approval to be unleashed from my seat as I sip my Perrier. I know that doesn't exactly sound like me but I've taken a vow of abstinence on the campaign trail. No Bombay Rum, no hanky-panky of any kind. That's to demonstrate to myself, if no one else, just how serious I am about winning this thing. Once I commit to something, I commit, be it to causing war and dissension, spreading nuclear weapons or winning a U.S. presidential election—I'm all in.

My chief campaign strategist, Donna Cass, chairman of the Business Roundtable, and former head of EXXON, leans over to re-adjust my silk bowtie. I've taken to wearing one because I like totally identify with conservative columnist George Will's sense of fashion.

Especially now that I'm a contender—a real contender. I may not have read PPE at Magdalen College at the University of Oxford, but I certainly want to look like I did!

Working well below her pay grade but in the name of an excellent cause, obviously, Ms. Cass blows hoary bits of snowflake dandruff off my shiny blue Brooks Brother suit shoulders. Let's face it: I look good, especially minus flakes of dandruff. Looking vigorously handsome and having access to substantive funding is a turn-on, both to the electorate and to women. Just ask Fidel and Jack Kennedy. It's the perfect combination because when all is said and done, magnetism counts. It's no wonder my opponent coped out. He looked as greasy at Tom DeLay. As a matter of fact, he was Tom DeLay. And I'm just so tickled that he backed off because, well, discretion is the better part of politics. (All I needed was to threaten release of that TIME magazine photo of him smoking a Cuban cigar over in Israel in 2003, and he'd have been finished as a presidential candidate. Americans don't like their Republicans aligning themselves with Fidel. Fortunately for me, I never permitted any pictures of Fidel and me together, except for my own private snaps. They're safely locked in vault down in Juarez, so they'll be no problem there. In any event, Ms. Cass earned her stripes by taking care of the Tom Delay negotiations. I didn't have to do a thing, except give her the green light to bust him.)

Ms. Cass hands me a copy of the latest addition of TIME magazine. "You'll want to look at this," she says. "Oh, Lord of Tender Mercies," I reply, staring down at it. There I am. Right there. On one-half of the cover, sharing the spotlight with my blue-eyed stepbrother, who's gazing out from the satiny cover page with a transcendent earnestness that might have played well, say, two thousand years ago or so; but today, in my opinion at least, reminds me of that helter-skelter look in my buddy Charles Manson's eyes as he conspired with Charles

"Tex" Watson, et al., to commit the Tate/LaBianca murders. Not that I would ever want to make that claim in public, mind you. I must always be careful what I say. Consistently appear discreet. That's not to imply that I won't stop at anything to win the presidency. I won't. I'll even consider radically altering my behavior, if necessary. Yes, I might go so far as to do just that—all for the sake of me and mine taking up in the White House First Family Residence and feeling fine.

Yes—I really can't get over it—there I am: One-half of *TIME's People of the Year 2019*. Is this a great country or what?

I flip through the mag's pages, feverish to see more. More about me. There're any number of candid pictures in there of me looking good—as a presidential candidate must. Doing things and saying things that would have been inconceivable just a few short weeks ago. Like meeting and greeting with regular people—just plain folks—from break of day until sundown; like posing for pictures with anyone who'll sit still with me; like promising dairy farmers increases in dairy program subsidies; like every other good Republican candidate who's ever come before me. Here, to be sure, I'm not at my most original. On the other hand, I'm out there promising to give, give, give, rather than just expecting to receive, receive, receive... Which is kind of amazing to me. Something of a miracle, actually, which is why, I'm guessing, the subtitle below the *TIME's* heading reads: *"Religious Nightmare or Political Miracle?"*

More than most, I suppose, I'm both.

In any event, I do so enjoy having my mug splashed across the cover of *TIME*, even if it means sharing face time with my stepbrother, who not incidentally comes off looking better than I ever would have expected. I have to hand it to him: He ages gracefully, too.

Add to this Charles Krauthammer's op-ed this morning published in the *Washington Post*, which Ms. Cass reads, in part, out loud to me over tea, and it's been a pretty good morning so far...

"If, as I suspect, the *real* Jesus Christ has finally hightailed it back to Earth, then we, as a nation, are twice blessed: Once because humanity's savior has returned to save our collective asses from the clutches of far-flung Liberalism; twice because He's come back as the Long-Awaited Savior of the banished Neocons to rescue them from the empty quarters of the political Outback. (All my depressed pals over at the *Project for the New American Century* are twice giddy, too! 'Tis the season to be resurrected!)

"Yes, my fellow Neocons, it's about to be morning again in America, so let's all get up for sunrise services, shall we, and pray especially hard this year for our neo-born king of American Imperium to be voted into office. His 'American Empire First' message is precisely what this country requires to overcome the dog-days malaise of those lamentable Obama Days..."

You get the idea. He goes on like that for quite awhile, somewhat embarrassingly so, but not totally. Let's face it, Charles's just wild about my candidacy. And I suppose—stepping out of my uncharacteristically modest character role for a second, who can blame him? It's just so gosh darn nice to be held up as anyone's last best hope—let alone the Neocons'. Naturally, I feel for those guys, especially after George W. flushed their fortunes into the Blue Plains Wastewater Treatment Plant on the Potomac River with his nutty war in Iraq. *What was he thinking?* Yes, Charles, I'm your guy: I intend to put America back on top, make the world safe again for Neocons, like Paul Wolfowitz, Norman Podhoretz, and the rest of Charles' good buddies down at the American Enterprise Institute in Washington.

249

At 36,000 feet, I look out into the ashy blue twilight through the narrow oval window of the aircraft, more than a little satisfied. My good cup of fortunes runneth over. It's enough to get me some religion: A titan win in Iowa; the front half-cover of *TIME*, a rousing endorsement by the distinguished neo neocon columnist Charles Krauthammer, and on top of all that, today's stunning tracking poll results, which have me up 8 points, +/or-3, which puts me far ahead of my most formidable opponent—MYSELF! All in all, it's been just great. My only inkling of regret are my poignant memories of all those swaths of decimated forests, eviscerated by decades of acid rain, which we flew over on take-off and I mourn. The odd thing—very peculiar indeed—is that I don't want to take any credit for having had a hand in destroying them in the first place by promoting Midwest polluting industries... That's just not like me. But that's beginning to sound like the new me. This after being able to resist every last one of those persistent phone solicitor's pleas from college kids at the Nature Conservancy. They were more like begging me to donate big bucks to help keep the White Mountains of New Hampshire alive, actually. But now it's all over. There's no more hope. It's done with. There are only the lingering memories of those incessant calls jangling like doorbells in my ears, making me feel pretty bad—an extraordinary departure for me. Like I couldn't have sent them a lousy $20? For sure, I'm grappling with my new sense of guilt and finding it to be a real nuisance. Why can't I just let dead forests lie? Why can't I just get on with my life?

At 41,000 feet, I tune in to CNN. I've become something of a news horse, no question about it. But it's part of my job to keep up with the campaign antics of my stepbrother. I've no remorse in doing it. He's a menace to society, plain and simple. The only trouble is, society hasn't recognized it yet. But after I get through with Him you better believe it's gonna turn tail and run every time it sees Him comin' round... I'm that dangerous—and that good.

Some of us have it—others of us don't. It's the way it is.

CNN launches into its New Hampshire Primary 2020 Coverage, like only CNN can, with electric relish. Ms. Cass offers me a diet Coca-Cola on the rocks, but I won't drink that corn syrup swill anymore. I insist on Evian sparkling water instead. I know, I know, I've changed—and changed remarkably. Well, knocking back Bombay Rum hardly seems respectable any more. And it's not like I should have to point out the obvious: Snorting cocaine is *definitely* illegal! So it wouldn't do to have me busted for it. Especially in the middle of a presidential campaign. So there's that to consider, too. What spins my mind is that before embarking on this crusade I never would have dreamed that running for office would have been anywhere near as entertaining as it's turning out to be. Or self-enriching. Now I get why politicians don't particularly mind taking it on the chin. It's the same kind of rush I used to get sniffing cocaine.

His Lefty Lordship pops up on screen. There He is again. Wearing a checkered red-and-black lumberjack shirt, no less. Stonewash blue jeans snug around his trim waist. Backwoodsman cap mounted on His head. Wood axe slung over His shapely shoulder. And I thought I looked good! His eyes show the necessary fire in His belly to win 270 electoral votes. Make no mistake. He's both on message and vibe. That makes Him dangerous. I check my own eyes as reflected in the airplane window. They burn just as brightly with desire, so I'm relieved. You can't fake that. To win the presidency, you've got to be smokin', like a downed power line on a hot wet night.

All in all, we're a fairly good match: I think we can all agree on that. At least—you'll have to admit—we're not your ordinary run-of-the-mill politicians. We've got some history behind us. Some gravitas. And, I like to think, some class.

Then it all happens television fast: The dog and pony show of the presumptive nominee for the Democratic Party.

His Liberalship stumping at the Merrimack's Restaurant in Manchester, angling for the Vote of the People Award, floating between tables and topping off morning coffee, like a bus boy on the run. This is not the same Christ I used to love (and despise). He must want the presidency real bad. The Washing of the Feet was one thing—understandable even, but topping off coffee for voters just to eke out a win? Come on now! Get a little dignity why don't you? Don't embarrass me! I am, after all, your stepbrother. Maintain minimal standards of majesty, please!

Plead as I might, we all know that it's generally hopeless. Once you step into the ambitions of being a politician, dignity is about as elusive as peace in Palestine. Well, more so, actually. Not to put too fine a point on it.

Nevertheless, even wearing His Halo of Indignity, He burns like a glowworm, giving off a fresh born-again aura. Ironic, isn't it? No one else seems to detect His diminished dignity or even care, so maybe it's just me. I've come to accept the fact that I see things differently at this late hour of my life. And actually, on closer examination, He doesn't look half-bad all duded up in His waxed cotton down L.L. Bean jacket, bell-bottom blue jeans and construction boots. Still, if you ask me, His lumberjack look suits Him better, but then I always did like check patterns, though in general I prefer a more tailored appearance in my presidential candidates. Don't you? Well, whatever. You know and I know that this is all about His angling for a Man of the People image. Poor fellow. It doesn't come naturally to Him, unlike me. In any event, publicity makes the candidate, not the clothes. And my stepbrother's got more than His fair share of it. So He's quite the candidate, actually. That much I'll admit, even though it pains me so to say it.

Cut to your not-so-everyday campaign stop: Concord State Prison. Which is what you might expect considering His Lefty Lordship isn't your everyday candidate. It's a campaign stunt for attracting jailbird votes and those of the oddball miscreant constituency. Of course, any candidate willing to recruit ex-Hell's Angels for His staff won't have any compunction against going after jailbirds either. After all, a vote's a vote—con or non-con. That's the way it is.

Still, I'm shocked—shocked I tell you to find vote-getting in the jailhouse!

But the Blues Brothers they're not. That's obvious from the way His Democratship and disciples-turned-powerful-political-operatives pile into the Big House as if they owned the place and were, in fact, on a genuine "mission from God"—not some rib-tickling Universal Pictures version delivered long ago to theaters near you by Jake and Elwood Blues, a.k.a. John Belushi and Dan Aykroyd. Indubitably, these guys own the field. They're credibility incarnate. It's impressive; it really is. Like someone should consider making a movie about them. In case my campaign doesn't work out, perhaps I should even consider representing them.

Disciple Winfrey stands shoulder-to-shoulder with Jesus as they go in. (Her film crew documents her every motion for her forthcoming HBO Special: *Oprah's Angels— Building Schools in State Pens*). I'm honored, of course, to have the folks at the Business Round Table backing me, but what I wouldn't steal for just one Oprah-type endorsement. It's worth millions—at minimum. Maybe more. What galls me is that He gets His for free. Don't you think that Congress should enact federal regulations banning the Oprahs of the world from exerting undue influence on the electorate? Just look at her: She's a walking PAC money, publicity machine. (I really ought to capitalize "Her" in Oprah's case, right?) On top of that, the others on Jesus' "Who's Who List" of publicity machine disciple celebrities come in strong seconds to Her as well. So I'm here to tell you that taking the Big C head-on will be about as easy as doing a midnight waltz up the north slope of Mount Everest. That's, of course, *if* He manages to wrangle the Democratic nomination away from the Green Geezer. And I won't lay odds on Him doing that. Christ's good, but the Green Geezer's—well, he's an automotive safety legend. Besides, he's had considerable experience helping defeat Democrats in the past...

As many a Republican fondly recalls...

Inside the Big House: The Song of Jesus. "Jesus! Jesus! Jesus!" the grateful cons sing out through the narrow bars of their prison cells. The Big He and His superstar disciples make their way along the concrete catwalk, meeting and greeting as many inmates as can poke their hands through the open bars and shake His hand. He's no dummy. One by one, He solicits their votes. Like they're really going to say no to their last best hope for a quick pardon?

I find it all quite moving.

Tears of contrition spill down their cheeks like rainwater spillover from a clogged gutter. I wonder: Could I ever shed tears of remorse like that? Not likely. But then again, this is the Year of the Miraculous, so *Times* says, so anything should be possible—theoretically.

I pin my sights on Martha. She's the best. You bet your drab, tasteless life she is. She receives each and every one of Her recidivist jailbirds with sprinklings of affection. It's been too long since the Big M has had a chance to hang with genuine cons—that's obvious. The fact is, She's a revelation to them. You can see it in their reaction to her. You can see it in their misty eyes. They're overjoyed and overcome with emotion. They weep; they try to embrace Her through the openings in the prison bars; then they boo-hoo so more when that only partially works, blowing their noses in the steady stream of white crocheted handkerchiefs she hands them. Why are they so overjoyed? Well, that's pretty obvious: If Martha can thrive—yea, triumph, after doing time in the pen, why not these New Hampshire cons?

So there's that. But Martha's best is yet to come. She comes bearing gifts, as only Martha can. Approved by the warden ahead of time, She doles out basketfuls of miniature faux fir conifers, like the fairy godmother hovering above on gossamer wings. It's a sight for convict eyes. Each is sprayed with cotton candy colors. Each is festooned with miniscule glass globes that float like soap bubbles in the spaces between the branches. They radiate sheer Light, total Joy. Much like my Martha. (I find myself unable to resist falling for Her. With Her powers, She must nibble on men like me for breakfast.) And every little limb is strung with candy canes! Such immaculate taste, Martha! They're the perfect seasonal complement for every inmate's drab jail cell.

Sure, you're thinking, Martha's over the top, what with Her attention to fastidiousness; but you'd be wrong about that. In my opinion, She should be applauded. Worshipped even. How much more convict-friendly can a person get? You don't see my stepbrother parceling out itty-bitty Christmas trees to the boys in the pen, now do you? No, He's down the catwalk wrestling for His next vote. It's Martha who's perfection incarnate. Not Him. Ask any con who gets their hands on one of those trees, if you don't believe me. What faux fir conifers will mean to them is indescribable, really. All year long they'll be sharing a little Christmas cheer, adding some light and a lot more joy to their cheerless cells. That's thanks to Martha. My Martha. Martha should be the one running for president—not my stepbrother. If She decides to step in, I swear that I'll switch parties and vote for Her.

Out in the prison yard: The center of attention in an orange jumpsuit universe, my stepbrother strong-arms more cons. From Elysian Fields to the slammer in no time. Anything for a vote.

Disciple Pelosi slaps "J.C.—the Dem—for President" stickers on the back of any orange jumpsuit she can lay her hands on. Which is pretty much what you'd expect from Nancy, ever the San Francisco liberal. Disciple Schwarzenegger barks out old time gospel clichés like an Austrian old time gospel preacher in a Baptist church in the Welsh uplands.

"I am de Way, de Truth, and de Life… sayeth de Lord Jesus Christ." Orange inmates snap to attention at the rumbling of Arnold's voice. "Listen up, you lawbreakers! Vote for Christ de Democrat on primary day or it won't be likely you'll be gettin' any pardon from da Big C!"

Arnold follows on wid, "Blessed are the clean of heart, for they shall see God—not de Yard."

Now why can't my speechwriters come up wid lines like that?

Arnold wraps up, using additional strong-arm tactics. "Now, big daddies, hear me once, hear me twice, 'cause I wanna ask you a question and u better answer it right or I'm gonna have to kill ya…

"Who's ur guy in de New Hampshire primary?

Come de roar of de cons: "CHRIST, de Big House DEMOCRAT, DAT'S WHO!"

What more could a candidate want dan dat?

A HMX-1 Marine helicopter hovers above de yard before descending, and driving de cons back against de fence. Christ & Co. fondly wave goodbye, and depart de yard, lifting off like a great green bug and disappearing into de hard winter sky. De cons get down on deir

256

knees, watch dem go, and den call out to de far empyrean, "Cons for Christ! De Lord of Our Yard! Cons for Christ! De Lord of Our Yard!"

His Conship sure has sewed up deir vote, all right.

I swig more diet coke on de rocks. At 42,000 feet, it hits me like a good, strong snort of angel dust.

He'll be a worthy opponent, all right.

Meanwhile, CNN's Hallmark greeting card to Candidate Christ continues under the camouflage netting of T.V. news.

Back on view wearing His flattering red plaid woodsman outfit, complemented, of course, by a rather sharp pair of black and charcoal zip-zag silk suspenders, His Politicianship poses before the denizens of the New Hampshire primary press, tapping sap through a wooden phloem at the base of a maple tree. It's all quite festive. The soon-to-be Grade B syrup dribbles out into a bucket, missing its mark, and sideswiping the bucket before landing on His backwoodsman boot. But the odd thing is that it works for Him. It actually makes Him look more adorably human.

Encased in a white polar snowboard jacket, removable contour hood with removable fir faux trim clamped down over his head and appearing every measure the valiant image of Antarctic expeditionary leader Robert F. Scott, His Adventurist dog sleds across a snowy, New Hampshire woodland. Sort of a show-and-tell for the Virility Channel, which is filming His woodland stunt, together with CNN. All goes well until He drives His sled into an unseen snow bank. Ouch! That's gotta hurt! He casually dusts Himself off, as if tumbles and spills were part of life, rights His sled, and takes off. That's what the public likes: A candidate that shows He's no quitter.

Emulating the campaign tactics of the King of Presidential Primary Libido Himself, Gary Hart, His Demship hurtles a French Lady Hawk throwing axe at a bull's eye displayed on the side of a listing barn.

It strikes the small central circle, for sure, but crashes through the rotten German siding, splintering it beyond repair. It's a marvelous show of strength, actually. And a symbolic use of brute force never undermined a presidential candidate that I know of, of course. In fact, at least subliminally, it's an absolute necessity, a sine qua non, particularly in the case of a Demmy liberal like my lovey-dovey stepbrother. Anything to counteract His dangerous, destructive pacifist image. In presidential politics pacifism is considered unacceptable. Fortunately for me, there's no danger that I'll project that kind of persona any century soon.

The captain turns the seatbelt sign on in anticipation of landing. Ms. Cass switches off the television. I turn it right back on. I'm not about to miss the end of CNN's profile on my stepbrother. There's that special something about Him that I simply can't resist. Maybe it's His sudden stumbling charm... or His newly pickled *je ne sais pas*. Whatever it is I'm vaguely attracted to it. Like I like the fact that He doesn't Lord it over us that He is who He is. He really does believe all that gospel jive about the meek inheriting the Earth. Frankly, I'm surprised.

Now He's standing out in front of the Timberland factory on a frosty morning shaking hands, blue-collar workers' hands—not smooth, I assure you. This much I admire about Him: He's become a *real* political animal. And He's an honest-to-God people person, too. I envy that. I do. Ordinary workers positively adore Him.

Except for one, that is.

"Charlatan! There is no Christ but Jesus—the Republican!" a factory workman snaps. My first reaction is: But, of course!

CNN zooms in on my stepbrother's startled reaction.

"Is not." He snaps back.

"Is too."

"Is not."

"Is too."

"Is not."

"Is too!" I hoot at the screen.

"The *real* Jesus be praised!" Ms. Cass cheers, looking right at me.

Elated, I take another swig of diet coke on the rocks. You can't ask for more than that. CNN gave me equal airtime.

Down in a church basement attending a Rotary Club luncheon. His Civic Associationship sits at a long table beside the dais, preparing to speak and make nonpolitical, nonreligious remarks (However does He restrain Himself? I sure can't.) and then pin a medal on a young person for participating in the 17th annual Portsmouth Polar Bear Swims, which raises money for the Rotary as well as a half dozen good causes, like the YMCA, Cross Roads House, Betty's Dream (whatever that is), and Big Brothers-Big Sisters. You can't ask for much more than that. Even the food on the table in front of Him looks great: Baked chicken, green peas and mashed potatoes, of course, just like William Safire talks about in his definitive political dictionary under the tongue-in-cheek heading, Rubber-chicken Circuit. Myself, I can't get enough. I could eat it early and often. And I'll keep on eating it from now under my Inauguration Day. What's really great is that I've been able to ditch doing all my own cooking as a presidential candidate. Was I ever sick and tired about being sick and tired about firing up a can of baked beans every night. Now I just float from one happy meal to another: Lunch to dinner to breakfast and then I start it all over again. It's a wonderful system they've got devised for us contenders. Really there is such a thing as a free lunch! Regardless of whether or not I win, one thing is definite: I'll have been well fed morning to dusk.

In the Merrimack Valley High School gymnasium in Penacook, as any self-respecting politician would if he or she could, His Holy Slugger poises with the 2019 World Series winners—the Boston Red

Sox—looking as though He wouldn't mind being one of them. (It pains me to say this, but they beat out my favorites, the Texas Rangers, for the American League pennant last year. I'm still crying.) Of course, I'm utterly convinced they didn't try hard enough. To cheat, that is. You know the old adage, "If you're not cheating, you're not trying." Not that I'd have asked them to do steroids or anything too controversial—but a corked bat or a spitball here and there at a certain propitious moment wouldn't have hurt their chances any. It's the least they could have done to get to the World Series. As anyone who knows anything about baseball knows, cheating's a perfectly respectable subculture of America's favorite sport. It has a venerable and distinguished pedigree, dating back hundreds of years. Cheating's a vital part of America's national psyche and I wholeheartedly support it—off the record.

His Holy Slugger hustles out onto the playing field together with the Red Sox World Series starting pitcher. Into the center of the gym, that is. My stepbrother assumes the batter position. Then comes the pitch. A line drive under the basketball hoop, and it knocks out a light in the scoreboard lights. An inside-the-gym homer! For someone who's never demonstrated any particular facility for athleticism—to put it really rather charitably—it's a beautiful moment. Even I applaud. Go Team Jesus! That's my stepbrother.

That concludes CNN's report—thank goodness. Any more endearing publicity like that and the Old Geezer might as well dump his campaign and go back to banging the drum for auto safety. No one—not even Nader—can reasonably be expected to compete against such marvelous publicity—no one except me, of course. Naturally, I'm anticipating CNN doing a similar puff piece for me—hopefully. The American voters need to know who I really am—or who I profess to be. However, I have every confidence that the voters will eventually warm to me. After all, they twice elected George W. Bush, so it seems to me anything's possible.

My Bombardier Challenger touches down in Concord right on schedule. I'm greeted at the V.I.P. lounge by two envoys from the Gun Owners Club of New Hampshire, who also happen to be extraordinarily polite. They set exactly the right tone right off the mark. First, they present me with a Browning BAR Mark II Lightweight Stalker—a rifle that'll make short work of any size game. I'm moved by their incredibly thoughtful gift, deeply moved. I can really use this. Along with the long rifle, they pass me a brown bag of granola, raisins and nuts. Something to tide me over until lunch, they say. How thoughtful can you get? Clearly, my appetite's become something of a legend. Some have even spread rumors that my true motivation for entering the campaign was to qualify for the rubber chicken circuit because I was undernourished. I suppose that's possible, come to think of it. I've survived on not much more than canned baked beans for generations. So I really appreciate the guys at the gun club bringing me a snack.

I thank them, of course. Ms. Cass thanks them, too. She loves guns more than I do. On the way out the terminal, I throw back handfuls of granola (It's just so nice to be eating right), as Donna totes my rifle in a handsome Kifanu Dark Horse leather carrier they provided. You can't ask for better than that. Granola and guns. That's the right way in New Hampshire.

Coming into town, I'm struck by the glacier beauty of the Old Man's handiwork, the majesty of white New England snows. And to think that just a short time ago, I was bent on environmental genocide... What was it with me? Why was it I was so intent on denuding the White Mountains, I wonder? Now it seems improbable, like an unlikely dream.

Our gun club escorts offer us an aperitif, but we don't even go there. Ms. Cass's a devout Christian and I'm a reformed drunk, so it's out of the question. No discussion. What continues to strike us is that they are so darn polite. But then I recall the words of the late great science-fiction writer Robert A. Heinlein who once wrote, "an armed society is a polite society." Well, he sure got that right. I'm here to bear witness to Heinlein's Truth. Politeness is next to godliness in the live-free-or-die state of New Hampshire. Which is just great because godliness is an essential part of being a bona fide Republican.

As we pull up to the gun club in a nice, long limo, I'm stuffed, I'm armed, and I'm ready to go on the record. Running for the presidency as a Browning BAR Mark II Lightweight Stalker-totting Republican makes me more than a little proud to be an American. It is, without doubt, the greatest honor of my life.

So thank you, America. Thank you for giving me this chance.

****

And I once thought trekking across Judea on the bony back of a jackass was tough. That was nothing, I tell you, nothing, compared with doing retail politics door-to-door in New Hampshire. It's an ass's destiny, for sure, but I have no choice, if I'm to fend off a formidable challenge by the Green Geezer, who's surging in the polls just a couple of days shy of the New Hampshire primary. His energy's incredible— just incredible. And he's as rambunctious as a Billy goat climbing a rocky mountain trail, even at the age of eight-five. That's what a clear conscience gives you: Bonus decades down here, endless decades up there. It's a pretty good deal, all in all. Others would do well to remember that. Bottle it and we'd all be rich! Rich, as in blessed. Then, of course, my work down here would be done way ahead of schedule and I could go back to my favorite chair on my favorite porch overlooking the Elysian Fields, put my feet up, and chill out for as long as I like, job done.

Oh, yeah right. That'll be the day. The day humankind gets a clear conscience!

Well, we all need to have dreams and ambitions to get up in the morning—particularly me. Otherwise I might stay in bed all day looking at scrapbooks of pictures of my mom and my first disciples, Matthew, Luke, and John, and on. I'm a sucker for the Days of Thorns and Roses. Those seem like the good old days, actually.

At the Birch Knoll Motel, I pour myself a hot bath. I dump in a ton of Epsom Salts because J.Lo said it was just the thing for my aching feet. J.Lo should know: She's an exquisite dancer and knows plenty about tender feet. Oprah insisted that I pour in loads of Bath & Body Works Cherry Blossom Bubble Bath, also, which I dutifully do. You don't want to mess with Oprah. Whatever she says is the Way.

I inhale the cherry blossomy scent. Praise the Lord for Oprah. I lower myself into the tub, place a warm, damp washcloth over my face, and rejoice in the bubbles. It's the highlight of my week. Nobody does bubbles better than Bath & Body Works. Nobody. I'm here to bear witness to that. And for the record, I make no apologies for rejoicing in the warm pleasures of my newly silky flesh. Mine hasn't felt this soft and smooth since I was a wee little baby lying in a manger wrapped in swaddling clothes, as you know. And my feet finally feel warm, warm like summer on the farm.

I dry myself off using a 100% cotton white terry towel with plain cam border before slipping into a Calvin Klein terry cloth bathrobe. I love the feel of it. It's got a shawl collar that fits like me a soft velour cloak of warm body armor. The truth is it makes me feel less like the King of Israel and more like the Lord of New Hampshire, which considering where I am is probably a good thing. I blow dry my damp hair in six-inch sections, like my style guru Madonna recommended I should. If I do say so myself, it ends up making me look pretty great. As I brush it and then muss it to give it that emphatic organic look, it comes out rather luminous, like a halo in the shiny dark. Usually when I let it air dry, it gives off the hopeless appearance of being somewhat greasy, not dazzling and lustrous, like I like. Madonna gave me excellent advice, as always.

Then I spruce up my outward veneer. I plaster my face with the luxurious lava of Taylor of Old Bond Street shaving cream, which I mix up in a wooden bowl, lathering it up just right with a Vulfix badger shaving brush that Disciple Mel laid on me to keep me looking wholesome, which is nearly impossible because of who I've become, but what can I do? I'm a politician. It's intoxicating—the scent, that is. It has about it the natural fragrance of herbal aromatics. Enough to drive the ladies wild, if I was in the market. I suds up so well I could definitely pass myself off as Khris Kringle, the Santa Claus in the 1947 Christmas movie, *Miracle on 34th Street*, if I wanted to. In the event you're ever looking for the perfect holiday family flick, I recommend it, and it's rated GP.

I have a go at chopping down a forest of dark stubbles on my cheeks with a Mastro Liv's Abalone 7/8ths Takeda Damascus steel straight edge razor. Of course, the sight of my own blood makes me go faint for reasons which should be understandable, so I'm concentrating intensely on doing a excellent job—the story of my purposeful life. Perfection is the thing with me, you see... Always will be.

Shaving done, without inflicting either a gash or a slash, I stare at myself in the mirror, disbelieving... Jesus of Judea is not who I see. But social progress comes at a price, so I grant myself leeway.

I roll on my stick of Crystal Body Deodorant, which incidentally is guaranteed to contain no aluminum chlorohydrate, is hypoallergenic and non-staining, and is made of 100% natural mineral salts. Importantly, it also has no added dyes, and is completely chemical-free! Disciple Jackson passed it onto me. He says that when he's out there on the front lines giving his big speeches, it keeps him dry. You can well understand why he was such a smart selection. Jesse knows his way around.

Cleaned up and calmed down after a relentless day of retail vote-getting in too many activist's living rooms, I plop myself down in front of the motel T.V., and turn it on, just in time for the only television on earth that's fit to watch: BBC World News.

I confess: I've become something of a newshound.

You can understand: At the end of another compromising day, it's the chocolate syrup on my French Vanilla bowl of ice cream... It provides me with all the bad news that's fit to simulcast, without the added indigestion of endless commercial interruption, and allows me to sufficiently re-charge so I can tackle my briefing papers—or as Pelosi calls them, my policy lullabies—before I sleep.

Those Brits know how to put everything in perspective. Every other night, more or less, BBC does a piece on us contenders. Last night they did a mercy piece on the Green Geezer, which I'm all for. He's done good work; I just wish he'd drop out, but there's no chance of that. He doesn't understand showing mercy on his fellow Democrats. Then the night before BBC shone the glory spotlight on yours truly. (It was almost embarrassing; I hardly recognized myself. To be a politician is one thing; to see myself on screen acting like a politician is to observe a disturbing mutation.) And tonight BBC is evidently airing a profile on my stepbrother—a profile on his rising star. He'll love that because he's become a world-class publicity hound. He used to be more discreet. But these days he drinks down publicity like alcoholics gulp down Beefeater Gin. The good news is our opposition research shows that he's managed

265

to wean himself off booze entirely. Instead, he confines himself to belting back Motley's tomato juice, which is progress of a kind, too.

Now for the greatest television on Earth: The BBC World News.

"Next, a profile of Christ—the Republican—in BBC's continuing series, *Holy Rollers on the Road to the White House*. "Will religion trump politics?" asks the anchorwoman, Kathy Kay, with a British accent so refined it makes me feel born again to be wild.

Now for the flattery report:

Pirated sound bites and poached campaign tactics comprise the bulk of the fluff coverage. But I choose to emphasize the positive: At least my stepbrother's comportment constitutes constructive engagement—thanks to the magnetism of democratic politics, which can have a civilizing affect on tyrants, as I've now seen.

Apoplectic at being cut-off mid-sentence, my stepbrother bangs his shoe on the table like Nikita Khrushchev at the U.N. General Assembly in 1960. On the edge of the bed, I turn as if to General Assembly President Frederick Boland at the U.N. sixty years ago, and reply as the imperturbable British P.M. Harold Macmillan did, by saying out loud that "If Christ—the Republican—is to continue, I'd like a translation…"

"I PAID FOR THIS MICROPHONE, MISTER MODERATOR!" he interjects dramatically: First rule of thumb for all you budding debate moderators out there: Never ever try to shut down a contestant mid-sentence. In the end, it only helps gets the candidate nominated.

"Tonight Christ—the Republican—distinguished himself in a three-way debate among his last-minute challengers, who jumped into the New Hampshire primary when the Hammer hopped out: Trent Lott, the repentant racist who swears that he no longer believes America

266

would have been better off if a segregationist had captured the White House in 1946; and Jeb Bush, heir apparent to the blown-out Bush family legacy, who vows that he's going to bring back 'harsh interrogation' techniques and reopen Guantanamo as fast as possible, if nominated and elected.

"But in light of Christ's muscular display of 'strong leader' qualities tonight, he's becomes the Republican to beat. This is BBC's Denis Gross reporting from Manchester, New Hampshire, and 'Making Sense of It All—Every Once in a While...'"

Kathy Kay elicits some additional swooning on my part. But it's not my fault. It's her voice, her voice! That distinguished British accent!

"Next, a profile of Christ—the Republican—on the campaign trail. He's a long way from Bethlehem... and an even longer way from Main Street Heaven. But the good news is: He's back! And he's no shrinking violet Republican! He's hard-core right—even when his opponents paint his policies as hard-core wrong..."

"Matt Draper gives us this Campaign 2020 profile..."

"In a word, this candidate, who calls Himself Christ, is at root a Wall-Streeter. Making the obligatory rounds from Rotary Club to high school gymnasium, he preaches the Gospel of supply-side economics at the altar of economists Robert Mundell and Arthur Laffer, praising their theories of Optimizing Marginal Tax Rates for the Benefit of holiest of high rollers: Quintessential Wall-Streeters. This in spite of the devastation wrought by the last great global depression, which brought financial ruin upon every house from Bloomington to Bonn to Bangkok...

"This, of course, is in marked contrast to Christ's Democratic counterpart, who preaches the Gospel of Prosperity According to the Virtues of Keynesian Macroeconomics. Which, if you don't know, which you probably don't, espouses the doctrine of tinkering with interest rates, taxation and funding federally-mandated projects to stimulate economic growth. But if you ask me, which you didn't, Keynesian economics has more in common with Christ's own Lift Up All Sinking Boats philosophy than Laffer's supply-side macroeconomics. But maybe that's just me. Back to you, Kathy."

I've got to say, the cool thing about Kathy is that she absolutely gets it, unlike those slugs over at CNN. Oh, sure, they're great with tele-entertainment, but they rarely dare to educate. That is to say, they're not above airing embarrassing re-runs of my dogsled mishaps, day or night, whereas BBC, for which my heart is full, isn't below taking on Laffer's resurrected theories and slamming them live internationally. That's my opinion, anyway.

Still, as Matt Draper said, I'm a Keynesian myself, generally speaking, even though we all know and must admit that life is not even vaguely fair, in spite of the fact that my life's story is dedicated to that single proposition. And truth be told, it doesn't appear to be getting much fairer, even though I'm back and strutting my stuff like a Las Vegas showgirl. But just you wait, Henry Higgins, because—obviously—an aspiring presidential candidate can only do so much. As in raise important issues, participate in national political debate and promote position papers, not materially solve or resolve real life problems. That's for after January 20th. Once I get the entire federal government yapping at my heels, push back my Oval Office chair behind my freshly polished Resolute desk with a filibuster-proof Congress in my front pocket, economic valleys will be raised up high and political mountains will be laid down low. Even greedy Wall Streeters and middle-to-low-income Main Streeters will sit down like lambs and eat vegetable sandwiches together. And please believe me, when I say that Mad Dog frauds like the Bernard Madoff of the world will be rooted out in a Cox-free SEC. I do, I swear on the golden heart of the Virgin Mary—my Mom—that global equity derivatives will be banned and quants and their evil cryptic commerce math will be banished in favor of straightforward arithmetic with easily identifiable plus and minus columns. America, under a Christ Administration, will encourage money to be made the old-fashioned way: By actually producing something of tangible value. A novel notion of late, for sure, but one worthy of consideration.

I'm all shark eyes as BBC's coverage continues on a day-in-the-life of my counterfeit stepbrother's campaign, because I know and you know that opposition research has its place and is all part of my job as a presidential candidate. The fact is, if I had done a little more of that kind of thing way back when, I might have smoked out old Judas before he ever had a chance to do me in. Imagine how different everything would have been, if I'd had another two thousand years to put it all right.

So the BBC stalks him into a ladies' luncheon at the Rotary Club in Nashua—a campaign gig I've already done. They loved me there, too. Believe me, they did. Had them eating the Gospel According to Me right out of my hand. But we all know why my stepbrother's there. He'll go anywhere and everywhere to get his mitts on a free chicken salad sandwich. It's in his nature.

Trying, and by every definition succeeding, in his full-bore effort to out-Jesus me, he holds forth like the preacher he never was but conceivably still could be. "The Texas GOP platform sayeth, and so I believe, our Christian shields must and will be raised in defiance against all nonbelievers of the Christian creed, so as to preserve, protect and defend our personal freedoms and national securities. As your prospective nominee, I will raise America's shields higher still in the name of liberty and Trickle-Down Charity!" The old ladies love that security stuff. Families first, and all that. Completely understandable. They smile; they applaud. He continues. "The basis of our basic liberties

269

and the cornerstone of our Western legal tradition are the Ten Commandments," he says in an even more determined tone, jazzed up by the warm rumblings of applause. "So we, as God-fearing Republicans, should stand in opposition to any government regulation that outlaws, limits or eliminates any public exhibition of our Decalogue or any other sacred Biblical icon, for that matter. We say: Leave our Christmas crèches alone!" More happy applause, with higher voltage. "And you better believe it when I say that if you send me to the White House, I'll veto any legislation that comes across my desk challenging our right to sing Christmas carols on the White House lawn, even in summertime!

"Take that, ACLU, take that!"

Then comes his standing ovation.

Beware. The Christian Right's on its way back!

But not before he appears before the New Hampshire Sierra Club urging the reluctant audience of ecologists to drill, baby, drill for Anwar oil. Well, what'd you expect from a dyed-in-the-wool Sarah Palin Republican?

Or, before he rides a hook-and-ladder on Main Street, Claremont, looking more like a genuine war hero than the bona fide imposter he in fact is. "Blessed are American political campaigns, for they may even help lift up the genuinely depraved..."

Or, before he makes a miraculous three-pointer at the West Concord High School gymnasium in front of the New York Nick's, who've bought into his bogus campaign. I, for one, believe that shot was somehow rigged. But I'll be damned if I can prove it.

Or, before he shows up at a 4-H Club, somewhere in New Hampshire, rubbing shoulders with the Girl Scouts Troop of the Green and White Mountains and cradling a box of vanilla cookies in one hand and a box of peanut brittle in the other. He takes a bite out of one, his face brightening. What I wouldn't give for a mouth full of peanut brittle right about now.

Or, before he hangs out at the Timberland Factory gates pressing flesh with sleepy-eyed blue-collar workers, and feigning to be what he never will be, no matter how hard he tries—a Man of the People. If my stepbrother were up for a Peoples' Choice Best Actor Award, he'd surely get my vote.

By this time, I've had enough. You can't blame me. As tolerant as I normally am, sometimes my stepbrother's duplicity is utterly too much and I require fresh air, tons of fresh air, to wash away the nausea I feel...

I step out into the Birch Knoll Motel night. The great tent of fuzzy stars wheel in an arc above my head like day-glow stars plastered on a child's bedroom ceiling and shining in the warm, comforting dark. Not quite the same view one gets of the firmament-at-large in Heaven, but tonight it'll have to do, because I've got nothing else going on. I look up, back towards my real home. My body aches for my bamboo bed, my soul yearns for the beautiful view out my old bedroom window and, of course, I want nothing more than having some quality time with my Old Man. But don't get me wrong: I'm not having any second thoughts. I'm certainly not thinking about bagging this thing called presidential politics and heading home. That's for sure. Probably I should, because as much as I'm genuinely fascinated by the groovy art of politics and the 24/7 flood of media attention, it just doesn't come naturally to me to ask for people's vote. Perhaps it should, but there's no way it does. Nevertheless, I'm not going anywhere. I'm on the job. I'm in for the duration. In this last reincarnation of myself, I'm a politician—first and last.

CHAPTER EIGHT

On the fluttering wings of a shining Sikorsky S-102 helicopter, generously made available to my campaign by my dreamy friends at the BRT (all perfectly legally, I hasten to add), I shuttle in from La Guardia, heading north northeast as the crow flies to my landing pad high atop the MetLife Building, which if you ask me sticks up like a swollen thumb from the middle of Manhattan's impressively spectacular skyline. Beelzebub's name be praised—they grease my fundraising propellers by day, steering me ever onward toward the hour of inevitably: My presidential destiny.

By night, they infiltrate my opponent's campaign skies with pilotless drones, jamming their strategic radar in ways I'd like to know about, but can't for reasons of deniability. Once we touchdown, I'm scheduled to maximize my NYC publicity by clogging up rush hour traffic for a while because my ample motorcade will swoop down to Wall Street so I can get photographed ringing the Opening Bell at the New York Stock Exchange. For a Republican, it certainly never hurts to be seen in the nerve center of global capitalism, even if it has seen a few bad years lately. May the rich get richer on the backs of the poor getting poorer. That's what I always say—off the record, naturally.

Obviously, I'll be honored as well to ring the Chinese gong for global free enterprise, because for us Republicans buying into capital market schemes is an act of godliness. The real Christ might not buy that, but I certainly do, even though in all honesty I'd prefer to the whole nation to sink into grinding poverty and bankruptcy because from poverty comes chaos and that's where I truly thrive...

In my book, pandemonium is tops. But not to worry, they'll be plenty of time for all that under my watch. The thing is to get elected first. And to do that I have to be on the side of the rich and very richer and those who want to get very rich. It's a role I'm resigned to play. Compromise is easy for me. I take to it naturally, which makes me the perfect presidential candidate, don't you think?

On the other hand, while wealth is the province of the few, poverty is the playground for the many, so if you think about it, it's really far more democratic to endorse poverty for one and for all, if you stop and think about it.

Okay, so today is Super Tuesday and my campaign could use any photo-op boost it can get to put more over my fellow opponents. I am the Last Great Hope of Lockheed and Northrop. If my stepbrother gets in, they can kiss their defense contracts good-bye. And the likes of Trent Lott, Tom Delay or, God forbid, Jeb Bush, will not triumph over my stepbrother. No way. The Grand Old Party needs *me*... I am their Great White Hope. So they will not double-cross me. Besides, word has been put out: There's no such thing as a secret ballot in *this* primary. We'll be checking those ballots not once, but twice. And come my kind of Judgment Day—the Day I enter into the White House through the Northwest Gate—any Republican primary voters who voted for the other guys will be put under an IRS electron microscope. Let the Word Go Forth: Don't Fuck With Me.

Which is why, I think, this will be the day I finally put a lock on the Republican nomination, putting me a gigantic step closer to winning the most importantly powerful job under the Eyes of Heaven: The U.S. Presidency. By sweeping Super Tuesday, I'll be ready to emerge from the cold shadows of history and I won't necessarily have to resort to knocking off my incorrigible stepbrother. To knock him off his game by sinking his candidacy in the voting booth is my idea of poetry. Besides, as any who's ever tried it knows—just ask Pontius Pilate, if you don't believe me—bumping off the Son of God in public is no easy thing, especially in an era where Swiss bank accounts are open to inspection by practically anyone, and e-gold money transfers can be traced from Singapore to Timbuktu, and the NSA can listen in to determine the color of your underwear. No new subterfuge is ever safe these days, no matter how deeply it's been buried in the catacombs of American political conspiracy theories—even if squirreled away below the spot where the real name of Lee Harvey Oswald's 1963 go-between at the Russian Embassy in Mexico City to Fidel Castro lies in preserved anonymity. So for now, sticking it to His God-head is the best bet, subject to any shifts in prevailing conditions.

I multitask as we approach Gotham airspace, with one eye on my Palm Pilot emails, another on a CNN Super Tuesday special news report about how high the turnout is in the southern states and the likely affect this will have on my stepbrother's chances of mopping up today, and a third on the massive, Manhattan, concrete skyline. All presidential candidates need to know how to multitask and if you must know, I'm doing just fine with that.

A second CNN website editorial, published by those monster liberals at the *New York Times,* encourages Democratic Super Tuesday voters to turnout like locusts to a wheat field to support my stepbrother's ascending candidacy—of course. Geez, what else would you expect? It's the NYTs, dummy! After knocking down his straw man opponent in New Hampshire—a former Live Free or Die libertarian turned Democratic nominee wannabe—and snapping up 86% of the electoral vote, He must be feeling pretty smug about His chances of locking up the nomination. So gooey good for Him. He's definitely entitled. Not that He would even be on the presidential campaign trail without me. It was all my idea—after all. I jumped into the race first— not Him. He just tagged along for the ride after I did, like any good little stepbrother should.

And judging by his impressive press coverage yesterday, which he got riding down Broadway on the back of a bumpy jackass, starting at W. 110th Street and ending at Times Square, racking in hundreds of thousands of urban primary votes, campaigning has gotten to be a real Thing with Him. Which I completely understand, because it's gotten to be a pretty big Thing for me, too, especially as my prospects of cinching the Republican nomination get tantalizingly close. So I'm all for Him enjoying the high that comes with candidacy. But watch out, little stepbrother, I'm warning you: Glee cometh before the fall, that's for sure.

In any case, He's definitely on a roll today, campaigning in Bruce Springsteen territory with The Boss himself—right there in East Freehold, New Jersey, near where he went to high school and learned a thing or two about the ordinary American experience and how to make extraordinary rock music out of it. Got to hand it to The Bruce. Lucky stepbrother. Just being with The Bruce and getting to hang with his E Street Band must make Super Tuesday, well, absolutely super! I really have to wonder: Why don't I ever get campaign gigs like that? Why isn't my staff that well connected? Where's my Bruce? Oh, never mind. I'm actually quite content to ring the gong at the New York Stock Exchange. The thing to remember in politics is that you've got to play primarily to your base. In my case that means the high, holy rollers and Fortune 500 crowd—not your everyday working stiffs like the North Jersey proletariat.

My good Business Round Table buddies and I ride out a spat of mild turbulence above the slow roll of the Hudson River. It could be worse. Down below, the liquid currents are bathed in Gustav Klimt gold. Nice. I like the fit of the tan leather seats. They make me feel as though I was really, really worth something. So perhaps that's my real problem: I suffer from a sense of primal worthless.

I hold onto Donna's hand because she's lookin' pale beside me, sweaty palms and all that, suffering from a bout of motion sickness. My partners in crime—I mean campaign financing—three amigo banditos in suits from Exxon, Chevron and Amoco—are strapped in across from me, looking like teenagers taking part in a circus thrill ride. They don't look so good, either. It's pretty bumpy up here. I try to reassure them with a manufactured smile. Let's hope it works. I don't want them spilling their breakfast in such a beautiful machine. My smile is pure pre-Commander-in-Chief stuff. One of those We Can Make It moments, designed for the Team. They're gonna make it, of course, 'cause they're with me. And demonstrations of confidence are absolutely everything in presidential politics—in addition to how to survive while flying through morning turbulence. In this case, I get my confidence from Donna. She made me down a tumbler full of Dramamine first thing, and I feel fine. No tummy distress whatsoever. She's like my den mother to me.

Outside, through the oval copter window, I glimpse a rusty tapestry of Jersey smog blanketing the Manhattan skyline—a foul far denser than that which stained the sunset clouds above Manhattan on 9/11. But it won't get me blue. I'm feeling optimistic. Invisible crowns of headless skyscrapers poke up into it and get lost, like the ends of pitchforks probing deep into layers of hay, like images out of Bram Stoker's *Dracula*. Once upon a time ago, just my kind of look; but no more. These days I'm more into that glory gold Gustav Klimt look. My mind's attracted to the brighter lights. It's not so outlandish really. Change can be good—even for me.

The copter starts to shake. Violently. And just when I'm starting to feel so good!

It's emergency time, like it or not, 'cause the crew slammed into a lost flock of Canadian geese. The poor dears! Our copter's going down. But have no fear: I am He, the Pilot-in-Chief. I eject my erstwhile

276

pilot from his seat and take control, handling the cyclic and throttle like toys, and straightaway, like a magician pulling white doves out of a black hat, I restore all power and lift to the Sikorsky S-102, before bringing it and us in for a soft landing atop the MetLife building. I wasn't about to let us go down, not even into a river that looked like Gustav Klimt gold.

And it gets better. I scramble out of the Sikorsky S-102 and am treated by the press as something of a lightning hero, which is a whole new profile I'm not opposed to getting used to. They embrace me as I embrace them. They caught every second of my death-defying theatrics and broadcasted it to millions. You can bet my press cycle will dwarf my stepbrother's little mule train ride down Broadway.

Rest assured, my 1034 convention delegates near.

Stuff hot Chili peppers Trent Lott; suck horseradish Tom DeLay. I was born a campaigner, a Republican hero. My only question is: Why didn't get with it much sooner? I could have run against Thomas Jefferson in the 1800 election and run every four years ever since! Campaigning is more than mere amusement—it's my version of daytime in Heaven.

Under Secret Service protection galore because I'm now such a hot political item, I enter into the MetLife building as a Lord of Manhattan. "Let's go light up the New York Stock Exchange!" I say, 'cause I'm feeling nothing if not good.

We appropriate the elevator, and take her down. I glory in the feeling.

52nd, 48th, 27th, 21st, 19th, 13th, 11th, 7th, 3rd, 2nd, 1st... Down to the basement of my soul I go, or so it sort of feels. On the other hand, I'm about to climb up into the attic of capitalism—which overlooks the trading floor of the NYSE, so this is bound to be a day of contrasts, for sure. My mind's in conflict, but new things are definitely happening, alarming things perhaps, and to be expected given my singular history;

277

but let's concede that my own personal evolution is akin to the advance of social revolution, so I don't much mind. I certainly won't lose much sleep over it. Not tonight anyway. It's no secret that I've always managed to survive quite well, thank you, by not allowing modern times to get too many steps ahead of me.

We egress by way of 5th Avenue, where my magical motorcade awaits.

"Hit the smog," I order from the back right seat. We fire down 5th Avenue like a slingshot paperclip released. We ride high to where I'll soon take on the holy mantel of the High Priest of Capitalism, the Last Great Hope of my Far Right Base.

Donna gets an emergency call on her I-Phone. Hmmmm, Inside Information. Osama's grandson has planted a bomb on my stepbrother's Jet Blue campaign plane—the one with "Christ—the Democrat" splashed across the nose, like graffiti. I feel compelled to warn Him, really I do; but on the other hand, isn't it the Secret Service's job to know such things in advance? But let's be perfectly frank: I may be on the eternal road to a higher state of evolution, but I'm not there quite yet. I'll have to be patient, content with baby steps for now. And if the worst should happen and my stepbrother and His gang go down— boom, boom—well, then—that's all part of the rough and tumble of American political life, now isn't it? Happily, I'll enjoy deniability. My fingerprints will be nowhere on a spectacular event worthy of the late great Lee Harvey Oswald—the immortal man who helped make assassination conspiracy theories a full-time cottage industry.

****

Clearly, I should have accepted Jet Blue's kind offer to upgrade my air ticket from coach to first-class. Not since I was holed up in my

Garden Tomb have my legs felt so cramped. Additional elbowroom as well as another eighteen inches of legroom is always tempting—I mean really tempting—but of course I was born to travel second class, so that's that. Traveling second-class by whatever form of transportation— airline, bus, tramp steamer or jackass is a birth thing with me. I don't do first-class. Not that that means I've got an inferiority complex or anything like that. It just means always having to say No to free upgrades and ride out the associated aches and pains uncomplaining. As a professional stoic, long learned in the ways of forbearance, I can take it.

Nevertheless, Seat 38B is nothing to write home to the Old Man about. For sure. They put me down next to a former shock jock from Milwaukee turned Michelin tire salesman after he got fired for a second time from radio station WFAN for making disparaging remarks about Eskimos or something. His name is Imus.

Now I remember who he is: The I-Man. Who let him on?

Cowboy hat drawn down low over the hood of his bushy eyebrows, he confesses that he bribed a harried mom, baby in arm, with a couple of first-class seats, just so he could sit next to me in second-class. (Everyone confesses to me. They can't help themselves, no matter how hard they try.) Now he wants to interview me because he needs a big break—something bad. With an exclusive, says he, he can get himself a new drive time radio show. Well, maybe.

From which to pounce on defenseless minorities? I ask.

Oh no. In order to promote racial diversity, ethnic reconciliation and general global harmony, he answers.

Hmmmm, should I really believe this guy?

Absolutely, he replies. No more sticking it to the Inuit Eskimos and humiliating them on air, he swears. No more racial slurs against nappy haired hoes on the Rutgers University women's basketball teams—ever.

Not the same Don Imus I remember at all, the one I used to listen to on XM Satellite Radio up there in the rafters of Heaven. Once upon a time, he may have gone mic-to-mic with Barbara Walters and the likes of Jerry Lee Lewis in his show-no-mercy High Lord of Shock Jock Radio Hosts Days, but those days are toast. For sure. There's no radio station in all of the Americas that will hire his ass—forgive my expression—a twice-fired geriatric radioman who beats up on defenseless Eskimos for the ratings. Among other minorities, I might add. There are limits, you know, even on America's airwaves.

But this I know: Imus has it in his head that I'm his redeemer. I'd recognize that dewy-eyed expression anywhere, because I've seen it everywhere. Of course I'm his Redeemer! Who else would be? I'm everybody's Redeemer, whether they know it or not. Which puts me in a class all by myself—I suppose—even if it still happens to be in second-class.

Anyway, second-class is a wonderful, happening place—the jewel in humanity's thorny crown.

Still, who I am to dash his hopes? Especially as he seems so really very earnest about his desire to give up bashing minorities and get on with the task of lifting them up instead—my line of work. So why not? If Disciple Jackson could forgive him for his on air "nappy-headed hoes" remark that got him fired from CBS Radio in the first place, why not me? I mean, I may be a Jew, but I'm not black—although there are those who claim otherwise. The truth is I'm more like rainbow inside. Just like Jesse and that old coalition of his, come to think of it. And if you really must know Rainbow Sherbet is my favorite.

Before I agree to do anything, Imus goes off on another tangent. The proselytizing health nut tangent. He tells me in excruciating detail

280

about the current state of his Stage 2 prostate cancer, insisting that it's way under control—in complete remission even, praise the Lord! In particular he sings the praises of Dr. Aaron E. Katz, Emeritus Chairman of Columbia University Medical Center's Urology Department, whom he credits, together with his wife, with plying him full of every kind of herbal supplement imaginable— ginger root, milk thistle, bitter orange, damiana, dong quai herb, ginkgo biloba, black cohosh, and green tea, to name the tip of the tip of the iceberg of supplements. He credits them with keeping him alive long enough and with sufficient mental clarity to allow him the opportunity to attack Eskimos and a host of other marginalized peoples.

Then, in a good faith effort to give me a helpful piece of advice, Imus informs me that, by the way, Dr. Katz isn't exactly cheap. He also recommends that quick as I can I schedule my own appointment with the good Dr. Katz to get my PSA levels checked. Any man over fifty, he exhorts, should get their levels checked annually. Considering I'm, well, well, well over fifty—I agree to do so at first opportunity. You never can be too careful, especially in light of my onerous responsibilities.

And about those inflated health care costs, Dr. Katz, supplements and all, I hereby promise that a Christ Administration will set out to fix them. Swear it to God. They've been far too high for far too long. Affordable health care is up there on my list of Things to Change during my first 100 days—congressional horse-trading permitting. Even though I consider myself something of a miracle worker, I'm no political marvel—not yet. Frankly, I'd be stunned and amazed to do even half as well as Obama did in his first 100 days. What president wouldn't? Obama set the new legislative standard. He's the LBJ of the 21st century.

Our captain—Captain Charles Jaworski—sounds very nice over the PA system as he welcomes us all aboard. "Flight attendants cross-check," he says in a commanding and confident way. The flight attendants go about their flight attendant duties as Imus and I buckle up before we push back from the boarding gate. Then, like a bird of magnificent proportions, pre-historic and jet-age simultaneously, JetBlue Flight 1549 rolls on toward Runway 1 Left/19 Right, which looks nice and clear to me. Imus lowers the brim of his cowboy hat, assuming the beyond cool position in his too small seat, but complain he doesn't dare, and flips on his nifty little digital recorder and puts it in my face. It looks like a miniature Sony to me, but what do I know about such things. Then he asks with an attitude that strikes as familiar, "Is now a good time, you left-wing charlatan?"

Well, I suppose it is. It's good to know that Imus is positioning himself for a comeback. So yes, I consent to the interview because as always I forgive him for his bigotries. It's in my job description. But the truth is, I need all the attention I can get. I'm the one running for president. So there we are: two old-timers looking to make our comebacks together. If you stop long enough to think about it, life, more or less, is really one long effort at making continuous comebacks. At least that's the way Imus and I see it.

Interview over after going on record stating that I will indeed open up the White House Gates again to the people, just like in Andrew Jackson used to do, and welcome in everyone—Republican and Democrat alike—and hold forth on Sundays on the West Lawn granting interviews with individuals who request a word with me. Even nappy headed hoes? "Just kiddin'," he answers his own question. That Imus. Once he gets his crocodile jaws into a piece of controversial meat, he's loath to let go.

At 32,000 feet, I look over at him and see tears running down the side of his codger cheeks. He's a pool of tearful emotion. Imus? Yes, Imus. It's been a long time. But now he knows, knows for sure: He's almost back. Officially. And for good this time. He's got an exclusive interview—with one of the most famous men on Earth—Christ, the Democrat. Not even CBS can refuse him now: Imus in the Morning returns. I'm happy for him. Besides, he doesn't seem like such a snappish crocodile after all. More like a backwater kind who's gone into Louisiana bayou retirement.

Even the King of Shock deserves a crack at redemption, I always say.

I look down at my wristwatch. Twenty-six minutes before we're scheduled to land at Logan Airport. Sparrow has me scheduled tighter than dill pickles in a jar. But it's not as if my well-intentioned, but hopelessly outmatched, opponent has a grasshopper's chance in the grass of ever hopping over my convention delegate lead. All I really need is the beautiful number 2,117 and it's all mine. They're all mine. Which is going to happen today. Not that I would have any objection to sharing them, with my own margin of victory, of course. In a democracy, one can only share just so many votes with one's opponent before one shares oneself out of a job.

I light up the boxy video screen on the back of the headrest of the all-too-small chair in front and tune in CNN. My earphones fit just right. CNN is showing a protest forming outside Logan airport. The protestors are there for me. They don't appear to be supporting my pro-abortion, pro-birth control position, not that I'm much in love with it either; but you've got to dance with them that brung you, right?

First rule of politics.

"Suppose Mother Mary Had Used Birth Control? Where Would YOU Be?" Good question. "Life Begins at Conception, Not at Resurrection!" Clever, quite clever. You get the drift.

Still, the bottom line is mine. I'm the candidate and I have to win and in order to win I have to bring my base with me. So there. So life's not perfect. Especially political life. I'm doing the best I can.

I flip the channel to MSNBC. They're doing a refreshing segment on the tweedy guys from Harvard's Hasty Pudding Club preparing to present me with the 2020 Hasty Pudding Award tonight. It's really quite endearing. And politically, it's a good bit. I certainly don't want people thinking that I take myself too seriously. What candidate for president does? It's all about maintaining perfect equilibrium. Like Philippe Petit walking the wire in the clouds between the phantom towers of the World Trade Center before they went down. Let's hope I'm half as good as wonder boy Philippe. That kid knew how to do a high-wire act. We have much to learn from him.

I jump over to WETA-Cable. Oh for it's none-commercial days, but a station's got to do what a station's got to do, especially these days. There I am, lined up with the whole Boston Red Sox team. I'm even wearing their uniform. They endorse me; I endorse them. Even though their last year's record was lower than low. A below .500 low. But it's explainable considering that their best two starting pitchers were on the disabled list, and their star shortstop as well as their top RBI hitter were suspended for suspected steroids, there wasn't a whole lot of hope for getting into the 2019 pennant race. Still, the Red Sox is my team. I love 'em to death, as Imus would say.

I can't top that, so I study my speech to pass the rest of the time before landing.

Eyes brush over my 3 x 5 note cards, written out in longhand for me by my beloved Disciple Pelosi. In this important speech she focusing in on my support for the agenda of the Massachusetts Fisheries Association in Boston, and I'll be talking about why a Christ presidency will support sustainable sea scallop farming off Cape Cod. Give the voters what they want. Besides, I've always been a big fan of giving as many fishes to the people as possible, as everyone knows who knows anything about me.

I'm all set. Next.

Sparrow has me onto the Tar Heel state to give a speech at the North Carolina Furniture Makers Association after I do the Fisheries Association. A candidate's day is never done, especially on Super Tuesday. Then onto Macon, Georgia to affirm my support for the peanut farmer subsidy—a must do stop if I want the Georgian peanut farmer vote today, which I dearly do. The truth is I like Planters Peanuts very much so I'd like them to stay in business and the peanut subsidy is the way to make that happen. After Georgia, I'll wing my way back up to the Buckeye State to give my standard semi-protectionist stump speech to the rubber factory workers in Dayton, who are barely hanging onto their re-treads. You can bet it'll sound both anti-NAFTA and free trade simultaneously. Like I said, it's all about balance. Keeping the right balance. Some might call that speaking out of both sides of your mouth, which as I understand it from the big boys in politics, is the best of all possible worlds, when you stop and think about it.

Then finally, it's onto the Golden State of California where I'm slated to attend a Gays for Christ rally at Union Square in Disciple Pelosi's Bastion of Liberalism—San Francisco. There I'll be handing out free condoms to aid in our campaign to stamp out AIDS because—and let's be perfectly frank about this—abstinence never has and never will be the thing.

After that, thank God! Sparrow and Dago have arranged a little down time for us all on the rooftop of the Sir Francis Drake Hotel, high atop the hills of San Francisco, overlooking the bay. We'll be slugging down Martinelli's sparkling cider, nibbling on organic California produce and tons of fresh Central Valley fruit. Yanni has volunteered to entertain while we watch the returns. For tonight, at least, I get to say adios to Motel 8. It promises to be a night of high expectations. I really can't wait.

I wonder how my stepbrother's doing?

I go back to watching MSNBC.

Good timing; they're doing a bit on his campaign. Imus snores beside me. I like his attitude. In real life, my stepbrother would be a real snore, if he weren't so damn dangerous.

There he is—banging on the big gong at the New York Stock Exchange, fanning the flames of industrial capitalism, when he could be out inventing more inclusive forms of global socialism. His most trusted disciples from the Business Round Table hang around him like vultures wearing heavy winter overcoats—political sycophants all. Naturally, they all want to get in on the ground floor of his administration and who can blame them? They don't know who they're dealing with. They have no clue. Still, for all his past faults, for all his notorious crimes, it's nice to see him doing something constructive for a chance—even if it is in the name of cutthroat capitalism. I really have to say that he's come a long, long way since that fateful morning when he bombed the hell out of Mel's in his F-16.

I nod off to sleep, for who knows how long, only to be awoken by a stewardess who orders me to buckle up for landing. Imus snores on, chin resting on the wall of his chest, buried under a cowboy hat. Determined, she leans over me to shake his shoulder. "That includes you, Mr. Imus-in-the-Morning." Startled, he cries out from the recesses of a disturbed dream, "I didn't say nothin' mean, I swear it!"

"I know you didn't—it's just time to buckle up."

He does and we watch a Maytag repair man commercial on CNN as our plane prepares for its descent into Logan.

As far as commercials go, this is a good one.

A uniformed Maytag repairman, a repair sign hanging above him, slightly askew, sits in his plain, bare office, waiting for the phone on his desk to ring. The clock on the wall ticks loudly, conspicuously. And there are no calls. Seasons come and go out the window. No calls. The repairman ages before our eyes. Still no calls. Finally, the phone does ring. Now a very old man, he slowly reaches for it, sunshine in his eyes. "Maytag Repair," he answers "May I help you, please?..."

Silence.

"What's that you say? Oh, I see…wrong number. Yes, good-bye, but thank you for calling."

He hangs up, the bright hope in his eyes gone.

We see him next sitting in a Maytag Repair Shop in Heaven, waiting by the phone, bright white clouds bubbling up around him. The repair sign falls off the hook. An announcer chimes in: "Maytag: The washing machines that need of no repairs—ever."

That's a good bit that. Imus chuckles, too. Agitated, a stewardess rushes past us, half walking, half running, moving toward the back of the plane, like a paperclip shot from a slingshot. "Sir, you must sit down NOW!"

Imus turns to me, as only Imus would, and says, "You know, I never met a stewardess who wasn't as hard-hitting as a New York Yankee's baseball bat."

Thank goodness for that; we could use some of that because standing in the middle of the aisle blocking the doors to the lavatories is a middle-age, overweight, and very sweaty jihadist with burning brown eyes, who is, if nothing else, intent on making his own comeback today, the Shiite way.

Yes, ladies and gentlemen of the press, we have an official terrorist onboard Flight1549, who looks the part. He's dolled up in traditional Arab dress—a white linen dishdash, cotton turban hat, and

287

contemporary belt made of C-4 plastic explosives. I prefer the rhinestone belt look myself, but who am I to get into the whole fashion statement question. It doesn't go with my job description.

Perspiring like a fat man in a sauna, he holds high the detonator cord, which is attached to a series of blasting caps impregnating each of the C-4 blocks wrapped around his mid-section. By my calculations, I figure the blast rate at about 24,000 feet per second. Not a good number for any of us.

"GOD IS GREAT!" he shouts, which I kind of wish he hadn't because I'm more of a fan of quiet discourse, not bombastic proclamations, myself. Bellicosity leaves me high and dry as well as flat. Besides, I never have and likely never will appreciate anyone for any reason using the Old Man's name for acts of violence. You can't blame me. It's a maintain-the-family-dignity-and-honor type of thing. It's practically genetic.

It's also a phrase that's become a terrific cliché. Couldn't he have thought of something a tad more original? Of course, God is Great! What else would He be? Minor?

Without so much as asking for any further input from our side, he denotes himself, blowing out the tail of the plane—Rows 40 through 45, including the aft kitchen. There goes Jet Blue's annual safety record.

We go down, with some woman somewhere near the middle section of the plane screaming, "Do something, Christ! Do something!"

Easy for her to say.

"I guess it's time to pony up," Imus cracks, "and prove you're no charlatan."

Well, I guess so.

Oxygen masks drop down, the usual thing when an aircraft is unnaturally losing altitude. There is the sound of howling wind.

"Do something, Christ! Do something!"

I definitely get the message. There's my cue. If I don't get off the dime, and soon, my Imus will be able to tell me that he told me so. Plus my presidential ambitions will end without even giving a concession speech. And of course, worse of everything, my unhappy stepbrother will waltz down Pennsylvania Avenue in the Inaugural Parade, happier than a victorious mugwump.

I can't have that.

I unbuckle my seat belt, trashing FAA in-flight rules, and confront the incline, a pitch of at least 70°. I'm assuming that I have a few minutes to think of something, anything to save us. I mutter to myself, unnerved by my sudden predicament, "Lord save me from all modern-day Osama bin Ladens... They really know how to take the fun out of flying."

From the front of the plane, I hear Disciple Schwarzenegger holler at me in his Americanized Austrian accent: "DO ONE OF DEM MIRACLES OF URS NOW OR ELSE I'LL HAVE TA KILL YA!!!"

He doesn't mean it; poor guy, he's just hysterical. Obviously, this is no action movie. It's life on the real side; and we're headed for a jet fuel cremation, not a majestic pinpoint landing. Not exactly what I had in mind for Super Tuesday. Not what I'd call a win.

I stretch out my arms, like the wings of a great and powerful eagle flying over rocky canyons. I raise my head up, as if it was the nose of the plane, and magically, the nose lifts, yes, stabilizes, rights itself—a bloody miracle.

Pretty soon we do a nice, steady flyby of the John Hancock building; I bank, my outstretched arms, and take us in for a three-point landing at Logan, smooth as morning sunshine pouring over shining glass.

Let's just say it's Miracle Tuesday.

Even Imus's impressed. After we come to a stop, he publicly acknowledges that I'm no charlatan—never was. He does a complete mea culpa, apologizing profusely to me and everyone else he can find on the plane for saying what he earlier said and then to show he really means it, he invites me to be on his show when it gets up and going. He's thinking about calling it, Imus Past Midnight.

"What you'd think?" he asks.

"I like it," I tell him, though if he gets a show it's likely to be a lot past midnight and many hours before dawn, but that's Imus' problem. In any event, take my word for it, the King of Shock Jocks is about to make another comeback—at whatever hour of the day or night his new show may be.

CHAPTER NINE

Seven-time World Wrestling Federation Champion, sixth Triple Crown Champion winner, five-time Tag Team Champion, four-time Undisputed World Wrestling Entertainment No. 1, first third generation wrestling superstar, two-time World Championship Wrestling Honcho, and one-time victor of the Royal Rumble, former Calgary Canadian Football League Stampeder, and member-in-good-standing of the Nation of Domination, Dwayne Rocky Malvia Johnson, a.k.a. The Rock, lays a black patch on the floor of the Republican National Convention Hall floor of the Comcast Wachovia Center in Philadelphia in his G-6155 Interceptor "Spy Hunter" roadster, getting the 2020 Republican National Convention off to a rip-roaring start under the cover of macho-macho. Thank you very much, fellows. You set exactly the right tone.

Car and driver careen toward the curved lip of the gigantic stage, doing 0-to-60 in something under three and a half seconds, which in my book makes him the most reckless figure in political convention history—other than George W. Bush, of course. Even today, W's mere presence on a Republican junkie's political junket is considered injudicious and fundamentally ill-advised by ranking party members. Poor George, these days he usually shows up, more or less inebriated, at Capitol Hill party fundraisers in his new capacity as prime cash bar bartender, having never really gotten over his drinking days at Yale and, of course, his, shall we say, little presidential indiscretion of failing to ferret out biological weapons in Iraq, prior to or even after his spectacularly rash invasion.

Rock's racy vehicle—primed for manslaughter—suddenly veers, targeting, it appears, a heavily populated section of my pledged delegates, rows 1-9 to be exact. This can't be good news 'cause I need all the pledged delegates I can get. And by the way—just so you know—getting votes is harder than it looks.

In seconds, they'll be convention toast. And there's nothing—absolutely nothing—I can do about it from this safe distance. The more I become a true political operator, the less of a miracle worker—even a satanic one—I am. Who would have thought I would have sold out my darker principles this early in the evolution of my career? But the allure of power—presidential or otherwise—does that to even the best of us. Okay, said another way—even the worst of us.

The Rock lurches forward in his terminator automobile. I sit and watch, fundamentally powerless to do anything to stop him. This comes as something of a shock. Specifically speaking, I don't do powerless. Donna and I hold our collective breaths. In the back of my mobile presidential suite limousine we breathlessly watch the roaring Rock, while gliding down hot Philadelphia streets, in the cool of our limousine,

291

headed toward convention hall, for what can only be the scene of my well-deserved political coronation—I hope. And of course, expect.

One thing's for sure: After regal treatment like this, I have no intention of hunkering back down in Juarez, win or lose the nomination, though of course the latter outcome is most highly improbable: I am, after all, WHO I AM.

Which is very understandable, if you think about it. No one gives up luxuries willingly—just like no one voluntarily chucks power. In my case, I've definitely grown accustomed to the sweet trappings of my new fate. So I consider them mine. A thousand times mine. Yeah, baby.

Just when it looks like the morgue for my pledged delegates, rows 1-9, The Rock stomps on the Interceptor's shooting brakes again and again, like he's trying to kill a dozen fleeing cockroaches on the kitchen floor late at night causing his Michelins to burst into balls of fire. Comes squealing and screeching, like the ratchet of too many gibbons placed in a cage. God-awful noise, that is. Tire smoke entombs the perimeter of the stage.

Then comes the quiet.

I grip Donna's hand, expecting the worst because it's in my nature. As the smoke lifts, the Rock's Interceptor appears, front end jutting out over the edge of the stage, still smoldering, like burning tires smoking at a downtown city dump.

I hear myself thinking: Thanks for not taking out my pledged delegates, Rock. I really could kiss that gorgeous hunk of a man. Think of all the last-minute delegate vote getting he just saved me from. That last crack's totally off the record, of course. The last thing a Republican candidate for president can afford is to sound too enamored of gays.

The Rock bounds out of the Interceptor. Step aside Sean Connery, Roger Moore, Timothy Dalton, and Daniel Craig: The Rock has come. A cool jade necklace swings like a pendulum from the thick post of his lumberjack neck, dangles down the North Face of his Mt. McKinley chest; red tank top accents his more than a little intimidating biceps; stonewashed denim blue jeans grip his tree trunk thighs like wet leather. The Rock being, well, The Rock, is poised for action.

He steps into the legendary roll of The Rock, giving the spellbound convention delegates what they ask for. Yes, he struts his stuff, according them—what else? The People's Eyebrow. It's to die for.

Pivoting in the direction of the full hall, he cocks his head, stage left, fires his magnificently muscular arms down and out, like a pair of projectiles. Then, in one very menacing fashion—displayed in close-up on the Sony—he lifts one eyebrow while simultaneously lowering the other. Wow! However does he do that? Good grief, I'm even terrified by the effect that gets, which is really, really saying something.

How can one not fall in love with this man? Talk about the perfect choice to open my—I mean—the Republican convention. We Republicans, we glory in unvarnished demonstrations of intimidation!

No lies be told, my Rock's the one who should, in fact, be running for Commander-in-Chief of the United States—not me or my wimpy little stepbrother. A big win for him and the Republicans could hold onto the White House and a majority in Congress for at least two terms—God willing, more. A Rock Administration would make George W.'s look like crumbling sandstone. It would be hard. Very hard, besting America's enemies in smack down after smack down. I watch him move, turning his People's Eyebrow to the other side of the hall. Enchantment, sheer enchantment. I swoon, at least as much as Donna Cass. He really is majesty in motion. To be sure, I plan to put That Look in my own presidential playbook.

The hall rocks—for The Rock. The Rock of rocks. My NRA's contingent goes, well, literally ballistic, firing off a hundred rounds or so from their AK-47s, Uzis, and 9mm Glocks they brought along for such an occasion. Those NRAers know how to have a good time. Guns and ammo. That's all they need. And The Rock. They adore The Rock. We all adore The Rock. He's our guy. And no one will ever take him from us—they'll have to pry him from our cold, dead hands first.

If he does decide to run for the White House—after I leave office, of course—he'll have my endorsement. No doubt about it.

Standing as erect as Queen Elizabeth crossing to her throne, The Rock proceeds to the Grand Podium. The hall is his. The whole right to bear arms Republican Party is his. We're all his! Thanks in no small part to his rugged charm, good looks, and the fact that he spared my pledged delegates from considerable harm.

Flying on an invisible starship toward popularity beyond bounds, he stands at the center of the Republican universe. By the power invested in me by my candidacy, I officially dub him—as Donna's my witness—Disciple Rock. He's drafted—whether he wants it or not.

Take that, Disciple Schwarzenegger. I've got my very own non-girlie man disciple now. God bless the child that's got his own.

Donna leans in to say what we've both been thinking: "If The Rock endorses you, you've locked the nomination."

I smile. Something I'm getting better and better at these days. Gone is that old gnarly frown of mine. My own mother wouldn't recognize me now.

Disciple Rock bathes in a deluge of affectionate applause handed him by the not-so-silent majority of convention delegates who admire his showman flair. If George W., Dick Cheney, Paul Wolfowitz, or Donald Rumsfeld has possessed even a smidgeon of it, they would have served my causes so much better in the days of the Iraq war and White House Rose Garden.

Rock pumps his meaty fist. Theme music from *Rocky*, the classic comeback movie, adds kerosene to the emotional fire of the hyped

294

assembly. Donna and I stomp our feet in sync with the delegate's monosyllabic chant: "Rock, Rock, Rock!" We're having a good old time! This must be a lot what fun looks like.

Anticipating The Rock's SmackDown against my welterweight opponents, Tom DeLay, Trent Lott, et al., I hope, I pray that their unequivocal demise will be swift and merciful and my triumph unassailable because, believe me, a brokered convention is about the last thing the party elite will tolerate. A split in allegiance is unacceptable. So it all comes down to one man—well, more than a man, really—The Rock. He can make it happen. He can make me president.

He only needs to deliver a backbreaking knee drop to Tom, a spine splitting scoop slam to Trent, and it's done. I'm in. So with his voice full with dreamy thunder, his corporal profile sheer grandeur, and towering over everyone and everything, something like the Rock of Gibraltar over the Mediterranean, he opens the convention deliberations, "Rock of Ages, Rock of Madison Square Garden, Rock of the Republicans, I promise you this: Come November, those clueless Democrats will wish they'd never climbed onto their mules, 'cause there's one truth and one truth only, ladies and gentlemen of the Grand Old Party: The true Son of God IS A REPUBLICAN!!! And the Lord Almighty never met a liberal He ever liked!"

The delegates' roar sounds like unfurling forest fire as The Rock rocks on.

"THEN LET'S NOT BE COY! LET'S NOT BE SHY! COME ON, LET'S BE OUTRIGHT RASH! EVEN BRASH! WE'RE THE PARTY OF THE WAR IN IRAQ AND THE GREAT RECESSION OF 2009, ARE WE NOT? WE'RE DISTINGUISHED MEMBERS OF THE WAY-RIGHT-WING, HOLIER-THAN-EVERYONE-ELSE, SCISSOR-KICKIN', KNEE-DROPPIN', SCOOP-SLAMMIN'

REPUBLICAN PARTY, SO WE'RE ENTITLED TO OUR PRIVILEGES AND ENTITLEMENTS, ARE WE NOT?

"ALLELUIA, ROCK!" hails a party member deep inside the hall.

"SINCE FAMILY VALUES ARE OUR LIFE—WELL, PRETTY MUCH, EXCEPT, THAT IS, IN THE CASE OF EX-GOVERNOR MARK STANFORD OF GEORGIA AND HIS ARGENTINIAN GIRLFRIEND... AND THEN OF COURSE THERE WAS ALSO THAT FORMER SENATOR ENSIGN FROM NEVADA AND HIS ERSTWHILE CAMPAIGN TREASURER LOVER... BUT THOSE DALLIANCES ARE NOTHING IF NOT HISTORY, SO WE REPUBLICANS HEREBY TONIGHT REAFFIRM OUR TRADITIONS OF FAMILY VALUES AND WHO BETTER TO REPRESENT THOSE TRADITIONS THAN..."

"Say it, Rock, say it!"

"I'M NOT ONLY GONNA SAY IT, BUT I'M GONNA PRAY IT! I THEREFORE HAVE THE SACRED HONOR OF SUBMITTING FOR YOUR CONSIDERATION A NOMINEE ABOVE ALL OTHERS, EXCEPT FOR MAYBE GOD HIMSELF! HE'S MORE THAN A LITTLE RIGHTEOUS AND PRETTY MUCH PERFECT, IF YOU ASK ME. HE ADORES CAPITAL INVESTMENT AND IS IN TIGHT WITH THE GOOD FOLKS AT THE BANK OF AMERICA AND MERRILL LYNCH—WHICH MAKES HIM ONE OF US!

"ON TOP OF THAT HE'S THE MOST PROMISING REPUBLICAN CANDIDATE FOR THE PRESIDENCY SINCE RONALD REAGAN BECAUSE BEHIND THAT PIOUS RHETORIC IN SUPPORT OF COMMERCIAL LENDING, GLOBAL HIGH-YIELD DEBT, AND GLOBAL EQUITY HE'S

ONE CHIN-LOCKIN', CLOTHES-LININ', MÙLE-KICKIN' S.O.B.!!!

"HE'S THE CHOSEN ONE TO RETAKE THE WHITE HOUSE FOR US IN 2020! HE'S THE ONE WITH THE MAJESTY AND POWER TO MAKE OUR PARTY RIGHTEOUS IN THE EYES OF THE PUBLIC AGAIN!

"Pray it, Rock, pray it!"

"SO TO ALL YOU UNPLEDGED DELEGATES OUT THERE, I'LL PRAY IT IF YOU SAY IT: GO FOR THE HEAVYWEIGHT, THE WORLD CHAMPION OF CANDIDATES! SMACKDOWN THOSE PARTY WELTERWEIGHTS! PLEDGE YOUR SUPPORT FOR THE TRUE SON OF GOD—JESUS CHRIST ON THE RIGHT!"

Oh, Rock. You're one beautiful guy. I owe you, big time—at least the ambassadorship to the Court of St. James.

Convention delegates give up a cheer, which comes across louder than an oncoming column of Bradley tanks: "SON OF GOD ON THE RIGHT!"

But The Rock can't quite hear. Cupping his ear, he strains to hear. "SAY WHAT?"

"SON OF GOD ON THE RIGHT!" they call out.

"AND WHY IS THAT?"

"CAUSE HE'S ONE CHIN-LOCKIN', CLOTHES-LININ', MULE-KICKIN' S.O.B.!!!"

Round of live ammo follow, bursting from every corner of the hall. CNN's cameras latch onto seas of bobbing, weaving hand-held signs, courtesy of the party faithful. They read: "ONE NATION, ONE SET OF VALUES!"; "MY G.O.P.; MY RELIGION!"; "JESUS ON

297

THE RIGHT IS MORE THAN A LITTLE JUST ALRIGHT WITH ME!"

The Rock looks down and smiles. It's a family thing for him. He loves his G.O.P. And the NRAers obviously haven't had this much fun since they were last on the firing range. As for me, I'm rather touched by their outpouring of affection and support. Rather moved in fact. How could I not be? I haven't had this much love lobbed at me since my mother held me in her arms the day I was born.

Then something irregular happens. For one brief moment, I feel, well, guilty. Guilty for having deceived so many wonderful people—my supporters—especially, come to think of it, The Rock. One thing I tell you true: I'm in BIG trouble if he ever finds out who I really am. If he does, I'll be on the run for the rest of his natural days, because they'll be no place safe on earth for me. He'll hunt me down so he can give me a SmackDown.

"They love you, Jesus, they really do," Donna says, quietly, touched and more than a little awed by the people's outpouring of affection.

"But they don't know the real you, do they?" she turns to me and says with eyes both penetrating and searching.

I'm petrified. Does she suspect that I'm really the charlatan of Christianity? If so, how does she know? How did she find out?

I tremble inside, which is not like me. Not at all.

"Rock's got it wrong," she continues, shaking her head. "You're no chin-lockin', clothes-linin', mule-kickin' S.O.B. If you ask me, you're a sweet little Lamb of God."

My fears are relieved. My taut face gives way to an aw-shucks expression. I can't believe my luck. I thought she'd figured it out somehow—knew that I'm Beelzebub. But she's still ignorant. It just goes to show that despite all my campaigning to date, I'm still qualified

298

to deceive. In fact, the campaigning may have made me better at it. I still believe I'm able to deceive the best of them—except for my stepbrother, of course. I've never been able to get anything over on Him, except of course I was more than a little instrumental in securing his death on the cross by colluding with my pal, Pontius Pilate.

The waves of applause carry on. And on. I could really get used to this kind of thing. In fact, I wish I'd known that adoration was so gratifying long before now. I might have gotten into politics much sooner. Politics, it turns out, is far preferable to snorting coke and downing Bombay Gin—by a wide margin. It makes my skin tingle.

We cruise past crimes scenes on Philly streets. Donna shakes her head sympathetically. "It's no way to live."

"That's no way to die," I'm thinking.

"When you're president," Donna says, "You'll pave the streets with gold."

"Maybe I will," I answer, kind of meaning it.

Like I said. I almost don't recognize myself.

Back on the boob tube, The Rock rocks the hall. "VOTE FOR MY GUY, UNCOMMITTED DELEGATES, AND IT'S SMACKDOWN TIME AGAIN IN AMERICA!!!"

Then The Rock lowers his voice, getting all very sincere, "One thing's for sure, my fellow Republicans, we rise and fall together, because we're first and last members of God's Team. To paraphrase the immortal words of the late, great Bud Grant, a successful team requires three things: Patient wives, loyal dogs, and great quarterbacks—and not necessarily in that order."

9mm Glock gunfire fractures the silence of the attentive hall.

"Our divine mentor, Jerry Falwell, pastor of the Southern Baptist Convention, founder of the Moral Majority, and political inspiration for our party's pro-family, pro-life, pro-defense, pro-Israel

Convention Ten Commandments, inspires us still. Even in Death shall He Live! And you can still be damn certain that he still blames 9/11 on gays, pagans, feminists and abortionists! He oughta have known. He had an Inside track with You-Know-Who!"

A barrage of AK-47s second, third and fourth that observation.

"We of course are the party of moral values—family values. Very family values. They're our guiding principles, shared by one and all, except of course by those occasional rogue party members that got through pre-screening. I am referring, of course, to our fallen friends, Sanford and Ensign, again. And Gingrich, too! But not to worry. They don't represent the majority—the Moral Majority of us—who populate a moral universe and choose to live by family values, following them religiously, as Easter follows Palm Sunday.

"Still, I must admit, in the name of full disclosure, that 8 of the Top 10 porn-consuming states just so happen to be Red States, which doesn't look good, ladies and gentlemen of the Republican Party. So, please, to all you porno, adult entertainment site roamers out there, GIVE 'EM UP! Family value hypocrisy's political suicide, don't you know? ESPECIALLY FOR REPUBLICANS!"

One or two Uzis ignite, raking the overhead ceiling with live fire. But the rest of the NRAers and the convention hall is silent, evidently none too eager to give up their adult site wanderings. Not just yet anyway... But I must admit, it took real guts for The Rock to say what he just said. Which is why The Rock is in my opinion, well, the party Rock of Gibraltar, and why I insisted that he have the first speaking spot.

Then from high atop his perch at Mt. Sinai podium, he delivers the party's Ten General Election Campaign Commandments, which always makes for good television, and the major networks cover it each convention cycle.

The Rock puffs out his chest, taking on the airs of Charlton Heston doing a decent imitation of Moses as Charlton Heston in Cecil B. DeMille's classic *Ten Commandments*. I saw that one back in 1956 when it first premiered and I'm still here to say that Heston as Moses really was believable. But Ramses as Yul Byrnner was, at the time, more to my liking. These days I'm more inclined to favor Moses' profile. Go figure.

"To win in November, we must be focused and to be focused we must sacrifice. Sacrifice for the sake of the Moral Whole," says The Rock. "Therefore as loyal members of the Republican Party Thou Shalt Obey our General Election Campaign Commandments! I Hand Them Down to You, Numbers 1-10!

"1. Thou shalt give up watching all afternoon college football games and playing golf until...

"AFTER the November elections!" the delegates respond in amplified unison.

"2. Thou shalt refrain from watching *24*, *Will & Gracie* reruns, and the Pat Robertson channel until..."

"AFTER the November elections!"

"3. Thou shalt suspend all target practice at your local firing range until..."

"AFTER the November elections!"

"4. Thou shalt forgo your annual pilgrimages to the Ronald Reagan Library in Simi Valley, California until..."

"AFTER the November elections!"

"5. Thou shalt not detour to hunt quail, deer, or squirrel—or shoot tin cans or watermelons in your backyards until..."

"AFTER the November elections!"

"6. Thou shalt not spend time shopping at Neiman Marcus, Brooks Brothers or Saks Fifth Avenue until..."

"AFTER the November elections!"

"7. Thou shalt refrain from joining any vigilante armed patrols along the Mexican border until…"

"AFTER the November elections!"

"8. Thou shalt not picket or blockade any abortion clinics until…"

"AFTER the November elections!"

"9. Thou shalt not bash the *New York Times* or all those liberals in Hollywood until…"

"AFTER the November elections!"

"10. And above all else, thou shalt not apologize yet another time for the foreign and domestic debacles of the George W. Bush Administration until…"

"AFTER the November elections!"

The Rock's our party's Moses, all right. I should reconsider his appointment to the Court of St. James and put him in my Cabinet. Otherwise, I risk squandering his prodigious talent. Donna concurs. We'll submit his name as Secretary of Energy for Senate confirmation. He's got just the requisite quota of voltage for that.

Here's another campaign pledge: A Beelzebub administration will bring on only the incomparable! Starting with The Rock!

You have my word on that.

Then comes a river of ads from our corporate sponsors, whose logos line the walls of my convention hall, including promos by the good folks at MeTube®, Hybrid Motors®, AT&IPHONE®, Standard Solar®, and Micromind® computers. They are then augmented by a diet of sixty-second visual bursts from the makers of Maalox, Tums, and Pepto-Bismol, who are not incidentally any of our convention sponsors, though they certainly should be because after getting a good look at our real sponsors, people of political good will—like me—get indigestion from the pervasive influence of corporate America on our national politics. I really care about these things, I really do. I know I've changed my tune, and I know that it's more than a little hypocritical coming from the mouth of a candidate whose primary backers are the guys and gals at the Business Round Table, but, hey, what the heck did you expect from me? I'm a politician, first and last, so hypocrisy comes naturally. In fact, I wear it as a badge of honor. Any reasonably decent politician does. You *have* to be hypocritical to be in this business. None of us was made of fairy dust, so it goes with the territory and is a matter of practicality. Democracy isn't free, you know. It costs big bucks to win at the polls— to get real political legitimacy. Convention hall space doesn't grow rent free on trees, either. Nor does airtime. It's expensive to broadcast on public airwaves. So somebody's got to dish out Benjamins. It's a necessary evil, we all know, and I disapprove of it on ethical grounds, of course, but I'm not above being practical in the name of promoting democratic institutions, especially when it also serves my purposes of getting elected to the White House. Now that's not so unreasonable, is it?

Now comes The Newt. From the Sierras to the Appalachians, there's no other Republican like The Newt, legend incomparable. For those of you too young to remember, please recall three little words: Contract with America. That's The Newt in a nutshell, the mind behind the contract, which led to the Republican takeover of the House of Representatives by Republicans in 1994. Beyond that, he's got a good argument for everything, and isn't such a bad Catholic, either.

And happily, like the rest of most of us, he too qualifies as a world-class hypocrite. Why you ask? Because he roundly criticized President Bill Clinton over his relationship with Monica Lewinsky when he himself was having, shall we say, extra-circular activities with his very own mistress. But The Newt being a hypocrite is no big thing and okay by me. He fits right in line with the other party faithful—I mean—unfaithful.

He stands at the convention hall podium with a Great Wall of Words projected like the immortal words of Abraham Lincoln chiseled on the walls of his magnificent marble memorial, preparing himself to do what Newt does better than anything one else: Make Contracts! His white, frosty hair glows celestial, like an abundance of haloes (more and more I find myself wishin' I'd some of those of my own), fashioned by a down pouring of stage light that radiate his bush with a fine wash of colorless rainbows. Newt makes quite a stir by doing very little. Mega-master of magnetism that he is, he exudes, positively and magnificently, charm like others ooze the promise of larcenous behavior.

Newt gets right to the big strokes, as is his custom and practice. With the flourish of playwright applying signature to the first page of his newly completed manuscript, Newt signs. Oh, does he ever. With the assistance of overhead projection technology, which I'll never understand, his signature glows under the projected words that capture the attention of the entire hall. These words, invented by and copy-written in the name of Newt, are just what you'd expect from Newt, given his strategic pedigree. They read: CONTRACT WITH CHRIST.

I turn up the sound. This could be good. "Last night I had a dream," he begins. "It was the most partisan dream I ever had. And in this dream certain voices made clear to me that the Republican Party was on the verge of winning a super majority again and putting our kind of person in the White House—not for one election cycle, not for two, but for the next THOUSAND YEARS... Yes, my fellow, Republicans, I said ONE THOUSAND YEARS!"

That last line goes over rather well. Everyone sings, "Alleluia!"

"And the reason is," he says pointing to the Great Wall of Words floating up behind him like billboards in Times Square in the night, "our CONTRACT WITH CHRIST!"

Lots more "alleluias" now.

"Therefore, I beseech you, my fellow Republicans, consider the terms and condition of the contract, as noted above. I offer them for your review."

The lighted contract scrolls upward behind the haloed Newt. It reads:

REPUBLICAN CONTRACT WITH CHRIST

As members of the Republican Party and as citizens seeking to elect our political persuasion to the House of Representatives, US Senate, and as president of the United States, we propose not just to change America's policies, but even more important, to restore the domination of our political brand and reestablish the bonds of trust between God and the Republican Party as well as the good people of America.

That is why, in this era of liberal dogma and understandably strident bipartisanship, we offer instead a line-item agenda for spiritual renewal and Republican Party political redemption, a written, binding commitment with no fine print, but also its fair share of loopholes.

This year's election offers the chance, after not nearly enough decades of one-party Republican control, to bring to the House and the Senate a new super majority that will transform the Congress into what it should have been all along: A House of God. That historic change would be the end of secular government that is too big, too intrusive, and too afraid to wear its faith on its sleeve. It can be the beginning of a Congress that respects God's values and incorporates a small number of them

305

whenever we can into the Constitution and of course, into the lives of American families, in a manner only a little bit intrusive.

Like Lincoln, our nation's first Republican president, we intend to act "with firmness in the right, as God gives us to see the right." Which means that of course we are right. Right on all levels and on all legislation passed by our Congress. To restore accountability in Congress by blaming only the Democrats for those rare failures that may in fact occur from time to time. (Let's face it, not even Republicans are perfect!) To end its cycle of scandal and disgrace, even though Sanford's and Ensign's (let's leave my name out of this, shall we? Remember, I converted to Roman Catholicism) mishaps are still turning in our minds. To make us all proud again of the way free and religious people govern themselves and abide by the Scripture—whenever possible.

On the first day of the 116th Congress, the new Republican majority in both Houses of Congress, with a presumed President Christ on the Right in the White House, will immediately pass the following major reforms, aimed at restoring God's and America's faith in the Republican Party, which first and last is the party of God and pretty darn righteous values—good for all.

Newt is good... really good. I'm going to have to think seriously about nominating him for my VP.

FIRST, require all laws of conduct that appear in the Bible to apply equally to Congress;

SECOND, select a prestigious, independent accounting firm to conduct an extensive audit of each and every member of Congress Ten Commandment violations, and to form a Special Committee on Violations of the Christian Code, and any abuse, fraud and waste created by the governmental practice of secularism;

THIRD, cut the number of non-religious House and Senate committees by one-half and increase the staff members for religious oversight committees by 100%;

FOURTH, increase the terms of all faith committee chairs from limited to limitless;

FIFTH, allow the casting of proxy votes in spiritual committees by any certifiable celestial voice or words of God reasonably construed to be genuine as believed to be heard by any devout member of such committee, so long as they are members of the new majority;

SIXTH, require committee meetings to be only held on Sundays and be open to both God and the public and the Pope;

SEVENTH, require a one-third minority vote to pass a tax decrease;

EIGHTH, assure a scrupulous accounting of our Federal Budget by implementing zero base-line budgeting, which we can ignore whenever we want to!

Thereafter, within the first 100 days of the 116th Congress, we shall bring to the Floor of Congress the following bills,"each to be given full and open debate, each to be given a clear and fair vote and each to be immediately available this day for public inspection and scrutiny," unless we decide otherwise, which we probably will.

1. THE MAKING RELIGION-IN-POLITICS MANDATORY ACT: Bill Text online at http://www.congress.gov

2. THE TAKING RELIGION TO THE STREETS ACT: Bill Text online at http://www.congress.gov

3. THE ECCLESIAL COMMUNITY INDOCTRINATION ACT: Bill Text online at http://www.congress.gov

4. THE FAMILY CHURCH ENFORCEMENT ACT: Bill Text online at http://www.congress.gov

5. THE AMERICAN CREED IMPOSITION ACT: Bill Text online at http://www.congress.gov

6. THE NATIONAL SECURITY WORSHIP RESTORATION ACT: Bill Text online at http://www.congress.gov

7. THE FAIRNESS IN FAITH FOR SENIOR CITIZENS ACT: Bill Text online at http://www.congress.gov

8. THE JOB CREATION AND WAGE ENHANCEMENT BELIEF ACT: Bill Text online at http://www.congress.gov

*9. THE COMMON SENSE DENOMINATION LEGAL REFORM
ACT: Bill Text online at http://www.congress.gov*
*10. THE FAITH-BASED CITIZENS' LEGISLATURE ACT: Bill Text
online at http://www.congress.gov*

*Further, we will instruct the House and Senate Budget Committees to report to the
floors and we will work to enact additional religion-in-politics mandates that may
occur to us between now and then, as well as budget cuts that we intend to make in
other legislation that does not enjoy a religious component, in order to ensure that the
secular Federal budget deficit is eliminated so that, if necessary, there will be ample
room for the enactment of all of these bills enumerated above, even if they require
additional funding through hog wild but well worth it deficit spending.*

*Respecting the judgment of our fellow citizens and patrons of the Church as we seek
their mandate, prayers and votes for religious domination in American politics, we
hereby pledge our names to this Contract with Christ.*

That Newt. He's a political genius—something of a religious titanic force, too. He's actually inspiring, once you stop long enough to listen to him. I take his points. Completely. Imagine my surprise: Tolerance is beginning to be an In-thing with me. I used to be so darn good at illiberality. Now I'm become a tad more reasonable.

Newt basks in the wake of his own breathtaking brilliance. Let's face it, he's just so gosh darn intelligent that it makes the rest of us... Well, I won't go there. But frankly speaking, he should be put in charge of just about everybody and everything—and then some. Newt turns his gorgeous mind on the sea of reverent delegates, shining his brainpower out across the open sea of night like the welcome light of a lighthouse.

"You've read the Contract With Christ, now I ask you, my fellow Republicans, to step right up and sign it! For the good of

Christianity! And the country! Above all, the God-fearing Republican Party! It's our means to ending our banishment from mainstream American politics, our ticket to restoring our monopoly on political as well as religious power, our foot in the door to a cozy spot in Heaven, once we pass onto that Great Party in the Sky!"

No shortage of "alleluias" in the hall for that line.

"Sign it, my fellow Republicans, and we will once again control America—if not a bunch of other countries besides—from now 'til Thy Kingdom Come! His Will Will be Done, if my new soubriquet ain't Pope Newt!! You have the word of a converted Roman Catholic on that!"

All I can say is that the delegates really go for that.

"Pope Newt! Pope Newt!" they start to chant.

Better that than, "President Newt! President Newt!" If they did that, I'd be more than a little concerned. We politicians don't like competition. Not at all.

As the chanting calms, the many splendors of The Newt continue. "Yes, my fellow Republicans," he continues, "sign it, and together we will take back the House, the Senate, and above all, the White House from those dim liberals who don't even know the difference between Baptists and Roman Catholics!

"As a Republican, I'm here to proclaim that the difference between the two is that Baptists don't believe in baptizing babies and Roman Catholics do!"

That last line gets a nice round of applause, as it should. Newt's just been awesome since his conversion. He's a natural born Roman Catholic. Politically, it was also a very canny move—a major leap forward in his political rehabilitation, which more than makes up for his romantic dalliance in the eyes of the party faithful. In fact, it accounts for him being anointed to High Priest of the Party by silent acclamation.

The truth is, we Republicans need our leaders to wear the white surplice of faith. And Newt's—well, he looks particularly good in a white surplice. He's the perfect choice for leading us down the convention hall aisle bearing the holy cross of Jesus.

Newt—I mean, what's not to love?

"Now rise, my fellow Republicans, and place your right hand over your heart and repeat after me..."

They do as they are told, falling in line like soldiers—onward Christian soldiers.

"I promise"

"I promise"

"to support all of the terms and conditions of the 'Contract with Christ'"

"to support all of the terms and conditions of the 'Contract with Christ'"

"which we believe will resurrect the Republican Party"

"which we believe will resurrect the Republican Party"

"from exile"

"from exile"

"and restore it to its former glory"

"and restore it to its former glory"

"so that it will once again dominate American politics."

"so that it will once again dominate American politics."

"This time, forever and ever."

"This time, forever and ever."

"Amen."

"Amen."

"So help me, Newt."

"So help me, Newt."

What's not perfect about the Contract? It's legally binding AND religiously-politically correct. Genius is too narrow a word for Newt! He's more like a Nuevo god, one floating above our dear, deserving party, watching over us by day and night.

God bless The Newt. May he one day sit at the Left hand of God.

Donna turns to me as we float forward, hermetically sealed, in the back of our pre-presidential limousine down dark Philadelphia streets, and says, "Now comes the moment we've been waiting for: The rolling roll call."

"Jesus be praised!" I answer ironically.

She clutches my dry hand, which actually makes me feel kind of guilty—which for me is saying something. She's such an ardent supporter, and I'm outright deceiving her, as well as half of America, claiming to be, well, Christ incarnate. On the flip side, I do feel, with each passing day, more and more like a authentic republican, which is, well, astonishing, considering my first love is dictatorship.

Sipping Babot, watching my Manifest Presidency unfold before me like the plot of a Dickens' novel, I prepare myself for the joyful inevitable: My coronation.

Newt introduces the rolling roll call vote. "We Republicans believe in the democratic process almost as much as we believe in religion in democracy. That's a fact. An historical fact because we are the party of the True Believers. So we don't select our presidential nominee by doing three rounds of rock, paper, scissors. Nor do we make pre-selections, regardless of my own personal preferences—which I assume have been duly noted and made public in the interest of full disclosure.

311

"Yes, we Republicans do what democrats do the world over: We vote. We vote because we believe, as Churchill believed, that democracy is the worst form of government on earth, except for all the rest!"

The NRAers send up a concurring volley of fresh gunfire. It makes Newt smile.

"So, my fellow Republicans, I give you grassroots democracy at its finest; I give you the Republican Rolling Roll Call!!!"

An overly keen delegate from the Great State of Missouri embraces the mike, grips it for her solo. Dressed in a festive convention hat, circled in floppy American flags, her party-sanctioned T-shirt, red and white lettering only, reads, Red States have the Ear of God.

"On behalf of the great state of Missouri," she begins with all deliberate pride, "where the Pony Express once rode both east and west and where Jessie James came to ride and die—I have the high honor of casting our 31 delegate votes for the next Republican president of the United States, JESUS—'We Always Knew You Were One of Us'— CHRIST ON THE RIGHT!!!"

Cut away to the blinking scoreboard projected next to CNN anchorman's head. The omnipotent number 1,191 shines, like wine in a chalice. It is the Holy Grail of Requisite Republican delegates to cinch the nomination, the number needed to get me within picnicking distance of the White House.

I'll admit it that I commit the sin of digit worship. Let's face it— in the nomination business numerals are everything.

Just when I was feeling optimistic, the majority of delegates from the Not-So-Great State of Florida cast their votes for Jeb Bush. That hurts my feelings. It really does.

Mississippi betrays me next, casting their delegates for Trent Lott, a doddering ex-segregationist. Off the record. No wonder they're this country's poorest state. They don't have the cunning of a first-year choirboy.

Probably they're still annoyed with me for leaking that false press story about Trent running a Confederate flag up the Capitol flagpole last February in honor of Abe Lincoln's birthday. Well, it certainly *could* have been Trent if, for instance, it hadn't been my dirty tricks department. But I'm over my Tricky Dick days, my Gestapo loving insanity. I'm focusing on the merits of my candidacy—and winning the old-fashioned way—by majority vote, which is refreshing. Eventually, we all want something positive. For me, it's politics.

The good folks from the Great State of Texas go for me, followed by my backers in Indiana, Nevada, North Carolina, South Carolina, Arkansas, New Mexico, Idaho, Louisiana and Tennessee. I pile up delegates like points on an electronic pinball machine as we drive along Susquehanna Avenue toward the convention center. From time to time I take my eye off my winnings and look out at the city going by. It's the strangest thing. I used to get a kick out of watching slums go by. Now I ask myself: Why should anyone have to live like this? Low-life bars flow by, their neon lights pushing back the nervous night: Velvet Lair, Lounge Lizard, and Eden's Nest. What a mess. Those folks should be drinking mineral water instead of Gilbey's gin.

Of course, six months ago I would have gone in and joined them. That's how weird my lot has gotten. Something very sinister is going on here. I promise myself that when I get elected, I'll launch a Beelzebub Plan to rescue the Philly slums. I'll propose and Congress will impose more rehab centers, additional block grants, greater enterprise zone, and an abundance of charter schools and hell, why not throw in more than a few extra public swimming pools to beat the heat in summertime? It's hot out there. Kids growing up require recreation—

313

something I never had. But I'll be there to give it to them. Why not? I'll be a river to youth.

Donna taps me on the shoulder by the intoxication caused by my sense of good will. Nervously, she points to the television screen. "Look," she softly says. "Trouble."

I don't doubt it. There on the screen, instead of the sights and sounds of my mounting delegate count, there are scenes of left-wing anarchists on the make. It's obvious by just the way they bandannas they have wrapped about their faces, showing only their anarchist eyes. I recognize those eyes. Eyes no longer mine.

They're staging a sit-in at the Comcast Center, barring anyone from entering my convention! These are the kind of activists that detect right-wing conspiracies in every news item not printed on the front pages of the *New York Times*. They're the kind to be feared and are probably the sons and daughters of those gasmask-wearing protestors in Seattle who did the World Bank protests in 2000. At the time, I actually thought they pulled the demo off really rather well. But that was when I was into all sorts of riot and mayhem and was a devoted fan of tragedy. (*Macbeth* was my favorite Shakespeare play, for instance. Now it's *All Well that End's Well*, for reasons obvious.)

But believe me, I've come a distance in my short time. I'm a true reformer now—the difference between Mikhail Gorbachev and Vladimir Putin, which demonstrates momentous, forward progress toward the strange case of my political enlightenment.

Thousands rampage down cordoned-off streets, overflowing police barricades like Pompeii lava flowing down narrow Roman streets. CNN covers it all—all except my Rolling Roll Call! Just my luck! Protestors chant at the silent building, as if it had ears. "SQUASH ALL REPUBLICANS!!!" I don't like that. Whatever did I do to deserve

314

disrespectful treatment like this? I mean really. I haven't done a truly evil thing in at least six months!

Frankly, I'm getting, well, kind of worried. What if the police don't—won't—take action to squash the mob? What if I'm blocked from getting into the convention hall altogether? What happens if I can't lay claim to my fantastic delegates? What if I'm forced to miss out on the moment I've been slaving for—my grand-eloquent acceptance speech? I mean, I can't let Pat Buchanan's beautiful prose go to waste. That would be totally unacceptable! And anti-democratic, too! Who do these protestors think they are? The Philly police need to knock heads. Being a democratic doesn't always mean having to say yes to freedom of expression. There're important limits, you know. For instance, one can't lawfully scream "Fire!" in a crowded movie theater. There is such a thing as drawing a bright red line between right and wrong, especially if you're a democrat of the Republican persuasion. Besides, I've learned that a little law and order now and again is not such a bad deal. It can be good for everyone. These are the things I know. Spiro Agnew had it just about right, campaigning as he did on issues of law and order. If I have anything to say about it, I'd like to weigh in on his political rehabilitation. But don't expect me or anyone else to attempt to resuscitate George W.'s calamitous legacy. Anyway, they wouldn't stand a chance. Not now, not ever. He blew his shot at a decent place in history the day he took on Iraq—and lost. Pyrrhic victories don't count in this business. Not one little bit.

I oughta know: To date my entire lifetime has been one big Pyrrhic nothing! An ocean of false triumphs! But I've been blessed. Look where I've ended up—in politics. Trying to make the big score, and doing my damndest—excuse my Aramaic—to get myself into the only history book that counts—the Good Book of Positive

315

Accomplishment. At this stage of my life, I'll do most anything to obliterate my dysfunctional record.

Hooded like a hangman standing atop the gallows, wearing a pair of Halloween pumpkin knife-slit eyes, disguising her feverish eyes which tower above a hastily torn air hole half a thumb down from the minor bulge of her pancake nose, an Anti-This-That-And-Everything-But-Principally-Me anarchist jumps up and down like a showboating monkey on a rock on top of a Crown Victoria police car abandoned earlier opposite the convention center. The roof buckles; the agitators cheer; she reigns triumphant. Thousands, perhaps tens of thousands of demonstrators bask in the high tide of undiluted pandemonium, come here to picket, unthinkably, me! For crying out loud, don't they know that I've changed? Can't they see through the old me clear through to the new one? The tender me, the loveable me?

I tell you truly: Anarchy doesn't look quite so inviting when you're facing the sharp end of it.

Sister anarchist slips her hand into her Marine jean camouflage pocket, and withdraws a can of spray paint like a Philadelphia derringer. Aiming, then firing, at the shattered proof windshield, she sprays her not very nice—not nice at all—sentiment in full view of a watching nation: "*SQUASH* ALL REPUBLICANS!"

It's not called the Loony Left for nothing. Wherever did she learn her protest graces? Let alone her pitiable syntax.

Then a funny thing happens to me, utterly unforeseen. From beyond the ancient withered forests of my confused intelligence, on the far side of the barrier rifts of my unhappy subconscious, on the other edge of the contaminated black backwaters of my moldy brain, and from the bottom half of the cesspool of my poor old sinkhole soul, I hear words never before thought, let alone spoken. They trigger sparks of electricity that jolt me like first-class offensive shock jock ethnic humor during the height of drive time. "Come, let us reason together."

I thought I was capable of everything, just not ushering up words like that.

Then when I though once was enough, it rides up again, comes again.

"Come, let us reason together."

Clearly, the positive influences of national politics have finally gone too far. If there were somewhere I could go to protest I'd go. I'd go to remonstrate against the undue taming of, well, yours truly. But it's too late to picket, to lodge any objections, to file a complaint. I've crossed over. I'm already in the shady land of NO EXIT. That's because, for better or for worse, I HAVE BECOME ONE OF THEM: A relatively decent person.

Politician though I am.

Forgive me, Father. I had no idea I was in anyway capable of doing such an uncharacteristically brave thing.

"TABLE REPUBLICANISM!!!" she bellows, her voice muffled by the voice hole, and sounding more like a moose horn than a bugle, as she leads her wild horses toward the edge of a rocky cliff. Doesn't she know that we're all little d democrats here? That we must act like little d democrats even when we don't agree with the views of opposition candidates?

Donna turns to me, alarmed. "This is going toward the wrong end of a one-way street."

"Not to worry," I interject, worried not in the least. It's show time, the opportunity to practice what I come lately to preach.

As we get within blocks of the Comcast Wachovia Center, they, the Attila-the-Convention, go on the offensive—everything offensive to

317

democratic values, that is. They hurtle thousands of recycled Evian and Smart Water plastic bottles at the ten-deep barricade of Philly's finest, who are all uniformed in blue, and armed with billy cubs and dark sunglasses. The shades alone give them complete authority over the looming anarchists. However, they remain unmoved. The bulwark of justice, yea civilization itself, stands firm.

I worry about the impeding bloodshed because Philly cops don't take any crap. But I also look at it this way: Law and order is key to my claiming my delegates, so all's fair in love and democracy. Come to think of it, all's fair in redemption, if the last six months means anything at all.

We turn a corner, adjacent to the Adam's Mark Hotel. I signal my driver to stop. It's high time I become, at least in part, the Christ I claim to be.

"Are you nuts?" Donna asks, petrified that I'm about to get myself strung up on a recycled cross on the old streets of Philly.

"You can bet not," I answer, with a wink. "In fact, I've never been of sounder mind."

As tear gas goes off and bedlam breeds chaos squared, I, Beelzebub, masquerading as the Son of God, Christ, step out into the evening riot, just happy to have finally arrived at the venue for my true transformation, and awash in the all but certain knowledge that the First Amendment is alive and well and thriving in my heart of hearts.

I wade out into the moss pit of activists, not wasting a single revolutionary second. This is where my heritage comes in handy. I fear nothing and no one. I am the epitome of calm, cool, and collected. I could easily do a deodorant commercial. It's seconds before the dame in the hood with Halloween pumpkin slits for eyes recognizes me for who I am from her perch on top of the dented police car. What took her so long? I'm trailed by Secret Service, who don't think much of my frontal approach. Not at all. My code name is Live Wire.

318

"IT'S CHRIST THE REPUBLICAN!" she hollers, her voice crashing like thunder over the fervid mob.

"SQUASH HIM!"

That's my cue, if there ever was one, my cue to write my first chapter in the Good Book of Positive Accomplishment. I'm just itching for it.

I turn back toward Ms. Anarchist, lift my arms, like any competent Christ would do, and wade toward her, before joining her on the rooftop of the squad car. It's not such an unpleasant thing to look into those beautiful Halloween eyes—even if they're anarchist eyes. She looks into mine. Perhaps she recognizes retired anarchist eyes when she sees them. We silently look upon each other as satellite cameras zoom in. Suddenly, we've gone live and national. The first words that come to me are—yes, that's right, what else could they be? "Come, let us reason together."

That stuns everyone, momentarily quelling the crowds, allowing me the perfect calm to dramatically interject, "Bipartisanship is not yet dead."

"A miracle," the hooded anarchist speaks softly through her air hole.

"Got that right," I answer. "Who'd have ever believed it?"

"Only Obama."

"In his first term."

On the marquee that circles breaking news in luminous letters around the outer skin of the Adam's Mark Hotel appear the words I've inadvertently radicalized myself to read: "CHRIST ON THE RIGHT GETS 661 DELEGATES. SON OF GOD WINS REPUBLICAN NOMINATION."

That feels mighty good. This time next year I may no longer need an invitation to watch the fireworks on the 4th from the Truman

Balcony. That view, like everything else 1600 Pennsylvania Avenue, could well be mine. Glory be. The prospect of winning may be enough to endear me to religion.

I know—that would be the ultimate miracle. But hey, it could happen. This is America, you know.

****

Minutes before the King of Kings—now the Candidate of Candidates—which just so happens to be me—is scheduled to deliver his Democratic Convention acceptance speech before the exultant eye of Internet television—my most important speech since the Sermon on the Mount and then some—I pace backstage, like a San Quentin inmate facing execution. I'm caged at the Comcast Wachovia Center auditorium in downtown L.A., where the blue tiger swallowtail Dems have come to coronate their guy for the presidency. It's not that I'm very nervous or anything; it's just that I'm finally recognizing the fact of all facts: I've arrived at the Point of No Return. Meaning that I'm wholly cognizant of the fact that once I give my speech, once I accept the Democratic nomination before hundreds of millions of people, once I commit to being the hands-on leader of my party—and not the Holy Roman Church—I can't go back to those golden but thankless days when I was Christ and nothing but The Christ. Yes, once I give my speech tonight—win or lose the White House—for better or worse, I'll always be known for what I am about to become: the 2020 presidential nominee of the Democratic National Party. Yes, I'll be the Chosen One, the Politically Anointed One, the One who no longer invests His primetime hours to turning water into wine. Instead, he's gone onto a whole new thing: Turning Red states into Blue ones.

But I guess I can live with that. Better to be alive and in play as Christ the presidential candidate than out of vogue and sidelined like some old Greek river god, such as hmmmm… Achelous. Anyway, anyone even remotely connected with party politics knows exactly what I mean. Either you're in or you're out. And, of course, you've got to be in to be In. Believe me when I say there's no halfway house in U.S. politics.

So I review once again what my beautiful acceptance speech. Disciple Pelosi, my august speechwriter incomparable to the incomparable, refers to it as my Speech on the Mount—the L.A. Mount. While I always thought my old, far more traditional Sermon on the Mount was pretty darn good, especially since I didn't have an editor or anything to go over it before I delivered it—and I was strictly self-taught—believe me truly when I say that it doesn't even hold a trickle of water to hers. Which is reassuring, since my old platitudes—profound as they may sometimes sound on any given Sunday—were generally received fairly decently over time, considering my limitations I can now cop to freely, without fear of loss of face. Obviously, I'm saying all this for the first time and without an ounce of humility. I suppose you finally get how politics has deeply affected me—to the detrimental. My natural-born humility, for instance, has utterly gone by the boards. Say good-bye, fellows. I'm completely over it! For sure, it's a tragedy, a genuine tragedy, but also a political necessity. As the world knows, humility is as politicians ain't. But one good thing in terms of my own personal redemption: I can always choose to forgive myself for what I do, what I become, what I may choose to do. Such a unique prerogative gives me considerable latitude in any future career moves I may choose to make. I know that it's unfair, but who ever said that life was fair?

Even so, not since I stood before that louse Pontius Pilate, knowing that it was pretty much curtains and that I was about to be summarily strung up on a god damn cross with common, un-bathed bandits, have I been under so much pressure to perform memorably. Talk about needing to cough up a command performance on demand! It doesn't get a whole lot more intimidating than this. Well, maybe for actors nominated for Academy Awards sitting in the audience on Oscar night waiting for the envelope to be opened it does, but not for the likes of yours truly. Even I wouldn't have the stomach to endure that kind of monumental tension.

I wring my hands, rehearsing my crowd-pleasing lines for the umpteenth time, endeavoring to make them my own—my very, very own—because, let's face it, even though I'm officially a politician now—the tone and tenor of the profession still eludes me somehow, doesn't come naturally to me—not like my native tongue—Aramaic, for instance; but Pelosi and her gilded words make it much easier on me than it might otherwise be at this critical—desperately critical—juncture because, as you know, everything but everything rides on this my nomination speech. Her words flow off the page like pure silk rolling down high museum walls. Yes, she's that good. Did I say good? No, I didn't mean that. I meant great. Great as Faulkner meets Mark Twain great.

It's like this: When I close my eyes and hear her words roll across my mind's sky empowered beyond all imagining, I ascend to a brand new level of speechifying. The words become more than words. Closer to music, like swelling Parisian sidewalk music wending its mesmerizing, tantalizing, electrifying way down inviting streets off Rue du Rivoli at the pinnacle of springtime and summertime combined. It has that much bounce, that much verve. Come to think of it, her words have managed to reaffirm my faith in The Word—and you guessed it, transcendental rhetoric, the kind they never much wrote—and I sure as hell never wrote in the first place. I was good but not that good. Now who needs miracles when I have words like Nancy's to toss about like shooting stars in public? They could make even George W. Bush sound like an oratorical genius. Or perhaps, if chanted just right, bring Michael Jackson back to life. Or, and I say this with my fingers crossed—make me President of the United States! They're that terrific.

News flash! The forty delegates from the Great State of New Columbia—a.k.a. the District of Columbia—cast their ballots for yours truly, which pretty much sums up why I was such a big supporter of D.C. statehood for all those years. It just goes to prove that no liberal constituency can resist an enlightened guy like me for president. Happily, with D.C.'s pledged and unpledged delegates that makes 2117 delegates, enough to put me over the top. Yes, ladies and gentlemen of the press, I've secured my party's nomination without even an assist from the Old Man.

I made it all on my own—with a major assist, of course, from my twelve disciples, whom I won't forget, believe me, when it comes time to pick my cabinet.

I'll be the first to admit it—*now* I'm nervous.

My palms perspire; my collar's moist; my forehead feels good and clammy. I find a window I can push open backstage. I poke my face out to catch some air. Notice I do not say fresh air. It's L.A. air and we all know what that's about. Above the parking lot sits the septic tank-colored sky. Below sits the Staple Center's lot, occupied by nothing but Volvos. Volvos of seemingly infinite shapes, colors, and models. From the 1960s to today. I like what I see because Volvos have always been and probably always will be my favorite auto since they're generally recognized as being the auto of and for the Democrat—as well as for the proletariat. For the collector's eye, it's a feast down there in the L.A. night. There're rows and rows of 122s, 144s, 164s, 740s, and V70s. Yes, Dems do love their Volvos. In fact, I never met a Democrat who wouldn't fess up to having at least *thought* about buying a Volvo at one time or another in their life. It must be in Dems' genes. The truth is, I wouldn't mind owning a classic blue V70 sports wagon myself. Even though I still don't drive. They come equipped with 4C multi-mode suspension and hot little Brembo brakes for ultra high performance. It's the ideal all-around family car. Safe as safe can be. It scored four out of five stars in EuroNCAP's ever so stringent safety tests! How 'bout them stars?

Car idolatry aside, I note a fairly large number of protestors circling round the lot, picketing for some kind of cause. Not for nothing, they file around the sea of parked Volvos, marching to the incessant beat of what sounds like Indian war drums. The picketers are dressed in Columbian Indian ceremonial attire, which should tell me something. They're as serious-looking as anything.

The leader calls, his marchers answer:

"WHAT DO WE WANT?"

"OXY OUT OF U'WA'S HOMELAND!"

"WHEN DO WE WANT IT?"

"NOW!"

"WHAT DO WE WANT?"

"OXY OUT OF U'WA'S HOMELAND!"

"WHEN DO WE WANT IT?"

"NOW!"

They go onto another chant after that because with protests it's always good to mix up the chants to keep your followers interested. He calls, they answers:

"NO RIGHTS, NO PEACE!"

"SELF-DETERMINATION IS A HUMAN RIGHT!"

"WHEN SHOULD WE GET IT?"

"NOW!"

You get the idea. But between those two sets of chants, the protestors pretty much exhaust the extent of their picketing lexicon, at least while I'm watching them.

'Course I should know something more than I do about their issue, but I don't, so I feel, well, disappointed in myself and somewhat inadequate. Oh, I know that it has something to do with Occidental Oil ripping off their ancestral lands down there in Columbia with the consent of the government, but beyond that—you can forget it.

He calls; they answer:

"WHAT DO WE WANT?"

"OXY OUT OF U'WA'S HOMELAND!"

"WHEN DO WE WANT IT?"

"NOW!"

It's a pretty decent bit, something a lot like politics. Making noise, being heard, getting something accomplished after an interminable amount of time—maybe, hopefully. I'm quite certain I'd be picketing for them, too, if I only knew a little bit more about their cause. It's conceivable I was briefed about the U'wa issue some time back during one of my many foreign policy briefings, but if so, I forget. I mean, I can't possibly be expected to remember *every* issue out there. The fact is—and I'll be the first to admit this—I don't have such a good head for policy details, not like Bill Clinton. Which isn't a good thing. On the other hand, neither am I possessed of his libido! Which isn't such a bad thing. Fundamentally, I'm a Big Picture Guy, and not the least bit ashamed of it, except at times like this when I can't remember every pertinent detail, which I guess is understandable and what you'd expect from a guy my age. You'd be hard-pressed to recall every particular, too, at the age of 2020.

I make a mental note to look into the U'wa issue in greater detail after I get myself elected and check my watch: Twenty minutes to go before my Speech on the Mount.

Saying goodbye to all those beautiful Volvos down there, especially the V70s, with protestors' chanting still buzzing in my ear, "OXY OUT OF U'WA'S HOMELAND!" I close the window. You betcha. Self-determination *is* a human right, by God! And the U'wa deserve it—just like everyone else.

On stage, the tetchy combo Slug metal, Thrash metal, Nu metal, Gothic metal, Glam rock, Desert rock, Garage rock band Rage Against Greed rage against, well, greed of all things. Considered the absolutely *plus autre* in guilt infested, angst-ridden entertainment these days, I just had to have them. In my book a little guilt goes a long, long way toward disempowering greed. And they definitely won't be a drag on the Youth Vote either. According to Wikipedia, Rage Against Greed has over twenty million devoted fans worldwide. With at least ten million of them in the United States and eight million of those over the age of eighteen, the band can do a lot for me come Election Day. Therefore, I don't mind a bit them peppering their lyrics with cuss words. It's all for a good cause—stamping out greed. "Fuck Greed!" is one of their main refrains. Not my kind of language obviously, but the young folks love it. It's how they stick it to the Man.

And you won't find me objecting to them torching the stage at the end of their act, either. I'm hear to tell you that incinerating guitars, burning amplifiers, and all that, is the No. 1 thing to do at concerts to beef up your fan base. The name of the song they're playing now is called—what else—"Greed Ain't Good." So much condemnation in so little time. It shreds the good name of greed, leaving it in tiny little burning scraps on the stage. At the start, they dedicated to Gordon Gecko, a.k.a. actor Michael Douglas, who, as the old-timers will recall,

326

played that reprobate corporate raider who epitomized greed in the 1980's Hollywood classic, *Wall Street*. My good Democrats are dancing in the aisles now. They're the perfect band for my perfect night. If I've learned anything in politics thus far it's that you've got to give the people what they want. Service Before Leadership: The First Law of Victory.

So I give my delegates what they want: "Greed Ain't Good." Take that Gordon Gecko. Take that.

While they scream against the greed, rage against rapaciousness, shouting until their voices croak, "Fuck Greed! Fuck Greed!" a less graphic, but no less compelling maxim scrolls the length of the proscenium overhead: "FRIENDS DON'T LET FRIENDS BE GREEDY!" If I do say so myself, I think it a rather excellent maxim, one I intend to use in my General Election campaign. Nancy thought it up for me. It will allow me to rage against greed without having to curse, not an altogether bad thing considering my new station in life.

I study once again the most important tag line of my acceptance speech. Good writers borrow. Great writers steal: "And so my fellow Americans—ASK NOT WHAT YOU CAN DO TO SAVE YOURSELVES—ASK WHAT YOU CAN DO TO SAVE YOUR PLANET!"

I have to admit: Saving souls is *so* passé these days. It's all about the Big Picture now. We are the World, and all that. Politics is like that. Shifting sands. I can live with it.

After the smoking guitars and smoldering amplifiers are wheeled off stage, leaving behind towering walls of smoke like a paddleboat, a paper Mache float rolls on. It comes in the form of a mountaintop, skirted with potted pines and painted sunset colors. It is surrounded by schoolgirls wearing gossamer gowns, dyed forest green. They are singing the 119th Psalm of Sustainable, borrowed from the *Bible of Ecology*, which I, not coincidentally, endorse, and incorporated in whole and in part in

327

my environmental platform. The psalm's refrain goes just like this—exactly what you'd expect: "Sustainability is next to godliness. The environmentalists will inherit the Earth." It's all part of us Dems being politically correct and fundamentally self-righteous, which is what we Dems do best.

Of course, I was born self-righteous. I come to it honestly.

Exercising his right to be self-righteous, a lone Dem in the hall shouts out, "It's the environment, stupid!"

And so, of course, it is.

I knock back a Tic-Tac, double-check my watch and get even *more* nervous. On the concrete pillar at my right, is a picture of my choice for V.P.—the Reverend Al Gore. Otherwise known as Go Green Al. He was the obvious choice. Eight years V.P. experience under Clinton, the world's leading soothsayer on global warming, and the guy who did the best self-parody ever on Saturday Night Live. Oh, sure, he's no Newt Gingrich, but taken together no one can ever claim that we don't make for the greatest straight-ass ticket in American politics since the days of Jimmy Carter and Walter Mondale. Common Cause, for instance, gives us perfect straight-ass scores, for instance. We're No. 10s. Tops in politics. Of course, I thought long and hard about my V.P. choice because, above all else, I want to be certain that there is an unbroken line in straight-ass leadership succession of this country should anything ever happen to me, which is not like, totally out of the question or anything. So Al's the one for me. His recent ordination proves just what a perfect straight-ass he can be—and has always been. He's straight-ass beyond any reasonable doubt. From head prefect at St. Albans School to Episcopal priest living on the farm down in Kentucky in his twilight years, he's as straight-ass as they come. Just my kind. And I'm also hoping that Tipper will consider writing another *Raising PG Kids in an X-Rated Society*. I need someone like Tipper, close to the administration but not of the administration, to beat up on Hollywood for exploiting sex and violence in movies and in the music business. She's just right for that. Tipper's absolutely fearless, God bless her. She's not afraid of Hollywood's moneyed power, not a bit. As for me, I'd really rather not upset one of my chief fundraising constituencies. I'm sure you can understand my reticence. Politics, I've found, is all about trade-offs. Live and understand. That's what I say. It's been quite a learning curve for me; but now, now I'm finally getting a handle on it.

Next on stage, arriving late, as usual, comes Disciple Jack$on. Je$$e, as all the world knows, is decidedly not a straight-ass. Not like Al and me. Which is obviously why I couldn't offer him the V.P. spot. Straight-ass is as straight-ass does and the American public wants straight-ass in their candidates. And Lord only knows, we can't all be straight-asses. Anyway, Je$$e is coming on to do something even more important than being vice-president, which as we also know, is about mostly about going to state funerals. He comes on stage to do some convention fundraising. He's not called Je$$e Jack$on for nothing, you know.

Even Terry McAuliffe, Bill Clinton's titan of fundraisers, has nothing on him. He's a virtual black hole for campaign contributions, absorbing them with gravitational might like light, and depositing them in the inescapable chambers of my designated presidential bank account. He raised $66 million for my campaign just last week because he's a genius at making Internet appeals. Je$$e's the King of $ and I, for one, can't wait to hear his pitch tonight to hundreds of millions of loyal Democrats, eager to support Christ the Democrat. Je$$e's a born-again fundraiser, all right, which is why I need him right where he is, whipping up fundraising miracles. Sure, if it hadn't been for his out-of-wedlock child, his reputation for being a shakedown artist, especially of Anheuser-Busch, and for his reference to Jews as Hymies and to NYC as Hymietown, and for more generally being renown as "The Mouth That Roared", which incidentally I have no objection to, and in fact encourage for fundraising purposes, I might have picked him for my V.P.—but that's water down the Nile now. The truth is, I wouldn't be standing where I am tonight without his expertise, so I owe him, which is more than I can say for Al Sharpton, who didn't raise a dime for me. You better believe that there'll be no ambassadorship for Sharpton, no matter how much he professes to be the de facto new leader of the African-American community.

Je$$e steps to the microphone, wearing his disciple robe, that makes him look, well, this side of holy. He's the King of the Microphone, that one, the most self-assured public speaker on the planet. I only wish I could speak that well. The fact that Je$$e hides all traces of disappointment about being passed over for the V.P. slot is testament to his commitment to the cause of getting me into the Oval Office. You have to admire him for that, especially since we all know that he had similar aspirations. He may be weeping like a child inside, but outside his cheeks are as dry as toast. Which is commendable since he only hinted about ten thousand times during the course of the campaign that he'd consider accepting the V.P. spot if I were to offer it to him, which I didn't. So I know he's feeling the pain, and that is exactly why I chose not to confront him about those anonymous postings that mysteriously appeared on my website and were likely, if not positively, ghosted by him trashing Go Green Al for his involvement in the Buddhist fundraising scandal during Clinton's re-election campaign back in 1996. But when Al said, "I sure as hell did not have any conversations with anyone saying this is a fundraiser," I, for one, believed him. In any case, I forgive Je$$e if he was the one who did put up all those malicious postings about my guy, which should come as no surprise to anyone because I tend to forgive everyone for everything.

Anyway, what's not to forgive about Je$$e? He was aide to Martin Luther King, Jr. at the age of 27. Enough said.

And so he begins to reel them in:

"They call me Jesse: Jesse as in Jackson, Jackson as in Jesse, the Reverend Jesse Jackson. Aide to Martin and now disciple to the King of Kings, I'm twice blessed, twice invested. I supported the activism of my beloved King and the politics of baby Jesus. So I think we can all agree that I am Somebody!"

"I may be Somebody and you may be Somebody and together we may be Somebodies, but the little baby Jesus—our most righteous, but not self-righteous Democrat since Jimmy Carter took the midnight train to Plains, Georgia and Barack Hussein Obama sang 'Calling me home, Chicago' while flying home on Air Force One for the last time— really is SOMEBODY!"

You see, this is why Jesse's special. Why, in fact, Jesse's Jesse and known the world over. He makes people feel good about themselves. Even me. Thanks to Jesse, I'm feeling pretty good about myself right now, too. It's obvious why, isn't it? I'm feeling pretty good about myself not because I just put a lock on my nomination—no not because of that. It's because I know—I mean really know—not just sort of kind of know—that I really am SOMEBODY!

Thanks, Jesse.

I do believe that the seated delegates seem to float about six inches off their chairs while listening to Jesse. They're that transfixed by the living Legend of Jesse Jackson. Who can blame them? They feel positively good about themselves. They're rapidly becoming the National Democratic Party of Somebodies, just by listening to him. As he becomes one with his message, his voice soars across the convention hall. Even the hall feels better about itself because it, too, is getting the idea that it's not just anyplace, but Someplace, for Somebodies.

"EVEN THOUGH WE DEMOCRATS DON'T OWN FANCY ALFA ROMEOS AND SHINY CADILLACS LIKE OUR FELLOW REPUBLICANS, RIDING AROUND IN SECOND-HAND VOLVOS INSTEAD…"

"WE ARE SOMEBODIES!" the Dems below refrain.

"EVEN THOUGH WE DEMOCRATS CAN'T GET ENOUGH CREDIT ON THE CARD TO SHOP 'TIL WE DROP AT GUCCI'S AND CHANEL LIKE OUR FELLOW REPUBLICANS AND HAVE TO WEAR HAND-ME-DOWNS TO THE DEMOCRATIC NATIONAL CONVENTION INSTEAD…"

"WE ARE SOMEBODIES!"

"EVEN THOUGH WE DON'T DO CHRISTMAS IN ASPEN OR SUMMER IN HILTON HEAD LIKE OUR FELLOW REPUBLICANS, AND HAVE TO SLED DOWN THE DRIVEWAY IN DECEMBER AND STAND UNDER AN OPEN FIRE HYDRANT IN AUGUST AND CALL IT A VACATION INSTEAD…"

"WE ARE SOMEBODIES!"

"EVEN THOUGH WE DON'T HAVE GOLDMAN SACHS OR MERRILL LYNCH TO MAKE US THE BIG, BIG BUCKS LIKE OUR FELLOW REPUBLICANS AND HAVE TO SCHLEP AT 9-TO-5 JOBS AND RELY ON PINBALL LOTTERY TO GIVE US SOME HOPE WITHOUT SMOKIN' NO DOPE INSTEAD…"

"WE ARE SOMEBODIES!"

"EVEN THOUGH WE DON'T HAVE PRICE WATERHOUSE TO ZERO OUT OUR TAXES ON OUR 1040s AND HAVE TO HIRE H & R BLOCK TO STOP THE IRS FROM

GARNISHING OUR WAGES WHEN WE FALL BEHIND INSTEAD..."

"WE ARE SOMEBODIES!"

Now genuine tears pool in Je$$e's eyes, and mine.

"AND EVEN THOUGH I WAS NEVER ELECTED PRESIDENT AND DIDN'T GET THE NOD FOR THE V.P. SLOT..."

"YOU ARE SOMEBODY!"

Jesse cries out, his voice taught with emotion. "UP WITH HOPE!"

"DOWN WITH NOPE!!!" the Dems in the hall

shoot back, floating about eight inches of their chairs.

Jesse gathers his emotions. He digs down deeper than deep to completely reel them in.

"NOW HOW MANY OF YOU SOMEBODIES OUT THERE WILL CONTRIBUTE $25, JUST $25, TO MOVE THE LITTLE BABY JESUS FROM THE OUTHOUSE TO THE WHITE HOUSE?"

I'm touched that he still calls me that—really I am. But Jesse's the only one who can. That's what being a 27-year-old aide to Martin, my star disciple and No. 1 fundraiser gets you: Latitude, some serious latitude.

About five hundred hands fly up. That's $12,000 for the asking, presumably in ones, fives and tens.

"NOW HOW MANY OF YOU SOMEBODIES OUT THERE WILL CONTRIBUTE $50, JUST $50, TO MOVE THE

LITTLE BABY JESUS FROM THE OUTHOUSE TO THE WHITE HOUSE?"

About a thousand hands go up. That's $50,000 for the asking, presumably in personal checks.

"NOW HOW MANY OF YOU SOMEBODIES OUT THERE WILL CONTRIBUTE $100, JUST $100, TO MOVE THE LITTLE BABY JESUS FROM THE OUTHOUSE TO THE WHITE HOUSE?"

About two thousand hands fly north. That's $200,000 for the asking, presumably on the AMEX card or in the form of IOUs.

"NOW HOW MANY OF YOU SOMEBODIES OUT THERE WILL CONTRIBUTE $1000, JUST $1000, TO MOVE THE LITTLE BABY JESUS FROM THE OUTHOUSE TO THE WHITE HOUSE?"

Every other hand not previously raised stands quivering at attention. That's $300,000 for the asking, presumably in the form of bank transfers.

Isn't my Jesse just wonderful?

He's completely smiling now, over his attack of self-pity. He puts his hand in his robe pocket and pulls out a check and lifts it up for everyone in the hall to see.

'NOW HOW MANY OF YOU SOMEBODIES OUT THERE WILL MATCH THIS—A CHECK FROM ANHEUSER-BUSH FOR $50,000 WRITTEN OUT TO THE COMMITTEE TO ELECT JESUS CHRIST THE DEMOCRAT?

"BUT DON'T ASK ME HOW I GOT IT."

Every hand in the joint goes up. Every one. It's a miracle. That's $200,000,000 for the asking, presumably in the form of home equity lines of credit. That's Jesse. And that's why Jesse gets serious latitude. He can call me the Little Baby Jesus until the end of time, for all I care.

In my Book of Prayer, Jesse's the Somebody of Somebodies because with my campaign war chest awash with cash, Reverend Al and I are within reach of the White House North Gate. I'm just so happy that the Supreme Court overturned campaign financing reform last year. Chief Justice Clarence Thomas did me a gigantic favor. Now there's hope without smokin' no dope.

On that happy thought, Je$$e exits stage right, pumping his fist *á la* patriots of black power. Unseen, off-off stage, Stokely Carmichael smiles in his grave. One thing's for sure: Je$$e's done himself proud. He's done what few, Dems if any, have ever done before. Unite the party in one grand act of campaign financing altruism. What my Dems have done they have done for the sake of the soul of the party and the American Republic, which, by God, I have come to preserve, protect and defend, so help me God!

Reverend Al Gore waddles in the wings as Je$$e sidles out, his clenched fist raised, his sense of Somebodiness at an all-time high.

As Reverend Al and Reverend Je$$e pass each other like shadows at twilight, As they do, Reverend Je$$e projects his foot into Reverend Al's path, like a grade school prankster, causing Reverend Al to stumble, but not crash. Which is precisely why I chose Al, not Je$$e, for the V.P. spot. Al may stumble, but he does not crash. Whoever said that politics was a contact sport knew a thing or two.

Quickly regaining his customary sense of waddling gravitas and shuffling dignity, Rev. Al takes to the podium, the stage floor trembling beneath his abundant weight. The Dems welcome him on with lusty cheers, celebrating in the aisles his glorious Greenness, his magnificent Nobel Laureateness, his awesome new Religiousness. His sparkling white collar, starched beyond stiffness into near concrete, catches the aerial lights. Al has come. The Dems are grateful, as am I.

Guggenheim Film Productions follows his tremulous steps with a dozen different digital super-high-definition camera crews, shooting footage for their next documentary film—all about Rev. Al., working title, *Roads to Righteousness: The Story of Al Gore*. It's bound to win him another Academy Award. You might say it's been preordained. And well it should be. How many men or women have the courage to perform "an act of re-purification," to quote Tipper, returning to Vanderbilt Divinity School at the age of 65 to study the Faith, so as to be able to devote his remaining years to the practice of my Faith before going directly onto even greener pastures, if you can imagine that, without passing Go.

Rev. Al settles at the mic. His enormous form, blown to extremities by his love for Col. Sanders' Kentucky Fried Chicken, dwarfs everything near him: podium, reading light, and mic. His slicked-back sheet of thinning white hair protrudes above his wide-body neck like a tortoises' neck from its shell.

In a hushed Tennessean accent steeped in stores of self-righteousness, accumulated over several generations, at least, he says, "Let the Powerpoint begin."

Houselights dim. A luminescent screen slowly lowers from the concrete sky above, delivered as it were from the recesses of the infinite. As it forms a wall to reflect the soon-to-be projection of Al's Holy Writ, a thirty-foot high ladder, suitable for wood-paneled libraries, is rolled out, set beside it. Al strings a lavalier microphone around his neck he picks up at the podium, before magically producing a green laser pointer. He never goes anywhere without one. Then from the back of the black hall comes a source of great light. A source of fortitude, a fount of wisdom, Al's Powerpoint presentation discharges. He lumbers to the ladder, climbs the tiny steps as the title projects, *A Convenient Piece of Fiction that We are a Planet of Moral Conviction*.

At first light, the Dems give Al a big hand. They have no doubt, as I have no question, that what we're about to see will be Al at his very finest.

Intricate graphs, complex charts, multitudinous diagrams dense with indecipherable formulas and floating algebraic numbers appear on screen, exposing revelations both profound and mysterious, and enigmas of the first magnitude, puzzles and problems that only a genius like Al could love.

Which is why Al has come to decode it for us.

At length, he reaches the top of the ladder. There he assumes the Professorial Position. Breathing hard, perspiring from his heavy climb, he fires up his laser pointer, directing it at the screen as a second title comes on, sparkling like water under noon sunshine: *A Revelatory Slide Show and Learned Lecture by The Reverend Albert Arnold Gore, Jr.*

Armed with all the unencrypted data of an ex-NASA astrophysicist, Al illuminates the problem. He paints a rather alarming picture of a world smothered in very high concentrations of moral turpitude. He maps out his whole case in three-dimensional bar graphs and pie-shape diagrams. We're living under a veritable cloud of immoral carbon dioxide, which is fast heating up ubiquitous depravity on the planet, creating human degeneracy on an unprecedented scale in the form of rapid global Moral Change. According to Al, it doesn't look good. Which I could have told them, but much prefer having Al articulate, as I myself would prefer to deliver the Good News.

So far, so good.

Anyway, the only way to remove this cloud of iniquity is to get religion into politics. According to Al, we're at the Tipping Point. We must act now because toxic levels of immorality have risen so dramatically since the beginning of the 21st century, peaking at all time highs of baseness and badness in the past decade as monitored by a global survey conducted by the Brookings Institute and published in its report, *EARTH 2020: Morality Lost*, are accelerating, nearing irreversible consequences for earth's vulnerable population. Al says these findings have also been confirmed by the UN Intergovernmental Panel on Morality Change and the Union of Concerned Moralists. In fact, there exists an uncommon global consensus among leading moralists, philosophers, and men and women of faith—ecclesiastical leaders of every denomination—that the earth's immorality quotient is higher than at any other time in history, and that therefore serious moral change is mandatory if America and the world is to stave off a new dark era of pervasive gloom and global fiendishness and save the species. Nothing less will spare us the fate of plunging into a death spiral of corruptness and roguery. These are perilous times indeed, says Al.

"Morality in the balance," he adds. "Read my book of the same title—still available on Amazon—to get the digital snapshot of just how bad things are and how much worse they can and will be if we don't turn this thing around—fast."

My sentiments exactly, which is why I find myself back on planet Earth.

"Make no mistake," he continues atop the highest library ladder in Christendom, otherwise know as Mount Morality, "America should and must ratify the Rome Accords for Morals Change!!! It can no longer delay. Time isn't on our side! Already 164 nations have ratified this vital international treaty to stop global degeneracy! And so too must America. Each day that it fails to ratify is a day of lost moral authority we must have at our disposal to combat morality change!

"I only have one reservation regardin' the Rome Accords—and I'd like to take this opportunity to tell you what that is. That those provisions endorsin' morality tradin' as a way of lowerin' worldwide immorality levels not be bindin' on the United States.

"Carbon tradin' didn't work to end global warmin' and morality tradin' won't work to end immoral behavior, either! Country X should never be allowed to increase its decadence quotient simply because Country Y enjoys a lower incident of decadence by virtue of a moral superiority arbitrarily earned, say by the proximity of the Catholic Church, for instance!

"Instead, what I'm talking about is a whole new incentives program that would allow every country to earn 'morality dollars' by demonstratin' quantifiable improvements in their populations' moral conduct over time! The more moral Country X gets, the more cash it gets. It's that simple.

"And by way of additional cash incentives, Virgin Airlines' CEO, Sir Richard Branson, Bill Clinton—case and point: moral change IS possible—and I have joined together to offer a $50 million prize to the first unaffiliated priest or unpublished poet who devises a non-invasive technique for reclaimin' the morality of certain persons through spiritual techniques who have been listed depraved and immoral by the U.S. Department on Morality (USDM).

"And we are also offerin' a $25 million prize to the first garage inventor or basement scientist who invents an invasive technique for reclaimin' eroded morality of certain persons through clinical techniques who have been listed depraved and immoral by the USDM!

"But back to basics. A Christ Administration we will never accept MORALITY TRADING. We will only seek to ratify the Rome Accords by attaching such a reservation. A Christ Administration will be about morality buildin'—buildin' mortality the old-fashioned way—by bolsterin' our efforts to do what we do best—do-gooderism!"

The Hall of Dems likes what it hears. They chant, "Do-gooderism! Do-gooderism! Do-gooderism!"

It's a treat to hear. If politics had saints, Al would be one among them.

"My fellow Democrats," Al concludes, "morality is, in fact, a sustainable resource! So let's resolve that we will all strive harder to climb Mount Morality in order to lower the precariously high levels of manmade immorality, which threatens life on our planet. Actin' together, I have every faith that we can and will end the convenient piece of fiction that we are a planet of moral conviction. Please believe me when I say that under a Christ Administration, we can and will reverse morality change because it's our morality and our planet and nothin' but nothin' can stop us NOW FROM GETTIN' MORAL!"

The Hall of Dems rises to its feet. "Go Morality Al!" they cry. "Go Morality Al!"

All of which is quite moving, even inspiring. If you ask me, Al's done it again. There never was, nor will there ever be again, anyone else like the Great Albert Arnold Gore.

After descending Mount Morality, Rev. Al waddles back to the podium, preparing to make my formal introduction. I wait in the wing, not so nervous, because the truth is Al's inspired me. I'm tanked up on his vision. His effect on me is the same as it is on others. Seriously, I'm thinking he could take over for when I set off into my retirement. He's just so incredible at what he does do—as well as what he doesn't do. I'm just mad about my Al. And the Old Man might just be, too. I'm really thinking that Al might have yet another encore performance in him. Can you imagine him in the starring role of Savior Al?

I sure can.

With talent like his, he might get me off the hook. I might finally be free to live my life unencumbered by humankind responsibilities, free to dangle my feet in the warm, running streams of the Elysian Fields without care or conscience over the fate of humanity.

340

"My fellow Democrats," Go Morality starts off, "While I am a Nobel Peace Prize Winner, I am NOT the King of Peace. While I am a nominee for vice-president, I am NOT a nominee for president. And while I think we can all pretty much agree that I am near perfect, I am NOT, absolutely perfect. NOT like my runnin' mate. Not like Christ the Lord. And while I get up each and every morning and look at myself in the mirror and say these few words, earnestly and ardently, 'It's a good day to be moral,' I can't possibly compete with the moral character of Christ the Lord. Which is why I am so darn proud to introduce Him. We can all do our parts, but He's the One, the only One, who has a shot at actually bringin' morality to our planet, to reversing morality change in the nick of time. He can neatly put an end to the convenient piece of fiction that we are a planet of moral conviction.

"We can count on Him, as always, to tell it like it really is.

"I'm talkin', of course, about our NEXT PRESIDENT OF THE UNITED STATES! I'm talkin', of course, about the ONCE AND FUTURE KING OF KINGS. I'm talkin', of course, about our SOON-TO-BE COMMANDER-IN-PRIEST! I'm talkin', of course, about JESUS—WE ALWAYS KNEW YOU WERE A DONKEY-RIDING DEMOCRAT—CHRIST!"

The Hall of Dems erupts into joyful pandemonium. That Al, he kicks ass. I couldn't have asked for any better intro.

Following on, Al raises his voice above all others—naturally.

"My fellow donkey-riding Democrats, I now have the high honor of introducing you to the godhead of the Democratic Party, the soul of America, the salvation of the planet, the guy destined to win the 2021 Nobel Peace Prize... and the NEXT PRESIDENT OF THE UNITED STATES...

341

"JESUS—PLEASE DON'T STRAY SO FAR FROM HOME AGAIN—CHRIST!"

At the sound of my rather elastic new name, three gigantic wooden crucifixes descend on cue and en masse from the iron rafters, lined up like little soldiers in a row. Back stage thunders snaps, imitation lightening cracks, the stage floor quivers, twitches, and jerks—I mean this time it shudders, really shakes like a leaf, not at all like that little wobble Rev. Al gave it waddling over to Mount Morality. My intro definitely has Cecil B. DeMille production values.

The DNC's heavy-handed theatrics will absolutely appeal to the Democratic Christian Right. They'll drink it down with a chalice.

Green velvet curtains, the color of Trinity, part before me. I step onto hallowed ground to claim my nomination, paid for in compromise. I pass by Mount Morality as I approach Al, who stands aside for me, hand outstretched, ready to meet mine. It's a good, good feeling all around, except for the fact that the rumbling and trembling makes me wish the *mise en scene* was more like an Ingmar Bergman movie.

The truth is it's great to even be in the same general space as Al, an honor almost. It makes one feel completely righteous, which is perfect for a Democrat. At the podium, Al and I shake hands as he officially hands me off to my appointed destiny. I give Al my blessing as he backs away, very nearly bowing, which I find embarrassing. After all, I'm only Christ and he's the Great Albert Arnold Gore.

I turn to face the Hall of Dems. It's a magnificent sight, so many do-gooders. But with Al gone, the world beyond seems a sliver of its former self, as if it had just closed in, a sudden infinity of limitations. It goes to show just how big my Al is.

"JESUS! JESUS! JESUS!" the Dems call out. "JESUS! JESUS! JESUS!"

I'm neither too modest—nor too humble—to acknowledge that I like the sound of that.

This is my night and I must admit that I hope the Old Man is taking time out to look down. I'm fairly certain I don't have to do too much hoping that my stepbrother will be tuning in right about now. Off the record, I'd love to flip him the bird on Internet television. Frankly, as I look about, and feel the love, and reflect on how far I've come in so little time, the only worry in the world I have is that I won't be able to measure up to Al. It may seem silly to some, but he's one hard act to follow.

But I'll try. Lord knows I'll try.

So with Disciple Pelosi's Speech on the Mount in hand, which blends the lemonade of religion and with the Bourbon of politics, I access the same voice the Old Man employs when making His presence felt to the lodgers upstairs all at once. "DEMS OF AMERICA," I bellow through the bullhorn of my larynx, "I HEREBY ACCEPT YOUR NOMINATION FOR PRESIDENT OF THE UNITED STATES!"

That blows the top off—literally. Trading in their Volvo parking lot protest for a frontal attack, the U'wa make a spectacular entrance, blasting holes in concrete walls and rooftops with explosive can openers, enabling dozens of guerillas, heavily-armed, to crash the Dems' biggest party in years.

Allstate® is really going to be pissed. Me, well, of course, I'm more than a little unhappy the U'wa have upstaged what promised to be a pretty decent speech.

It's enough to make Jesus cry, which I do inside.

Fulsome clouds of smoke invade the hall. Random gunfire terrifies here and there and everywhere; cacophonies of hysteria make for a place of sorrows, a house of horrors. The U'wa National Guard is

343

taking over. The scene looks like an image from an al-Qaeda fairytale. It's snowing down concrete dust everywhere, coating the hall in wonderland colors. Dems duck for cover, searching for sanctuary below the metal underbellies of thousands of clattering folding chairs. I, of course, remain standing, resisting any and all forms of intimidation to the last—violent or otherwise. Besides, it just won't do to have the Next Leader of the Free World appear in an AP photograph, circulated worldwide, cowering underneath anything.

So naturally I insist that the nice Secret Service agent who offers to scoop me up to safety step aside. You can understand why. My motto has always been and always will be, dignity. Mary Magdalene taught me that.

Armed with grenade launchers mounted on AK-47s, the Columbian invaders emerge from concrete blizzards blowing this way and that like eclectic fashion-conscious militia. For instance, they wear fine silk stockings over their faces to disguise their identifies, ceremonial U'wa feather headdresses for a hint of color, minus, regrettably, something on the order of Zappos' Stuart Weitzman Fever pumps with 4-inch high heels in Cognac Tartaruga patent leather. Those shoes, instead of high-top marching boots with hobnob heels, would have agreeably complimented their down and dirty camouflage bulletproof vests and baggy but pressed guerilla green trousers, except for the fact that they would have inhibited any kind of fast escape, especially over broken slabs of concrete.

Through the porous ceiling, U'wa warriors slide down makeshift ropes fashioned from jungle vines yodeling like Latin Tarzans. Others breach cavities punctured in walls, bounding out like Alice-in-Wonderland commandos. None are wearing DNC credentials. So I throw this out for consideration: Perhaps if those credentials were just a

344

little easier to come by—a friendly suggestion for the 2024 credentials committee—we'd be spared these kinds of histrionics.

It's mad dog madness in here. It may make for good television—it's got action, it's got intrigue—but really crummy atmospherics for speechmaking.

But then a young man's voice, as warm as Amazon sunshine dusting rainforests, sings in my left ear—my one good ear. My right ear is not so good. Ever since I transported back to Earth on the Divinity Express, I've experienced negative ear pressure, and the odd popping sound, which makes my everyday listening experience one of dissonance rather than harmonious. From time to time, it's more than a little disconcerting, making life sound more like a Ferris wheel ride at the county fair than plain ordinary, invited by his courteous call.

In any event, I turn to look, to listen. There stands—I swear—a facsimile of Simón Bolívar. I recognize him as the one leading the demonstration out back in the Volvo-packed parking lot, but now he's changed into Columbian guerrilla costume, and carries a AK-47 instead of a picket sign. He emerges from the veils of concrete mist, radiating that special glow that only true saviors of a great cause emit as they arrive at the doorway to their destiny. I know him for what he is: A more militant me. There but for the grace of God I go!

His luminous, dewy eyes could have been mine two thousand years ago or so—way back when I was like, totally naïve and everything and believed that I really could solve all of the world's problems in one quick lifetime. Boy, did I ever get that wrong. But in those days I was blessed with the undiluted optimism of youth. Now, well, while I still have hope without dope, I'm a trifle more circumspect about the time it will take to go down the path to evolutionary progress. Not that I don't hope for a global miracle to happen and speed things up considerably.

"Lord Christo," he says, conveying a deep sense of self-righteousness equal to or better than any Democrat I've encountered lately, "I'm Señor Berito Cobaria, elected leader of the U'wa people, chair of the Strike force for our Ancestral Homeland Preservation Unit, and general all-around Grand Puba of the U'wa."

"Honored to meet you," I respond, exercising my phenomenal patience and tolerance yet again in light of trying circumstances.

"No, Lord Christo," he says, genuflecting on bended knee, "the glory's all mine." That puts a positive check in his column because there's nothing quite so endearing as a militant showing his pacifist superiors respect.

Sounding all but contrite, young Cobaria continues earning Brownie points which, believe me, he desperately—and I do mean desperately—needs.

"We apologize to interrupt your grand important occasion, Lord Christo, but the graves of our ancestors will be desecrated by Oxy Oil soon."

"I gathered that," I say, trying to sound sympathetic and not too miffed. "I saw your protest and made a note to learn more about it once I took the White House."

"So you believe we come not to sponge a post-convention speech dinner."

"Or freeload at the open bar... yes, I believe."

"We come to save the U'wa people."

"From Oxy Oil."

"The Anti-Christ of Conservation."

"The Beelzebub of Environmentalism."

"And take Rev. Al hostage for his crimes against the U'wa people!"

"Crimes? What crimes?"

346

"His crimes against the U'wa people! How could you not know, Lord Christo? He owns 30,000 preferred shares of Oxy Oil! He profits from the oil devils that robs our graves and takes our holy lands!"

And I thought Rev. Al had been thoroughly vetted! Whatever was my staff thinking? Whatever was my VP thinking?

"So if you do not do as we ask, in thirty minutes we will nail your Rev. Al to the cross!"

Now, of course, the three wooden crosses standing in dark silhouette in back of me take on a rather more sinister aspect. If you ask me, this Señor Cobaria is sounding more and more like Pontius Pilate than Simón Bolívar.

Al waddles back on stage, after hearing his name. His mere presence seems to shrink by half the enormous cavity of the open stage. "Do you know who I am, young man?" he asks, sounding as cantankerous as an old math professor. "I'm Albert Arnold Gore, the Great. I invented the Internet! I was the world's No. 1 soothsayer on the perils of global warmin'—other than the boys at the Intergovernmental Panel on Climate Change! I was, am, and always will be, an Academy Award-Nobel Peace Prize winner! And now I am a two-time V.P. nominee for the Democratic National Party!

"So believe me when I tell you, young lad, that your public tantrum won't go down very well in the head prefect's office!"

"Be that as it may, Rev. Al, we're the ones holding YOU hostage, so if you ever want to eat Kentucky Fried Chicken again, put up your hands and shut up!"

Al's not going to like the thought of that. He lives for fried chicken.

Naturally, I find this situation intolerable and abhorrent because if anything happens to Al I don't have a credible replacement candidate. That is to say, should I ever elect to go into retirement someday, which isn't like, entirely out of the question given the stress and supreme aggravation that comes with the job of being Christ, the world is owed a Plan B. That's right. If history has taught us anything, it's that Earth needs some kind of back-up Savior—a Savior in reserve. And I think Al's just the man for the job.

So you bet I intervene.

"What can I do for you, Señor?" You bet I'll negotiate with terrorist. I need Al, the Democratic Party needs Al, the world needs Al. In fact, there's a case to be made that the whole universe needs Al! Everybody needs Al! The entire U'wa need Al!

"Unless you American Dems pass tonight a resolution denouncing Oxy Oil for its crimes against the U'wa people, unless you pledge much cash for the preservation of our ancestral homeland— made payable by credit card only, and call for U'wa peoples' right to self-determination at the UN—tell the world that Oxy Oil should get the god damn hell out of our cloud forest on Internet television, man, are we gonna nail Oxy Al to the cross now!"

"Well, there's no need to use inappropriate language with me, young man," I brusquely shoot back. I do so find any kind of vulgar language offensive, don't you?

Looking downright sheepish, as well he should, his eyes lower to the floor. "Sorry, Señor," he says.

"Apology accepted," I reply, restoring characteristic warmth to my voice.

But the truth is I dare—no, double dare—Berito and his feather-headed gang of rainforest pirates to try and nail my big Al up on any cross they choose. Like, there's just no way, José. He's three hundred pounds of sheer body mass! And another six hundred pounds of divine inspiration, if not more! That's nine hundred pounds in the aggregate! Impossible! Al's the Heaviest Weight of them all.

But thankfully we're not there yet and I don't intend to let it get that far. I'm not only Christ, the nominee. I'm also Christ, the peacemaker, even though for the time being, at least, I'm draped in the primary colors of the American flag and have taken up saying the Pledge of Allegiance in the morning instead of the Lord's Prayer.

Which goes to show that you just never know what life may have in store for you.

Now Berito's cloud forest guerrillas stand positioned about the Hall of Dems' like chess pieces on a checkered board: Queens, knights, bishops against our defenseless pawns, checkmate all but certain. They look passably colorful, too, trussed up in bird feather headdresses and all. The big difference between them and me is that I don't, as a general rule, carry around AK-47s with rocket launchers to try to get my way. I use subtler tools, like moral persuasion and divine intimidation. Berito and his boys should try it. Guns are for amateurs. They're good for wars, but lousy for making world wonders.

So having co-opted my one big night that understandably I've been looking forward to for the past six months or more and having elevated this hostile takeover into primetime melodrama (forgive the hint of bitterness in my voice, even I can't control myself sometimes), setting the stage for a 21st century crucifixion on Mount Morality with Al playing the starring role this time, and not—thankfully—me, Señor Cobaria and his band of feather-head terrorists (colorful as they may be), they add salt to the wound by starting up a ping-pong chant denouncing Al, when I should be waxing political about my new world vision!

Life often disappoints, but politics eternally exasperates.

"What do we want?"

"Oxy Al out of Oxy Oil!"

"When do we want it?"

349

"NOW!"

"Oxy Al out of Oxy Oil!"

"Up with U'wa people! Down with Oxy Al!"

They go on like that for quite some time.

It's all very embarrassing, especially for Al. But of course he deserves it. *Whatever was he thinking holding onto those 30,000 shares of Oxy Oil?*

In light of the mess he's in because of the lack of a proper vetting process, which is all myself because I thought Al was golden— no one's safe from last-minute revelations—not even me. That's a frightening thought. So next time, I intend to have myself vetted, just in case. Clearly, one can never be too vigilant. And playing it safe is the key to incumbency.

"What do we want?"

"Oxy Al out of Oxy Oil!"

"When do we want it?"

"NOW!"

So to negotiate or not to negotiate? That is the question.

Obviously, this one has plagued heads of state for centuries. On the one hand, Israelis just say no. On the other, South Korea just says yes. Case and point: Their handling of the hostage situation with the Taliban in Afghanistan. By pledging to remove their troops, they freed 21 of their own. So there's a legitimate ideological divide between the dos and the don'ts.

My idea for a new world order is one in which we can sit down and reason together even when we're being unreasonable—particularly when we're being unreasonable. It may sound all touchy feely and everything, and yes, I'll admit, I may be impossibly naïve, but who can really say for sure until we give it the old New Testament try?

My voice clear and steady voice, dripping with patience and nothing but patience, I say, "Come, Young Berito, let us reason together."

We arrive at the apron of the stage and dangle our feet over the side, as though sitting down by the banks of the Nile. And despite the presence of his AK-47, I still feel love for Berito. But I have considerably less tolerance for my V.P. Though I'm not into playing the blame game and must ultimately take full responsibility for muffing the V.P.'s vetting, it must also be said that Al should have known better. More than anyone else, he was aware of the U'wa history. Now I recall that U'wa supporters stormed his campaign offices to protest his family's ownership of OXY stock during his bid to be elected president. The one that was stolen from him and given to the man who gave American presidents a bad name, that nitwit, GW.

But Al, whatever were you thinking by not divesting? If anyone should have known this could happen, you should have.

Which goes to show that not even Al's perfect, difficult as that may be to believe.

Turning toward Mount Morality, where Al stands with his hands up, as requested by the feather-headed guerrilla standing guard, I say, betraying not a whisper of exasperation, "Please join us, Al. Let us reason together." Berito nods his consent and V.P. Al shuffles over, followed at gunpoint.

Al does as he's told because, among other things, he knows that I'm the Nominee and he's the Vice-nominee and that Vice-nominees do as they are told when instructed by the Nominee. And of course it comes naturally to him because he's had loads of practice doing exactly as he was told as V.P. under Bill Clinton.

So the three of us assemble on the Banks of Reason, a.k.a., the Comcast Wachovia Center stage. There's Young Berito at my left hand; Rev. Al at my right, which should make for a captivating Time Magazine cover next week and propel the story of this sideshow into a new news cycle, hopefully winning Al and me more sympathy votes come Election Day.

We politicians celebrate opportunism, you know.

Al makes quite a stir as he sits down beside me, as you can probably imagine. The platform rumbles, its underpinnings shift. And like an empty Japanese garden in the bleak mid-winter, the Hall of Dems is bathed in silence, as my wonderful delegates sit in their metal seats, under watchful armed guard.

Though admittedly this situation isn't great, I'm reminded of a saying by President Kennedy, which puts it in a better light: "When written in Chinese, the word crisis is composed of two characters. One represents danger and the other represents opportunity." You get my meaning, of course.

And as I prepare to perform my very first act as negotiator to demonstrate the wisdom of my policy of engaging terrorists, angling, as well as ever living in hope, to wrap this thing up briskly, so I might still have a chance of delivering even a few precious minutes of Disciple Pelosi's classic speech before we leave primetime behind for good, I sit there, my feet dangling over the edge and visualize a successful conclusion to my mission, like all the best self-help books suggest. I even envision its name, which I'd be honored to call, the Comcast Wachovia Accords.

Then, I work mentally backwards, conjuring up each step toward achieving my goals.

It's not sexy, for sure, but peace work never is, which probably explains why I never became a sex symbol. But I like the name and it's in keeping with other great peace accords, like the Guatemalan Peace Accords, the Paris Peace Accords, the Dayton Peace Accords, and the Oslo Accords. It ranks right up there, in my opinion, at least.

I begin by soliciting Young Berito's side of the story—what any arbitrator worth his Nobel Peace Prize would do. He tells his peoples' sad story in poignant detail. You've heard it mostly before, but you'll hear it again because it's that important: Oxy Oil's been raping U'wa homeland for more years than he can remember, despoiling the sacred earth as if it were a city dump, violating the spiritual integrity of its ancestral burial grounds as if vandalizing a temple, pirating crude oil beneath its heavenly rainforests, sucking out the very soul of the earth and making an obscene profits at the expense of life itself.

And it gets worse: The U'wa people, including Berito's cherished grandma, have been forcibly removed from the place of their birth, relocated in a strange, inhospitable land, so that Oxy can drill, baby, drill.

And the Columbian government has ignored their pleas and Internet petitions. Entreaties to the UN have largely fallen to the wayside, although the UN Human Rights Committee did find that the Columbian government violated the U'wa right to self-determination by removing them from their holy land. Even the U.S. Congress turned its face away, failing to pass a resolution supporting their basic human rights. Worse, last year the White House didn't send the U'wa a greeting card at Christmas, which had been its custom and practice since the Carter Administration!

Berito cries copious tears.

It's like this: Nobody loves them, nobody cares about them, nobody intervenes on their behalf. The injustice goes on and on. And now his children will never get to live in their true homeland, hear the sound of early morning rain drumming overhead on cloud forest leaves, the sound he heard as a child, the sound his parents heard, the sound his grandparents heard... You get the drift. It's an aural holocaust.

After listening to all that, which serves as my official pre-White House briefing, I'm more sympathetic to Berito, despite his desperate theatrics, which is not, of course, to say that I in any way, shape or form, condone, endorse, encourage, promote, defend, sanction, champion, favor, abet, back or otherwise stand behind, or excuse, defend, or justify his heathen, barbarian, brutish, bestial, thuggish, ruffian, savage tactics.

Have I made myself clear?

I now invite Rev. Al to tell his side of the story.

Al's as contrite, apologetic, regretful, sheepish, rueful, shamefaced, remorseful, sorry, repentant, and just plain guilt-ridden as a television evangelist caught under the sheets in a New Orleans whorehouse by a prying reporter from the National Inquirer. Which is a competent start, since I'm still more than a little miffed with him, considering Berito and his boys are about to string him up on the cross, an experience I do not—most emphatically do not—recommend, commend, propose, speak favorably of or speak well of, or endorse, to Al or anyone else. Period.

Al summons all three hundred of his natural pounds to his defense, fessing up to owning those thousands and thousands of shares of Oxy Oil stock before the probing eyes of my pledged delegates, Berito's men and every Internet camera in sight. Teary-eyed, he claims that he had meant to sell them off after the 2000 election, but evidently completely forgot about it because he was discombobulated, which he hopes we can all understand, what with the nail-biting and fretting over the hanging chad Florida recount business and the terrible drumming he got from the Supreme Court in *Bush v. Gore* which, by the way, he still hasn't fully recovered from and perhaps never will and which may very well account for his monumental blunder, which again he can't

354

emphasize enough, he's deeply, deeply sorry for, incredibly regretful of, and phenomenally guilt-ridden about. That goes from now until forever.

(Al also takes his opportunity to re-emphasize that he still believes the Florida recount was rightly a state matter for the Florida Supreme Court to decide and that Rehnquist Court gravely erred in assuming jurisdiction over the Palm Beach hand count question.)

That aside for the time being, and feeling sorrier than sorry can say, Al implores the U'wa to put his infelicity in proper context—a brilliant tactic, and one you'd expect from the Great Albert Arnold Gore.

In furtherance thereof, and all but throwing himself on the mercy of the U'wa, he proceeds to list his sizeable, considerable, appreciable life raves.

You Go Gore.

To wit, and common knowledge to all us Gore fans out there and here, he 1) alerted the world to the frightening dangers of global warming and rapid sea rise at considerable personal expense and which the Nobel Peace Prize cash couldn't possibly make up for, especially since he had to share it with all those guys on the Intergovernmental Panel on Climate Change; 2) was the best former next president of the United States since Jimmy Carter became the best ex-president of the United States; and 3) enrolled in Trinity Divinity School for a second time in order to undergo a process of re-purification so that he could achieve the highest achievement of them all—The priesthood—and while there did very well, like he does in everything else in life, getting straight As and making the dean's list each semester and everything, and then was finally ordained a real priest and became known as Rev. Al before going on to practice the Faith, until he got The Call to become Jesus Christ's running mate, which pretty much brings his life achievements up to date.

Like, wow, I can't even top that!

Then, for all his global and spiritual accomplishments, magnificent and earthmoving as they are, he completely breaks down. He's beyond contrite. He's gone.

"You've got to believe me, everyone! I NEVER meant to harm anyone, not one U'wa! No, not one!

"I love the U'wa people; I think of myself as a born again U'wa—even though I made money off the drilling rights to their homeland for far too many decades!"

Then comes Al's Greatest Inspiration, the crowning idea of his career.

He draws out his iPhone OSZ9.2—the latest in high tech communication, of course—from beneath his cassock, speed dials his Merrill Lynch stockbroker, and shouts instructions to him like he was calling in a spreading fire, "SELL ALL MY OXY STOCK, BEN, SELL IT, NOW! PREFERABLY AT A WHOPPING LOSS!"

You bet Young Berito likes the sound of that. His eyes dance a blend of Salsa and Maringa. Not even Mat Damon ever smiled like that, and his smile was seen around the world. In fact, Berito's so taken by Al's contrition, so moved by his sell order that he leans across and pats Al's knee. "There, there," he says, "I wasn't really going to crucify you... I was only teasing you, Al. For the publicity, amigo. We're on the same side now."

Now I like the sound of that.

Then Berito casts off his AK-47. It makes a terrific racket, very theatric. He wipes tears of compassion on his sleeve. Compassion for Al, ex-shareholder of Oxy Oil stock; new partner in the cause of mutuality.

Al is touched, relieved, chastened. He burbles, "Oh, that's okay, I knew you wouldn't be able to hoist my bod up on that damn cross, anyway..." Then the two embrace, with me sandwiched in between. And that's okay, too, because this is exactly the way the whole world will be under a Christ Administration: Adversaries communicating across empathies.

Sensing the moment of my opportunity arising from the danger of crisis, I whip up a draft of the Comcast Wachovia Accords on the back panel of Nancy's speech, setting out the following binding terms and conditions:

THE COMCAST WACHOVIA ACCORDS

Whereas, the National Democratic Party resolves to denounce Oxy Oil for its crimes against the U'wa people on Internet television every chance it gets and agrees to insert said denunciation (otherwise known and hereinafter referred to as The Denunciation) in its party platform;

Whereas, we the National Democratic Party pledges to hold a Internet-thon fundraiser within thirty (30) days to raise funds for the establishment of an urgently needed U'wa Legal Defense Fund;

Whereas one hundred percent (100%) of said funds will go directly to the U'wa Legal Defense Fund, with zero (0) percent retained by the National Democratic Party to cover overhead or administrative expenses;

Whereas, the National democratic Party calls on the Columbian Government and the U.N. to honor the U'wa right to enjoy self-determination and get off the dime and grant it to them;

Whereas, I, Reverend Albert Arnold Gore, agree never to purchase Oxy Oil stock, either preferred or common, so long as I shall live;

Whereas, I, Señor Berito Cobaria, both in my personal capacity and on behalf of the U'wa people, agree never to threaten bodily harm against Reverend Albert Arnold Gore again, either directly or indirectly, personally or through third parties, so long as I shall live.

Now THEREFORE, *in consideration of the mutual covenant and agreements contained herein and other good and valuable consideration, the parties agree as follows:*

1. To put aside their differences and hereby remise, release, and forever discharge each other of and from all manner of action or actions, causes of action, claims, allegations, complaints of any kind or description whatsoever, damages, judgments, petitions, grievances, and/or demands whatsoever, including but not limited to those relating to the ownership of Oxy Oil preferred shares by V.P. Al, and threats of crucifixion against him by the U'wa People, and in particular by Young Berito and his band of urban guerrillas.

2. Parties hereby acknowledge that they have read the Comcast Wachovia Accords and fully understand all of the same and that they have had the opportunity to consult with the National Democratic Party's Nominee for President, Jesus Christ—the Democrat—prior to acceptance of the terms and conditions stated herein.

IN WITNESS WHEREOF, and intending to be bound thereby, the parties have caused this Accord to be duly executed on this 6th day of August 2020.

Before the signatures are dry, the Hall of Dems bursts into a National Democratic Hugging party— just my kind of thing, which must be like, totally obvious by now.

Then when all the hugging's done the Secret Service drags Berito, et al. off for booking, which comes as no surprise to any of them. While the terms of the Accords are binding under state law, they do not shield them against prosecution under federal law, in particular under U.S. Code: Title 18, § 1203, which criminalizes hostage taking, made punishable by any terms of years or life imprisonment. Sorry about that Berrito, but not to worry. We Dems will honor our commitments to the U'wa people. And you can count on me putting in a good word for you with the judge at trial. If need be, at your sentencing, too. I'm always moved by those willing to sacrifice for the greater cause.

Still, all in all, it was a very good night for the U'wa people. Minimum input, maximum publicity, acceptable casualties.

And it was a passable night for me, too. For one, I finally got myself nominated. For two, I proved JFK right. I turned Danger into Opportunity, grabbed victory from crisis. As for my Speech on the Mount, well, I can always record a version of it for WeTube and post it tomorrow. Americans deserve to hear Nancy's phenomenal speech. Sermon on the Mount move over. And for three, I think Al and I get big votes out of this. We showed that we were FDR material. That we had nothing to fear but fear itself.

Take that, Beelzebub.

CHAPTER TEN

Colbert—Stephen Colbert—of the Colbert Show and Czar of the Colbert Nation, that born-again comedian—you know, the skinny one in an undertaker's suit—who delivers his funnier-than-thou sermons from high atop his late-night pulpit at Comedy Central Cathedral wearing, among other things, his latest from his special bowtie collection he bought off Washington Post pundit George F. Will at a yard sale after he gave up the lot for a more traditional regular old necktie-look— the single most liberal act in the history of Conservative George—dating back to the time when he was still punditing on This Week with George Stephanopoulos on Sunday mornings, about five hundred plus weeks ago, if memory serves. So, as a consequence, Stephen gave up his own traditional tie-look, not because he was in love with the bowtie, *per se*— no, not at all. No, for him, he put on a bowtie out of a sense of moral, social duty because in his mind, at least, the gesture was about restoring balance to the universe. That is, if George was going to go liberal necktie, he'd be damned if he wasn't going to go conservative bowtie—to balance the elemental political forces at work on the universal stage. A world without bowties is a world bereft of conservative values, which is exactly why I myself have taken up putting on bowties on the daily campaign trail as I head into this General Election season. No real Republican presidential can be seen without them. Bowties say conservative values. On the other hand, I also run the risk of appearing priggish, like George always did, which is why I'm sitting here in the Green Room about to do the Colbert Show because once I get through it there's just no possible way that anyone at anytime will ever be able to accuse me of being priggish—no matter how frequently I wear bowties. In any event, you have to admire Stephen for what he did on behalf of the universe. That's the kind of comedian he is—a comedian with a conscience—which may be an oxymoron, a contradiction in terms, but there you have it. The world needs more born-again comedians with consciences like Stephen speaking from an ever-expanding number of late-night pulpits, don't you think?

Speaking of whom, he's on the air right now, beaming his rascally grin into the hearts and homes of America's political elite and ante disestablishment types alike. He swirls in his studio chair, like a kid on a barstool. He jabs the Klieg-lit air with the tip of his forefinger, as if poking a low-hung piñata. His comical face is a powder keg of risible mischief about to explode. Like a bald eagle coming in low and fast, about to pluck up lunch, the studio camera swoops in on one jocular Stephen Colbert, who then proceeds to blow his comical top in close-up.

"Tonight, from the show that's not too proud to bite!" he whoops, waggish eyes shiny bright as asphalt streets doused in Gatorade. "Holy Ghost or Beelzebub Incarnate, what have presidential candidates come to these days? If you have to ask, you'd better vote Green Party!"

360

Caption 1 appears at Colbert's left cheek, "Ralph Nader—this is your last chance!"

Naturally, to watch Stephen in motion is to watch a wave of perfection. I sit in awe—more like in rapture, actually—inside the Colbert Nation Green Room, as Stephen blasts off like a Titan rocket from his studio silo. Say what you will about Colbert—a hoot, a coot—he's armed and dangerous.

Turning to the camera at a different angle, he bellows, "Then, who painted the cross on the Capitol flag today? Was it the Religious Right or the Christian Left?"

Caption 2 appears: "Phone home, Jerry Falwell: All's forgiven!"

Another position, another angle, Colbert twists, then shouts, his impish hilarity infectious, his embrace of the ludicrous this side of magnificent. "My guest tonight is slumming for votes; I prepped for it by watching a Ted Turner colorized version of *Mr. Smith Goes to Washington* twenty-two times. He's no Jimmy Stewart, and definitely no Jack Kennedy, but I never promised you ANYTHING!

"This is the Colbert Report, where bite makes might and politics ain't nice!"

Caption 3: "He never promised a love nest in The Bunker to his interns, either."

Silvery clouds blow across the sky like giant wads of cotton candy; schmaltzy trumpet riffs erupt, making me want to eject from my seat and stand at attention; a picture of the Statue of Liberty twirls like a cheer leader's baton in a computer-generated graphic of safe patriotic space. Now I'm in the mood to salute. Then comes another computer graphic of Colbert Himself, waving an American flag in a computer generated breeze, this century's Yankee Doodle Dandy parading down Main Street. He's no George Cohan, but then this isn't 1942, either.

In a miniature sweeping gesture that epitomizes the comic debonair and way cool of Stephen Colbert, he removes his rimless glasses while staring down the barrel of the camera. What most men aspire to be, Colbert is. Of Colbert, let this be said: He's the Abbot of Funditry; Apostolic Administrator of impish roguery; Prelate of clownish blasphemy; Cardinal of frolicsome rakishness; High Priest of tricksy gung ho-ness, and when he has to be—and wants to be, which is always—teasing dean of the annual White House Correspondents' Association Dinner roasts. His 2006 barbeque of George W. was a classic in jest.

As the audience fanatically applauds, a second animated eagle swoops across the stage, looking for sautéed political tidbits. The camera dollies in, approaching Stephen Colbert faster than a kid on a skateboard. He sits behind his desk like the pope in a mortician's suit, agitating his open hands every which way in a mock display of humility.

"Thank you! Thank you! Please! Folks at home, please do not change your dial because I'm in the mood to be born-again—Yes, really, right here on TV—baptized with only my original George Will bowtie on, beside the Waters of Brooklyn!

"You won't want to miss that, folks!"

Now I ask you: What more could you ask for in a comedian? And to think that only a few months ago I was so admiring of despots like Pol Pot and Joseph Stalin. No longer. I can't quite explain what's happened, but one thing's Comedy Central certain to me now: Presidential politics is toxic stuff.

The light goes on in the Green Room. That's my cue. I'm on. In the Colbert Nation, it's General Election time.

They sit me down alone at the roundtable for the interviewee on a set built adjacent to the one Stephen's currently bogarting, while yucking it up with the studio audience. Whatever his joke—at whomever's expense— the Colbert audience laps it up, like raspberry jam from his fingertips. I look around. Nice set. Beside me is a backdrop made of Lucite, stain glass panels laced with predictable patriotic imagery: The all but phallic Washington Monument, the robust breast of the U.S. Capitol, and bracketing America's primordial sex symbols are the beaks of two Lucite stain glass eagles, poised to peck at the enemies of hilarity. What's with the Father of the Colbert Nation and eagles, anyway? I understand—at last—wanting to be on the side of angels, for sure, but on the side of the eagles? It must be a Founding Father Syndrome kind of thing.

As I sip mineral water from a Colbert Nation mug put down at my place by a post-David Letterman intern and prettified with an abundance of eagles—what else? Stephen belts out "The Star Spangled Savior," parodied especially for me.

> Oh, say can you see by Christ's divine light
> What so sadly we saw at his last crucifying
> Whose bright blood and clear tears thru the perilous terror
> On the cross we watched were so tragically streaming?
> And the Roman's dread stares, the lances bursting his flesh,
> Gave proof through the millennia that our Savior was still

somewhere.

> Oh, say does that star-spangled Savior yet rise

O'er the land of the devout and the home of the occasionally contrite?

"To answer that question," Stephen spouts, "as well as, I hope, to own up to exactly what he was doing up in Heaven with God knows how many nubile interns, divine beyond all saying, for all these centuries—plenty, I'm sure, to be the envy of even my colleague, David

Lettermen, and his treasure trove of Bunker Mates—is our star spangled savior Himself, Christ—the Republican! False Prophet or True Hope? I'll let you be the judge of that!"

The studio erupts with a kind of newborn glory hallelujah clapping. Stephen skips willy-silly over to the studio tabernacle where I sit, topping the audience applause with the ridiculously righteous exclamation, "It's Rapture Time, folks!" while waving his arms about in ways that would make the average grown man look positively idiotic—but not Stephen. No, there's not a speck of idiocy about him. He's molten comedic genius, pure and simple, the lampooning Charlie Chaplin of late-night Internet TV. And I'm psyched about just sitting at the same table with him, especially since it's not everyone who has the motive and opportunity to pull the wool over the eyes of the entire Colbert Nation. Of course, for me it's strictly a matter of business, presidential business, for sure, but business nonetheless. Otherwise, I wouldn't entertain doing anything so low down and ornery—not anymore, that is. For one thing, though I myself am not a Christian—not yet at least—I've grown to respect my stepbrother's faith quite a bit since I began impersonating him. It's not all bad. Of course it's not all that great, either. Perhaps I'm suffering from Christianity Syndrome and that's why I've begun to think the way I am. Or maybe I'm a victim of Democracy Syndrome. Or both. It stands to reason. I pretend I'm Christ and inadvertently become more and more like him, even become sympathetic to everything he stands for. That is, I gradually become less religiously challenged—although, Heaven knows, I still don't want him to beat me at the ballot box. Talk about unintended consequences. I can only hope that my surprise transformation—astonishing above all to myself—will be worth it in the last analysis. Anyway, the aforementioned confessions of a mutating personality are strictly

364

between you and me and definitely, definitely, definitely off the record. Got that?

Stephen plops down in the seat across from me, infused with irrepressible Christian glee, characteristic since he's a super Christian—working as a Tele-comedian. He grips my hand, my poor, soar hand. "Thank you for coming, Jesus, thank you!" Actually, the honor's all mine because I need him more than he needs me. We presidential candidates require all the publicity we can get. "But before we begin," he adds in deadpan, "let me state for the record that even though my guest and I are as Christian as they come, we have nothing but respect for other religions because in the end we believe there's more than one road to salvation through our Lord Jesus Christ."

Big laugh.

Stephen bores in on me.

"Now, there's something I urgently wanted to talk to you about. I'm still a little upset with you that I missed the Rapture. Ever since I was born—and born a devout Catholic in Charleston—I wanted to be there for the Rapture and now I've missed my chance because I wasn't given the simple courtesy of a heads-up. No press release. No nothing. And believe me, I would have paid cold, hard cash to have reserved a place at the corner of Hollywood and Vine to see you come down through all that smog. So what went wrong?"

"I never knew you cared, Stephen."

"But I'm a devout Catholic!"

"So I understand!"

"Don't you think we Catholics should be entitled to front row seats? After all, we put more hours in than Episcopalians."

"This is true."

"Damn right it is."

"Forgive me, Stephen, for I have sinned."

"Thank you, Christ—the Republican. You can come on my show anytime."

"There's only one condition."

"What's that?"

"You call me by my right name: I'm Jesus Christ—the Republican, not the Democrat."

"You mean they booked the wrong candidate?"

"Guess so."

"I may look like a comedian and act like a comedian, but deep down inside I'm really just a jackass."

"Got that right."

"Still, there's a 50-50 chance that you're the real Christ, right?"

"At least 50-50."

"Which means I may have doubled my chances of getting into Heaven."

"It's called hedging your bets, Stephen, intentionally or not."

"Got that right. Remind me not to fire my producer."

"Just say the word, Stephen, and I'll issue you a first-class ticket, good for 60 days."

Stephen blanches at the thought.

"Well, I don't want to get there *that* quickly."

"Why not? It's a pretty nice place."

"To tell you the truth, I'd much rather wait until Hell freezes over…"

"That could be a very long time in light of global warming."

"If you don't mind me saying so, I'd rather go second class and take my sweet time."

"Suit yourself."

"Not that I would ever want to give our viewers the impression that I'm trying to buy my way into Heaven with a little free air time…"

"Don't worry, they figured that out long ago."

"You think?"

"I think. But to tell you the truth, Stephen, you earned a ticket long ago."

"I did?"

"You did. The night you roasted George W. Bush at the White House Correspondence Association Dinner. That did it."

"No kidding. I never knew that."

"Of course not. But I'm here to tell you that you won over the Old Man that night, for sure, even though He knows that you're a Democrat."

"You mean…?"

"Yes, God's a Republican."

"Well, as you die and are reborn…"

"You never suspected, right?"

"Not once. And it will certainly come as a big surprise to all my liberal friends, to say nothing of the liberal media."

"I guess Fox News is going to be quite happy to hear that."

"I never would have suspected."

"No reason you should have. It's a secret ballot, you know."

"Still—God a Republican?"

"Well, why do you think I'm one? It runs in the family."

"So basically most of us Democrats are screwed when we go belly up."

"Got that right. But it's not too late for folks to switch parties and vote Republican. Vote for me, that is."

"I guess we're all gonna want to think carefully about that."

"Got that right."

"Not that anyone could ever accuse you of using intimidation tactics."

"Not if anyone knows what's good for them."

"So why's God a Republican? What's the attraction?"

"He's big on Rush Limbaugh, for one. He loves talk radio, listens to it 24/7. He's obsessed, if you ask me."

"You don't say."

"I just did. Loves Rush, loathed Bush. Go figure."

"So even George W.'s going to have a rough time getting in, even though he is—well, one of your kind."

"After what he did to the Republican Party in the wake of Iraq and the Great Recession of 2008? No chance."

"What about Dick Cheney?"

My head swivels slowly back and forth, in mock pity.

"Hopeless, uh?"

My head bobbles yes.

"Couldn't have happened to a kinder, gentler duck hunter."

"The truth is, Stephen, the Old Man tolerates the Christian Right but His heart's with the James Baker-types. His all-time favorites are Olympia Snowe, Jim Leach, Susan Collins, Arlen Specter, Christopher Shays and Richard Lugar."

"So He's a liberal Republican."

"More like moderate to liberal."

"I only wish I'd known."

"Now you do."

"So He's like you?"

"More like I'm like Him. I like small government, low taxes, and a big military to protect my religion and my nation."

"I'm with you. The bigger the military, the safer the Colbert Nation."

"Big military? Coming from a Democrat?"

"I'm a staunch defender of Colbert Nation, so I want no expense spared in the defense of my realm."

"So you're a closet Republican! One of us!"

Explosive applause. Stephen turns on his audience. "Stop sucking up to my guest! No, I'm a Scoop Jackson Democrat! A Colbert Nation nationalist!"

"*Laus Deo!*" I cheer and toast him with a Colbert Nation coffee mug.

"So, how's the campaign going for you so far?"

"As you might expect."

"So you're optimistic about your prospects?"

"With the Old Man on my side, the race is mine to win."

"But doesn't your opponent say the same?"

"He'd be wrong."

"But you both can't be right."

"True. I'd be right; he'd be wrong."

"Well, that makes it simple."

"Also true."

"Prove it."

I pass Colbert a piece of paper. "The Old Man's endorsement," I tell him. "Sign, sealed and emailed."

The spectators cheer. He turns on them again. "I said stop sucking up to Jesus! ONLY I GET TO DO THAT! Now let me have a look." Colbert scans the document, holds it up before the studio lights, examining the elegant watermark. "Looks genuine enough."

"You better believe it."

"So you think this is proof positive that you're the true Hallelujah Savior and not Beelzebub Himself or worse—George W. Revisited?

"I do."

"May we speak frankly?"

"Of course."

"Perfectly frankly?"

"Absolutely."

"You won't take it personally?"

"No chance."

"The truth is, Stephen, I didn't come back to Earth to run for the presidency."

"Then why did you come back?"

"I came back to run for the presidency of the Colbert Nation. I came back to win your seat. Both the Old Man and I have always been fans and it seems like a pretty good gig..."

"If you can get it."

"That's right, my friend. IF YOU CAN GET IT!"

"I think you know the answer to that..."

"Why, you snake..."

"Careful, Stephen, remember who you're talking to."

"But what will I do if I lose the election?"

"Which you will..."

"Which I will."

"Then it's back to Charleston for you!"

"No! Not Charleston!"

"Yes, Charleston."

"Anywhere but Charleston! YOU CAN'T DO THIS TO ME!"

"Oh yes I can. It's called term limits, Stephen."

"They passed that law in the Colbert Nation, too?"

"Yes, in the Colbert Nation, too."

"But you could have any late-night nation presidency you wanted. Why mine?"

"Because the Old Man wants to knock the Letterman Nation clear off the air and you haven't done it yet."

"But why the Letterman Nation?"

"Because of that little thing called The Bunker."

"Oh that."

"Yes, that."

"Now I see."

"Yes, I thought you would."

"He was pretty steamed about that, uh?"

"He's still more than a little ticked. That was a bed too far, even for celebrities. He never should have lured all those interns up there, desecrating the top of the Ed Sullivan Theatre like that! Anyway, it's been decided. I represent the Republican morality police and we're gonna take over and our first step is to wage a coup against the Letterman Nation. That's why I'm running, Stephen."

"Sounds perfectly logical to me."

"One more thing: The Old Man expects His Republicans to vote party-line each and every time. So when Dave admitted that he'd voted for both Republican *and* Democratic Party candidates, well, understandably, the Old Man went ballistic. You wouldn't have wanted to have been there for that..."

"Guess not."

"Absolutely not."

"Well, what's an ex-president supposed to do back in Charleston?"

"I recommend taking up the ministry. You'd be an asset to Catholicism, Stephen. And if you go quietly into that new night, I'd be happy to put in a good word for you."

"With you-know-who?"

"With you-know-who."

371

"Well, you've got my endorsement. Who wants to be president of the Colbert Nation when I can be a deacon in Charleston?"

"So I have your permission to put your name on my campaign literature—Jesus for President of the Colbert Nation—Endorsed by Stephen Colbert Himself?"

"You do."

"That should be good for a ten point bump in the polls. Thank you."

"And your appearance here tonight should guarantee me at least a 4.1/10 audience share. Not too shabby for a comedian on his way out."

Stephen and I look at each other across the table, thinking the exact same thought at the exact same moment. We shout it out loud at the same exact second.

"IS THIS A GREAT COUNTRY OR WHAT?"

The audience cries out, "GOD SAVE THE COLBERT NATION!"

"That's all for tonight, folks!" Stephen interjects. "Just remember, tonight's show may be dead and about to be buried, but on the third day it shall rise again and ascend into Heaven where it shall be viewed at the right hand of God!

"This is the Colbert Report!"

The lights go down on the stage and Stephen offers his hand across the table.

"Well done," he says. "You're welcome back anytime. And I mean it—I really could use a little help getting into Heaven when that day finally comes—and mind you I'm in absolutely no hurry. I may have been raised in Charleston, but I was born in Washington, DC., and you know how that city is, what with all those politicians. There's just no way that some of that shit doesn't rub off on you, I mean, me. So as I said, a little help would be much appreciated."

I tell Stephen that he can count on me.

Later, back in the Green Room, he and I rubbish David Letterman some more just because it feels good. I've also heard tell that Letterman's having my stepbrother on next week, so unfortunately that will likely get him a 5.1/10 share or so, which is not the best of news, but I can live with it considering the Colbert Report will have done fine by me, especially since Stephen gave me his endorsement, if in jest. The voters will never notice the distinction anyway. But the really cheery news for me is this: Donna tells me that I was kind of funny. Imagine that: Beelzebub, a cut up. Strange days indeed. It just goes to show—as if we needed reminding—that anything's possible in the Colbert Nation.

Back in my hotel room, at the end of another day of grip and grin, I crash, like a body falling through plate glass. My strength is drained. It must be the salutary affects levity is having on me. Comedy is another kind of art and one that has been previously out of my league. Tragedy used to be, well, fairly easy for me. I could do it without thinking much about it. But comedy, now that's real work! Nevertheless, as a politician running for the presidency of whatever nation, I must learn to do it and do it well. Any politician, of whatever partisan stripe, who's trying to get himself elected has to buckle down and study the trade. To my knowledge, only Richard Nixon got away with a comedic tin ear. But then look what happened to his administration. It bombed. Completely bombed. Don't want that. So I fully intend to improve my humor, practice it when and where I can. If you ask me, learning to wisecrack well is a more or less noble ambition. And these days I'd like to join the pack. The H.L. Menkens, the Mark Twains, the Jay Lenos, the Johnny Carsons... The big boys, the Comedy Greats. The Lords of Laughter. It all goes with wanting to be seen as a fairly decent chap. Yes, to get myself elected but also just because. Obviously, I still have a long way to go on both counts, but progress is as progress intends. And why not? I've done tragedy. Have I ever done tragedy. So it's time to move on. In the words of that immortal bard Samuel J. Snodgrass as he was about to be led to the guillotine, as quoted by Cosmo Brown in *Singin' in the Rain*, "Make 'em laugh, make 'em laugh, don't you know everyone wants to laugh."

That's the new, improved me in a nutshell. I'm with Cosmo Brown and Samuel J. Snodgrass: Tragedy be gone. Make 'em laugh.

Is this a great campaign, or what?

****

It was my idea to do a face-to-face sit-down with David Letterman on The Late Show, so I can't blame anyone but myself for what might happen tonight. Disciple Dago was the first to voice concern about the idea. He called it a potentially dangerous exercise in self-mockery and public ridicule. Disciple Sparrow wasn't too keen on the plan either. She said, let's be blunt: It's a strategy dumber than stupid pet tricks. (Well, no one can say that freedom of expression doesn't have free rein in my campaign.) But Pelosi nudged me on, saying that unless I softened up—massaged was the word I think she used—my stupendously unfunny campaign image and made myself out to be, well, more Vaudevillian, it would be like signing my political death warrant. Evidently, the voters need to know that I'm not all entirely too humorless to live and that once president I'll be more like the deft and witty JFK than the dreary Richard Nixon. Of course, she's right. I have to shake my Christ the Humorless image. After all, a little jocularity will help me sell my programs on Capitol Hill and to the American public when the time comes. Humor can be a great communicator. Ask Ronald Reagan. He communicated best when he left the public rolling in the aisles. So I'll do my level best to mimic his profound funny side. Levity is next to Heavenly and that's the creed I intend to live by from here on out. As Harry Callahan said in *Sudden Impact,* "Go ahead, make my day... with a little levity." Okay, I added on that last part.

But let's face it, after my stepbrother's blockbuster performance on the Colbert Report, I need to switch personas—really fast. He's up seven points in the polls, already, and rising daily, thanks to his public tête-à-tête with Stephen and attendant good publicity, which is proof positive that Americans don't like their politicians taking themselves all too seriously, which I can understand. I might have fared better back in my Palestine days if I'd lightened up. But I was young and too inexperienced to wrap my mind around that idea. Everything had to be so, so serious. Now I know better. The Old Man warned me about lightening up, too. And it's not as if He doesn't practice what He preaches. Not too many people may know this about Him, but there are times when He can actually be quite a cut-up. In fact, the guy can be a regular Steve Martin when He wants to be. Some days He makes the Elysian Fields positively roar with laughter.

Okay, I inflate, but you get my point. He's no unsmiling statue of Zeus at Olympia, for sure. I've even heard it said that He's a hoot, once you get to know Him.

So that's why I'm doing the David Letterman shuffle, despite the fact, as we now know, that once upon a time ago David did more rendezvousing in The Bunker with his intern love nest mates than joke writing. But hey, who am I to judge? These days I'm just an ordinary politician eking out votes—one vote at a time—one joke at a time. Gee whiz, the more elastic I become, the less I remember who I am.

375

Still, to win the presidency is worth the price of forgetting. The thing is to defeat my *^%&%$%#@$#@%^& stepbrother, at any cost.

My new level of modest self-confidence in my ability to go humor is directly attributable to the good works and the inestimable patience of my mentor, Disciple Schwarzenegger. God bless his Two-Terminator soul. He's been the godfather, the Grand Poobah, call him what you will, of my more comical state of mind. Each night this week after hours he's tutored me on my hotel balcony over popsicles—strawberry popsicles I recall—on the ways of laughter. On top of everything else I learned this: There's no such thing as too many popsicles. They help wonderfully to concentrate the mind.

Apart from the good humor lessons, Arnold also regaled me with stories about his pumping iron glory days, which were all pretty terrific, and an inspiration considering weightlifting is not one of my great strengths. He also managed to widen my internal zone of confidence, telling me that one day not too far away I'd be bidding my stepbrother—only modestly funny in our view—"Hasta la vista."

Even though it amounts to rejoicing in the expectation of the failure of others, it nevertheless made me feel phenomenally—well, let's be frank—good. I'm only human sometimes. Besides, this is democratic politics, definitely not dodge ball in the Garden of Eden. So you have to make allowances, especially for me.

Of course, I can't hope to rise to the level of Go Morality Al. He's the master of self-depreciating humor and sits at the right hand of the Comedy God. I myself am content to live in his burlesque shadow. I accept my limitations. I only hope to self-depreciate enough to get by. The remainder of the guffaw glory I hope will go to Al. He's nearly good enough for the two of us, so some of it will naturally spill over to my benefit as well. Spoken like a true politician. Always looking out for

No.1. Father forgive me, I know what I have done. I've mixed politics and religion.

I'm on in twenty seconds. I'm about to part the curtain, wag my tail like a damn basset hound and go on. Well, that's show business, that's politics, that's doing what you gotta do to win 270 delectable electoral college votes under a flashing neon sign of self-promotion lit up like Times Square on New Year's Eve.

Just look at what I've gotten myself into.

Dave leans into the microphone anchored to his desk to make my glamorous introduction.

"Ladies and gentlemen, please check yourself for ticks, because my next guest is the Democratic nominee for president of the United States—and the only person in the entire solar system who refuses to play Stupid Pet Tricks! This is guaranteed to be more fun than humans should be allowed to have! Let's give a warm welcome to Jesus 'You've Got a Lotta Damn Gall' Christ!"

I'm on.

"Hold onto your wigs and keys, everyone! Here comes the Holy Man!"

Paul Shaffer conducts the CBS Orchestra in a gut-busting version of "Jesus Christ Has Risen Today." (If you ask me, NBC was a fool's fool for firing Paul for stealing studio chalk, as Dave maintains.) He makes this electro version certifiably ROCK! It's never sounded so Top-40 commercial. Never. Episcopalians would be well-advised to bring back the 1940 Hymnal and have Paul write new arrangements. Better than Gothic, Glam, or even Heavy Metal Rock—Holy Rock—a fairly good hook for bringing on the next generation of Holy Rollers, too.

I walk underneath the bright lights. For this one brief moment, I own Ed Sullivan's theatre. The audience greets me as though I was Brad

Pitt and Matt Damon combined—a celebrity's celebrity. They matinee-idolize me. Disciple Jackson's right: NOW I REALLY AM SOMEBODY! If New Yorkers think I am, then I am. They have an unerring instinct for who is and who's not A SOMEBODY. Believe me, this makes the whole stumping for votes 24/7 thing seem, well, marginally kind of worth it, except for the low blow to one's sense of dignity. Even as I walk I can feel the Great Walls of Dignity come tumbling down. But who needs dignity, right? Not when the White House's at stake. Not then, anyway. Which is why the applause, the acclaim is all very nice. It makes losing one's dignity entirely tolerable.

And to think I'm walking in the hallowed footsteps of such musical greats as the Beatles, Sonny & Cher, and the Smother's Brothers, to say nothing of Madonna. God is Great, def!

Anyway, dignity's vastly overrated. Politics is about—as dem taggers in Watts say—"GETTIN' DOWN WIT DA PEOPLE!" Lose da dignity, and da whole world is urs.

Dave and I greet each other amiably. We sit down; Dave behind his big studio desk; me on the comfortable couch next to it. We look as cozy as Koala bears sharing the same fork in the Eucalyptus branch.

"Lordy, lordy, lordy, yes sireee, Christ," enthuses Dave. "Landing you was harder than resisting one of my mom's Thanksgiving pies! Were you playing hard to get or what?"

"This—this was being coy, Dave. Holding out in Heaven for 2000 years before comin' back for the Rapture on Hollywood and Vine—now that was playing hard to get."

Blistering applause. A studio filled with many guffaws. That puts me one-up on Dave with the hot Second Coming jokes. I'm off to a satisfactory start, one worth shedding those extra pounds of dignity for. Besides, no mater what it's worth: I get to sit on the exact same couch Madonna once cushioned her buns on; Courtney Love put her tush on;

Julia Roberts, Isabella Rossellini, Tom Brokaw, Robin Williams, Eddie Murphy, Tom Hanks, Jerry Seinfeld, and Bill Murray took a load off on. Even that Republican Maverick, John McCain, who sided with George W. on Iraq. And don't think the Old Man and I didn't give old Obama a helping hand way back in 2008. No way we were going to let another Bushian Republican do one more four-year stretch in the White House. We'd have stuffed the ballot boxes ourselves to get the desired results. He and I aren't above a little Chicago-style politics when the fate of the world hangs in the balance. Not that we want that passed around. Don't even think about it. Your eternity depends on it.

"I may be high on coffee, cheap speed and donuts, but gosh darn it, it's great to have you finally on. This oughta buy me enough extra credit with Rev. Beal to keep me in the church directory!"

"But not near enough to get you a feather bed in Heaven come Judgment Day."

Dave goes pale, white as a bed sheet. He feigns a cough. He straightens his tie, sips down hot coffee from his mug. Mistakenly or not, he splashes hot coffee in his lap. He hops out of his chair, madly brushes his lap with a napkin. Then he kneels down at the base of his swivel chair and adjusts the height. He sits down again, stirs his coffee with a No. 2 pencil. Finished, he flips it like a baby baton, attempting a patented Johnny Carson one-handed catch. It clatters on the desktop. Faking frustration, Dave flings it at the camera—but it goes wide and crashes to the floor beyond the frame, shattering like a sheet of plate glass.

"Hold onto your wigs and keys, everyone!" Dave announces with a mixture of despair and good humor. "Not even Christ's willing to forgive a guilt-ridden Presbyterian Midwesterner for what went on in The Bunker all those years ago!

"Lordy, lordy, lordy, yes sireee, Christ, I'm in the shithouse now!"

"Yes sireee, Dave, as I understand it, you set an all-time intern humping record."

"Is there no way to make amends, Jesus?"

"Gifts to the Magi?"

"I bring gifts to the Magi!"

One by one, Dave extracts choice articles from underneath his desk. First, a baseball card. Then, a CBS tote bag. Next, a plastic bottle of Lipitor. Finally, bundles of cash.

"I'm willing to give you my very own only slightly creased 2007 Barry Bonds baseball card?"

"Tempting, but that a steroid season, so it's not enough."

"What about this official CBS tote bag, with travel toothbrush, Crest toothpaste, plastic comb and boot polish also included?"

"Again tempting, but I already have my own boot polish, thank you, so it's not enough."

"Okay, then, I'll throw in my last spare bottle of Lipitor—unused. It reduces bad cholesterol 39%-60%, when exercise and diet are not enough."

"I don't do drugs, Dave."

"You know that you're making this difficult for me, don't you?"

"I do."

"Lordy, lordy, lordy, the stakes are mighty high. So here's my final offer: I'm putting down $20,000 in cold hard cash that I won fair and square in Texas poker the other night playing double or nothing with actress Anna Paquin for the $10,000 she beat me out of on my show years ago. Believe me, Jesus, I NEVER GOT OVER IT!"

"Tempting, but no dice, Dave."

"Then how am I supposed to pass my troubles to a monkey on a rock?"

"The Three Kings did better than this, Dave."

"You think?"

"I know."

"The Old Man is looking for signs of redemption, Dave, not hard cash."

"Not baseball cards?"

"Not even Barry Bonds baseball cards."

"Well, imagine that."

"But I know a way that you can get that feather bed."

"Tell me, tell me, please."

"Renovate the Ed Sullivan Theatre Bunker upstairs and turn the sin room into a political madrasa."

"You mean to train Islamic terrorists in the ways of anti-Westernism?"

"No Dave, turn it into a schoolhouse for repentant Republicans who agree to convert to Democratic Party orthodoxy."

"You mean you want me to homeschool a new generation of late night comedians?"

"That, too. Because what the world needs now is laughs."

That gets a laugh.

"Down fella!" Dave barks. "I'll handle the jokes!"

He turns on the audience, admonishing them. "Remember," he says, "this is not a competition, it's only an exhibition—please, no wagering."

That gets another laugh. Then he comes back at me.

"Speaking of upstairs, it must have been a tough decision for you to leave Valhalla to come back down to the land of too little comedy, uh?"

"Like Disciple Schwarzenegger said in advance of his decision to run for the governatorship of California: 'Dat was da most difficult one I ever made in my life, except da one when I decided to get a bikini wax.'"

The audience howls, which sends Dave into low orbit. Smacking the flat of his palm down on the desk, he bays, "I said *I'll* handle the jokes around here, big fella!"

Big laugh. I throw up my hands in mock surrender. That pleases Dave.

I notice that it's cold in the studio. I shiver in my seat.

"It's freezing in here, Dave."

"If you can't stand the central air, get out of the studio, big fella."

"But it's colder than a fish locker in here."

"We like to keep our comedy fresh."

"I'm rapidly becoming a meat popsicle, as Korben Dallas says in the *Fifth Element*."

"That's my plan."

"What plan is that, Dave?"

"Cryonics for Christ.

"It happens like this: We freeze you today so we're guaranteed to have you around tomorrow. This time out we're not taking any chances. You're grounded, big fella. We're puttin' you on ice. There's no more Valhalla for you any century soon. The truth is the world needs you every bit as late-night comedy needs me. Which is a lot. So we're gonna put you right where we can always find you. In the fridge, on ice. We promise to thaw you out each time an urgent situation requires your divine assistance. But we will accept no more unexplained absences. The world can ill-afford to wait thousands of years between your visits any more than it can do without my comedy.

382

"Believe you me, history will thank me for this."

"Your public service to God and Comedy?"

"You betcha."

"I am at your service."

"I just knew you'd be a good sport! It's no wonder I'm a Presbyterian!

"We'll be right back, folks, with a special edition of Stupid Pet Tricks, after a few suspect words from our desperate sponsors. Tonight's edition will be hosted by the Do-gooder of all Do-gooders— our very own soon-to-be Cryonic Christ—before we lay him out on the ice!"

During the commercial break, Paul Shaffer and the CBS Orchestra crank out a rather moving rendition of "O Holy Night", a song recalling the tender embrace of my mother. Dave, too, is moved to tears. "So very fitting, Paul. So very fitting. It's never too early for Christmas tunes." That was something to remember, a beautiful shared moment with my fellow comedians.

Back on the air, Dave launches into his rather kooky imitation of horseracing announcer Dave Johnson's racing call, "Ladies and gents, down the stretch they come!" which is followed by unleashed cheers for Paul and his great, little band.

"Folks, we're back on with Jesus 'You've Got a Lotta Damn Gall' Christ and his very own special edition of Stupid Pet Tricks!"

Times have definitely changed since Caesar Augustus decreed that the world should be taxed. We didn't have Stupid Pet Tricks back then and no doubt the world was that much the poorer for it. I just hope and pray that the Old Man isn't looking down. His heart isn't what it used to be, you know. I'd prefer to spare Him any sudden shocks. Still, if He does get wind of my antics here tonight, He's got to practice tolerance. He needs to understand that politics is about dignity be

383

damned, that anything goes to get elected. Besides, what the world needs now is laughs. More laughs than a basket full of singing monkeys. And hands down I'm the right candidate for the job. I'm the one—the only one—competent enough to usher in a Golden Age of Laughter, which will relieve our grave and somber world from its miserable and humorless existence—once and for all.

Well, Dave and I, that is. And Stephen, too, I suppose, although I'm still marginally unhappy that he gave away free airtime to my stepbrother. Jay Leno? He's too Republican for me. So it's just us three politically correct Promoters of the Comedic Faith.

Let salvation by comedy begin.

Pope Pious III Himself stands on all fours on the top ledge of a twelve-foot high aluminum ladder on stage. A regular on Stupid Pet Tricks, Pope Pious III is a white fluffy feline, of some conceit, understandable in light of its national notoriety. Tonight, he is under orders to partake of the first rite of Holy Sacrament. That is, chomp down a communion wafer—administered by your celebrant extraordinaire, who also finds himself on the eighth rung of aforementioned ladder under the searing halogens, feeling, well, let's face it, stupid, bereft of even the remotest prayer of ever reclaiming my dearly departed dignity.

But in pursuit of the White House, as we all know, I must be fearless, must be completely game for anything and everything. Be prepared to descend to new lows in search of high comedy to win votes; yes votes, glorious votes. No price is too high, no act too undignified, to advance my candidacy from over Here to over There.

Paul's open roll snare drum sounds, portending great things to come. Wafer in hand, I turn to the studio audience, and note in an understated way, I might add. "This is only an exhibition, not a competition. Please... no wagering." That gets a laugh. As well it should. I borrowed it from Dave. Good comedians borrow; great comedians steal. I haven't ascended to greatness yet, but believe me, I intend to get there. These days, comedy is next to godliness.

Pope Pious III turns his snoot upwards, pointed towards the Fresnels showering down light. That's my cue. I step one more rung up the ladder and take the Host from the paten, a whole wheat wafer, 1 3/8" in diameter, embossed with a simple rendering of the Christian cross. Making the Sign of the Cross over the paten, I say in a tone both reverential and fun, "May the Body of Our Lord Jesus Christ preserve your soul unto life everlasting." I incrementally lower the wafer down toward the little nose pointed the way of all Heavens. And as it comes to rest, stupendously, miraculously, fantastically, it balances: Communion wafer stabilized on snout.

Pope Pious III snaps his head, flinging the Host upwards like a beach ball, waiting for it, mouth wide open, to come back down, before devouring it whole. The gallery bursts out in a blaze of applause. I'll be the first to admit it; the Pope's got talent. Everyone else recognizes it, too. We're all very impressed. I genuflect, then start back down the ladder as Pope Pious stands where he was, basking in the deserved fame, wrapping himself in blankets of limelight. It must be nice.

But a funny thing happens to me. I feel less than a lot undignified as I go down. A weight has been lifted, inexplicably. Then instantly, I recognize why. As faith knows no limits, neither the Holy Sacrament knows no prejudice. A Sacrament is a Sacrament is a Sacrament. No matter who gets it, it's still sacred. Even for felines, named Pope Pious III.

Johnny Depp, the Late Show's loyal mascot, who is, in fact, a big, blue, and beautiful Macaw parrot, swings upside down on a bird

385

ring in a rattan cage mounted center stage on a plain, wooden stool. I stand next to him, holding the paten in my left hand, about to assume my celebrant duties again with my right. On the paten sits a silver Chalice, filled with good wine. Next to it lies a 2ml glass Eye Dropper, loaded. Johnny, being Johnny, is spouting off his customary Dave Letterman non-sequiturs non-stop. He's quite the showman: "Something from the meat case, Linda? Something from the meat case, Linda? Not a man, woman, or child alive today who doesn't enjoy a lovely beverage. Not a man, woman, or child alive today who doesn't enjoy a lovely beverage." He won't be shut up.

"Johnny want communion wine?" I ask.

"SQUAWK! Johnny want communion wine," he cracks.

I make the Sign of the Cross with the Eye dropper over the silver Chalice, and say with a degree of profundity, and without the slightest indication of any kind of prejudice, either inferred or implied, due to the fact that he is, after all, a parrot, "May the Blood of Our Lord Jesus Christ preserve your soul unto life everlasting. Amen." Then I guide the dropper through the cage until it touches Johnny Depp's beak.

Compressing the squeeze bulb, a little at a time, Johnny chugs the Precious Blood down. Naturally, once the dropper's dry, as any pirate parrot would, he begs for more.

"Johnny want more. Johnny want more."

I harden my heart like a pharaoh. "Not until after you recite the first of my commandments." I can be tough when I want to be. "There's more to this trick than quaffing down vino, you know."

There is no discernible pause between the end of my sentence and the beginning of his. He's on the job.

"Love the Lord your God with all your heart and with all your soul and with all your mind! Love the Lord your God with all your heart and with all your soul and with all your mind. SQUAWK!"

386

That perfect delivery earns him a complimentary dropper-full of the grape.

"Now for the second."

"Love your neighbor as yourself! Love your neighbor as yourself! SQUAWK!"

Another flawless recital, another gratis dropper-full of vintage communion wine. He guzzles it down, like only a pirate parrot could. Then, I suppose out of gratitude, he does me one better. "All the Law and the Prophets hang on these two commandments!" he spouts. "All the Law and the Prophets hang on these two commandments! SQUAWK!"

How can you not love this bird?

You can forget about my hardened heart. I indulge him with a fourth dropper-full of wine. Well, why not? It's consecrated wine, and parrots—just like people—are entitled to the rites of salvation, anytime. And more is usually better.

But now he's drunk. Parrot drunk. Which means, of course, trouble!

"Captain Jack Sparrow! Captain Jack Sparrow! Where's the deck of the Black Pearl? Where's the deck of the Black Pearl? SQUAWK!"

This was not in the script.

"No, you're not Captain Jack Sparrow and this is not the deck of the Black Pearl! Remember! You're just a parrot named Johnny Depp and this is the set of the Dave Letterman Show, not the deck of the Black Pearl!"

"Captain Jack Sparrow! Captain Jack Sparrow! Where's the deck of the Black Pearl? Where's the deck of the Black Pearl? SQUAWK!"

"I said…"

"Johnny want communion wine! Johnny want communion wine! SQUAWK!"

Things appear to be getting somewhat out of hand, so Dave intervenes. Thank the Old Man for that. It would definitely hurt my numbers if I were to be seen losing my temper with a drunken parrot.

"Wake the kids and call the neighbors, folks, that was Pope Pious and Johnny Depp performing a special edition of Stupid Pet Tricks, with Jesus 'You've Got a Lotta Damn Gall' Christ, who has demonstrated once again why they don't let chimps be late night talk show hosts!"

Johnny's drunker than six pirates in a bar in Singapore. "Bootstrap Bill! Curse of the Black Pearl! Bootstrap Bill! Curse of the Black Pearl! SQUAWK!"

Then he passes out. In all my days I've never seen a parrot so drunk.

"We'll be right back for the Top Ten Reasons why the American public should let Jesus Christ park his donkey at the White House on Inauguration Day after more slippery words from our overwrought sponsors!"

Funny, Dave, funny. The good thing about Dave is that he's taught me not to take myself so seriously.

Cut to commercial. Johnny's handlers cart him off. I reclaim my seat on the couch where Julia Roberts once sat.

Meanwhile, Paul's German Shepherd seeing-eye dog, named Stevie Wonder Dog, puts his paws up on Paul's Roland keyboard and starts playing that Yuletide hymn of Yuletide hymns, "Oh, Come All Ye Faithful." I must say that his wraparound shades look way cool. The seasonal tune brings to mind one of my presidential ambitions: To stand on the Ellipse and throw the switch to light the national Christmas tree.

A paid political commercial in support of my stepbrother's campaign concludes with him staring into the camera and stating, with new, cultivated sincerity, "Don't trust the White House to just anyone:

Vote Republican." I'm all for equal access, mind you. Just not for him, even though I know he's undergoing rehabilitation.

"We're back with the King of Kings—that special Lord of Lords who never met a prostitute he couldn't make go straight!"

The audience roars its adoring approbation. Which makes me feel, well, like the King of Kings that I really am, even though I'm not acting much like Him these days.

"He's been kind enough to agree to recite the Top Ten List of the Reasons why the American public should let him ride his donkey down Pennsylvania Avenue bareback and park it at the White House North Gate come Inauguration Day! Ladies and gentlemen, I give you Jesus 'Oh my aching ass' Christ!"

Oh sure, it's true, Dave's definitely pushing it, but then this is politics, isn't it? And in politics, you have to make allowances. This much is written. Even when they come at my expense, I say, Just Say Yes to Jokes.

I take out the Top Ten List. Believe you me, how well this goes over tonight is more important than an endorsement from the AFL-CIO. I have come to my much-anticipated rendezvous with comedy. This is not where the rubber meets the road, but where the politician meets the holy man.

I leave behind the spot where Julia Roberts once sat as Paul's drum rolls. If you want to know the real Julia Roberts, you must see *Notting Hill*, especially that scene where Julia's movie star character, Anna Scott, stands before Hugh Grant, who's playing an unassuming travel bookshop owner in West London, named William Thacker, imploring him to love her, and looking like the most beautiful girl-next-door in the world. "After all..." she says, holding back tears, "I'm just a girl, standing in front of a boy, asking him to love her."

See the movie and you'll understand my reluctance to leave the spot where she once sat.

"This is an envelope, not an invitation. Please do not attempt to approach the spokesman as he reads," I intone, straight-faced. Dave follows-on by putting his feet up on his Cadillac desk, clasping his hands behind his head, and dreamily interjecting, "I am nothing if not interested and attentive."

That gets a laugh. That Dave—he's just so good with the funnies. I'm all envy. In the event my presidential bid goes down the tubes, which is, like not altogether impossible, and I can't get myself back on track with the Holy Man act, I'd consider starting up a House of Laughs, maybe in L.A., and do a combination religious/political stand up routine. Well why not? Sarah Palin made it work in Vegas.

Who knows? Dave might even go in with me—50-50. We could feature comedy 24/7. Ooops, I mean, 24/6. On the seventh day, even we comedians must rest.

"Now here we go," I boom out, hoping like Hell the Old Man is nowhere near in sight. "The Top Ten Reasons why the American public should let me ride my donkey down Pennsylvania Avenue bareback and park it at the White House North Gate come Inauguration Day!"

Below my bony ribs on screen a snowy White House becomes visible, lit up like the Mormon Tabernacle. Erected on the North Lawn is also a wooden cross, like one of the ones the Romans used to be so big on back in the days when crucifixions were all the rage. On screen, the Top Ten List appears as I bark the numbers out, one by one.

"Number 10.

"I PLEDGE TO COMBAT GLOBAL WARMING BY RIDING MY JACKASS TO ALL OFFICIAL STATE FUNCTIONS WITHIN SIXTY MILES OF WASHINGTON.

"Number 9.

"I PROMISE TO ELIMINATE THE NATIONAL DEBT WITH MORE THAN SMOKE AND MIRACLES.

"Number 8.

"I PLAN TO DELIVER THE STATE OF THE UNION IN ARAMAIC, SO NOBODY IN THE COUNTRY WILL KNOW JUST HOW BAD THINGS ARE.

"Number 7.

"I VOW TO END FRACTIOUS PARTISAN POLITICS IN WASHINGTON BY BRINGING THE HOLY SPIRIT OF BIPARTISANSHIP TO IT.

"Number 6.

"I INTEND TO RECHRISTEN MARINE ONE, JESUS ONE, AND AIR FORCE ONE, GOD FORCE ONE.

"Number 5.

"I WILL INSTALL A NEW HOTLINE IN THE OVAL OFFICE LINKED DIRECTLY TO HEAVEN BECAUSE WE ALL KNOW MY OLD MAN IS A JEALOUS GOD AND PRONE TO SUDDEN BURSTS OF ANGER.

"Number 4.

"I HEREBY COMMIT TO WASHING THE FEET OF EVERY WHITE HOUSE GUEST INVITED TO AN OFFICIAL STATE DINNER.

"Number 3.

"I COMMIT TO GRANTING LIFE-LONG AMNESTY TO THE FIRST MILLION VOTERS IN THE STATE OF TEXAS WHO PULL THE LEVER FOR ME.

"Number 2.

"I AGREE TO PARDON GEORGE W BUSH FOR ALL HIS TOMFOOLERY, BUT NOT DICK CHENEY, NO NEVER.

"And the No. 1 reason why the American public should vote to let me ride my donkey down Pennsylvania Avenue bareback and park it at the White House North Gate on Inauguration Day is—

"I VOW TO PASS LEGISLATION IN MY FIRST 100 DAYS IN OFFICE MAKING IT A FEDERAL OFFENSE FOR JEHOVAH WITNESSES IN EACH OF THE 51 STATES TO PROSELYTIZE ON FRONT PORCHES BEFORE 12 NOON ON SATURDAYS!"

Dave's distinguished production credits show up next: Worldwide Pants Incorporated. They're followed by a second caption: There is No Off Position on the Genius Switch. Then the screen fades to black, and I'm outta here, content in the knowledge that I've helped myself tonight. Still, it's a long, rough road to the North Portico and my White House entrance without a hard pass. Dave said it best when he turned to the camera after I left and said, half in earnest, half in jest, "I wouldn't give his troubles to a monkey on a rock."

He got that right. It's tough being Christ Come Candidate.

Later, at the hotel and in my room—a long cry from that drafty old barn in Bethlehem—Go Morality Al, my disciples and I debrief, after one or two or maybe even three—I can't quite remember—glasses of some fairly passable Argentine wine, I hit the hay, figuratively speaking, of course. Hay is for barn animals, not someone 270 electoral votes away from the White House.

I dream fairly spectacular dreams. One featured Morality Al and I skateboarding down the Santa Monica pier wearing tee shirts inscribed with bubble graffiti letter words, front and back. The words on the front read: "It is easier for Morality Al to go through the eye of a needle..."

And on the back, "Than for a politician to enter the kingdom of Heaven."

Weird, I know.

But I hope you won't hold it against me, because on Election Day I'm really going to need your vote.

CHAPTER ELEVEN

"Good evening, I'm Jim Lehrer of 'The News Hour', broadcasting from the Field House at Washington University in St. Louis, Missouri, and I welcome you to a 90-minute town hall debate between our two candidates for president of the United States. Tonight's debate is sponsored by the Commission on Presidential Debates. The rules have been agreed to by each of our two candidates, and all gunplay has been strictly prohibited.

"On my right, needless to say, is our Republican nominee, the Son of God on the Right. On my left, as might be expected, is our Democratic nominee, the Son of God on the Left, who also claims to be the authentic Holy Ghost, made flesh again. Oh, what a tangled web politics and religion weave! Recent DNA testing has proven conclusively these two candidates are in fact related—which means one of them is definitely Beelzebub. Now it's up to the voters to determine which one. It's up to them to put their finger on the truth. We can all imagine the serious ramifications of electing him, but then again, how much crummier could it be compared with electing George W.? That's another question for another day, for sure, but clearly if Beelzebub were to be elected, it would likely mean the end of Christianity at the White House as we know it. No more Easter egg rolls on the South Lawn. No more Christmas tree lightings down on the Ellipse. No more wooden crosses parked on the North Lawn and proclaiming the national faith. And worst of all, no more wearing Christianity on proverbial presidential sleeves, before, during, and after campaigns. Imagine that.

"Still, even if Beelzebub should manage to slip through the White House North Gate on Inauguration Day, like those supreme state dinner party crashers—Tareq and Michaele Salahi—there's no need to abandon total hope. Recalling the words of once upon a governor of Mississippi and erstwhile chairman of the Republican National Committee, Haley Barbour, 'In politics, nothing is as good or as bad as it seems,' with the possible exception of George W., of course. But let's not traumatize ourselves by walking backwards into Baghdad again. To paraphrase Haley, in democratic politics, no politician is as good or as bad as he or she may seem. That goes for Beelzebub as well. Democratic politics has a salutary effect, even on ornery despot

"Our debate tonight has the candidates seated in chairs surrounded by an audience of 'uncommitted' St. Louis-area voters. Or so they say. They were determined to be 'uncommitted' in a poll conducted by the Gallup organization, which never errs, except by a margin of error of +/- 4 percentage points. Under the rules agreed to by the two campaigns, audience members wrote out their questions on one side of their 3" x 5" cards earlier this afternoon and those cards were then delivered to my offices by two armed guards from the Pinkerton Agency where I have grouped the questions according to subject matter and swear on Edmund Murrow's grave that no one knows the content of these questions except for me and their authors and that they have not left my sight, except once when I had to visit the little boy's room for a minute or two—no more.

"I will ask the authors of the questions to ask their questions at the microphones placed for their convenience at the end of one of four aisles and request they refrain from showboating, which is a right reserved for our candidates only. As the Dean of Moderators, however,

394

I get to do whatever I please, whenever I please, however I please. I retain the right to ask any follow-up questions I like or, if necessary, call in the Missouri National Guard to force the candidates to actually answer my follow-up questions, instead of evade them, which is not like out of the question. I also have the right to call in federal marshals at any time to break up any brawls between the two candidates that could break out for reasons real or imagined. At my presidential town hall debate, fisticuffs are outlawed.

"As moderator, I am required to issue this disclaimer: The News Hour and PBS take no responsibility whatsoever for the content of this program. Nor, we are at pains to say, can it be rated in advance, for reasons obvious, so parents please, keep your mute buttons at the ready, if your children are up and about. You never know what these politicians will say.

"I, for one, am with Mark Twain. There should be a room in every house and an auditorium in every university to swear in. It's dangerous to repress such emotions.

"The candidates will have the opportunity to question each other, with personal attacks encouraged. Outright exaggerations, absolute distortions and unreserved lies are discouraged. Telling the truth is a plus, and makes the candidate eligible for extra voter brownie points, redeemable on Election Day.

"There will be no opening statements, but each candidate will have two minutes for a closing statement. The first candidate who delivers a closing statement of one minute or less will earn the Dean of Moderators' official endorsement—which granted may be worth less than a vote by the District of Columbia's non-voting delegate in the U.S. House of Representatives, but it's all I've got to give: One man, one endorsement. That's all, folks!

"And may the real Christ win.

"Now let's welcome our two opposing candidates to the Clash of Comedians, Mr. Jesus Christ—the Democrat—and Mr. Jesus Christ—the Republican. Welcome to the Clash of Comedians. Kindly take your seats, and let the Clash begin.

"As pre-determined by the two candidates drawing straws at an undisclosed location this morning, and with the final results tabulated and delivered by Price Waterhouse to my offices by Pinkerton Government Services late this afternoon, tonight's first question goes to Jesus Christ—the Democrat—from Dywane Tanner, a former eco-terrorist, who did time at USP Leavenworth for firebombing a Hummer dealership in Fayetteville, Missouri back in 2012. At the time, his destruction set a new record. He incinerated 43 H4 SUT Luxury Hummers in one night. At $74,400 a pop, he hit the Hummer Empire right where it hurt: In its Shanghai bank account. And he would have gotten off scot free except for one thing: He bragged about his incursion on Facebook. Fortunately for him, once he got into prison, he 'found' Gandhi and became a do-gooder pacifist, just like Christ.

"How do we know? On the First Day, his parole record states that he helped put on a new roof at Leavenworth using photovoltaic shingles donated by Unisolar. On the Second Day, he designed and installed a solar energy system to power the prison laundry room. On the Third Day, he engineered a clean green energy machine to power up and down prison cell doors, making Leavenworth the most energy efficient prison in the nation. So successful was Mr. Tanner that last month Mother Jones featured Leavenworth on its front cover, labeling it, Eco-Friendly Incarceration. Because of all his good solar works, Mr. Tanner was paroled, so his solar vision could be set loose to solar-up the world. Some call him the Christ of Ecology, delivering the Gospel According to Ecology to a planet hungry for clean energy. He is also the president of SolarEarth, a non-profit based in Washington, D.C., that is dedicated to defending the planet from the environmental harm caused by the Hummer Corporation by promoting solar.

"Mr. Tanner will pose a question on the environment. Mr. Tanner, where are you? Oh, there you are... the one wearing a Hummer's the Mother of All Bummers sweatshirt. Mr. Tanner, the floor is yours."

"Thank you, Mr. Lehrer, but for the record, it was ecotage, not sabotage, that what I did. But let's not go there right now, because frankly, and forever, I've seen the light—which came by route of solar power. Not that I'm not tempted—and I mean really tempted—to put a blowtorch to the odd Hummer parked on the street every once in a while. Those bright door sill plates, those heated leather-trimmed seats, those Vortec™ 6.2L V8 engines make for almost irresistible targets, don't you know?"

"Mr. Tanner—your question, please."

"*Oh right, my past violent tendencies aside, I'd like to take this opportunity to also put in a good word for my former compatriots at the Earth Liberation Front, some of whom are doing time in Leavenworth. Hey Mark, Hey Brian, Hey Shelley! Hey everyone else, you know who you are! I'm always thinkin' 'bout you!*

"*Mr. Tanner...*"

"*Right, I'm just saying that despite the so-called illegality of their actions, they did really good work and they're still my friends. Their only fault—and mine, too, mine, too—Lord only knows, was using the Hammer on the Hummer instead of the Velvet Glove, which is understandable in light of the fact that the Hummer is contributing the extinction of thousands of defenseless species up and down the planet. If that isn't violence, if that isn't wrong, if that isn't environmental genocide, I don't know what is!*"

"*Mr. Tanner, please!*"

"*Oh right, sorry! One final note, if there's anyone in the viewing audience— anyone at all—wishing to make a contribution or would like to volunteer to picket*

397

with us at Hummer's Shanghai headquarters, and doesn't mind getting thrown into the Laogai System for a few years—max!—please go to our website to sign up. That's www.SolarEarth.org. *Or if you can't spare the time away from friends and family, please consider instead making a generous donation! We accept AMEX, VISA, DISCOVER, MASTERCARD and, of course, PAYPAL!"*

"Mr. Tanner—your question—AS IN EXACTLY NOW!"

"Oh right, sorry about the wait. But once an activist, always an activist! That's what I always say, anyway.

"So what's your position on weaponizing solar power and turning it on the Hummer?"

Shocked, the Dean of Moderators shouts, "Mr. Tanner! Take that back!"

"Oh, it's okay," I jump in. "But before I answer, I'd like to thank Washington University and the people of St. Louis for hosting this debate tonight. It's an honor to be in the home state of one of America's greatest presidents, Harry S. Truman. Wasn't he the one who said that there isn't a problem in this country or the world that can't be settled if approached through the teaching of the Sermon on the Mount. What's not to love about old Harry?

"Even if he was responsible for dropping A-bombs on Hiroshima and Nagasaki and wiping out over a hundred thousand people in a flash, I can still git down wit him— as dey say in da hood. Of course, like old Harry, I'd rather have peace in the world than be president, but also like Harry, I was forced by events to seek the presidency and I will not shirk from my duty to keep Beelzebub out of the White House. Again, I'm with old Harry: I just told the truth and you thought it was hell! And you'd be right!

"You better believe the Old Man and I deliberated over his admission ticket to Heaven. Of course, we did. The atomic bombings poised huge moral questions. Naturally Bess was a shoo-in when her time came, but Harry—well, Harry was another matter altogether. It took some fancy flights into the land of moral gymnastics to get him in., but we finally did. And he's been an absolute charm ever since—to say nothing of being a big hit with the children. That's because he shells out good advice. And I quote: 'I've found the best way to give advice to your children is to find out what they want and then advise them to do it.'"

Harry's wit brings me great applause, which I happily pocket. On the other hand, my opponent attacks.

"I'm shocked! Shocked, I tell you, that my opponent would suggest that the Heavenly Father and I would—even for a split-second—have hesitated to let Harry into Heaven. From the moment he was forced to apply, he was welcomed! Those damn Japs deserved what they got coming to them! The man saved thousands of American lives! Thousands of lives! HE HAD TO DO IT! HE HAD TO DO IT, I TELL YOU!"

"Did not!"

"Did so!"

"Did not!"

"Did so!"

"ENOUGH YOU TWO! THIS IS GOING TO BE A CIVILIZED DEBATE OR I'M DECLARING TIME-OUTS FOR EACH OF YOU!"

"Sorry," I say, deeply embarrassed. I *hate* the way my stepbrother brings out the worst in me!

"Yes, sorry," he intones, playing the part of a contrite debater. "But anyone who takes a jab at *my* Harry lights me up with indignation."

"Now that's better. Let's get on with it without sideswiping each other, shall we?"

We've both been sat down in public. How embarrassing. But Beelzebub started it.

By way of greater apology, my eyes lifted towards the brushfires of studio lights showering down, I add, "Forgive me, Father, for I have been rude." Then, turning to Mr. Tanner, stealth ecotagist that he is, I take on his loaded question. "Remember what I have said, Mr. Tanner: Thou shalt love the Planet with all thine heart, and with all thy soul, and with all thy might. This is my first and greatest policy tract. And while I do not advocate weaponizing sunlight, even for the purposes of making bonfires out of Mother of All Bummer car dealer lots, and will not condone, even in the name of green justice, members of the Earth Liberation Front taking Louisville Slugger baseball bats to Hummer daytime running lights, a Christ Administration will—on its first day in office—undertake to propose legislation to ban all Hummers IN THE NAME OF THE ENVIRON. You and I both know what those words mean, don't we, Mr. Tanner?"

Mr. Tanner bows his head, looking contrite.

"They're the very ones you scrawled in the middle of the night in chrome green spray paint across the chrome fuel filler doors of Hummers parked in Fayetteville, back in 2012, right?"

Mr. Tanner nods, ashamed.

"In short, Mr. Tanner, I pledge to use the tool of law to do whatever needs to be done. We shall ban them from the face of America. We shall ban them on the seas and oceans. We shall ban them in the air. We shall defend America from them, whatever the cost may be.

"We shall ban them on the beaches. We shall ban them on the landing grounds. We shall ban them in the fields and in the streets. We shall ban them in the hills.

"First clean the inside of the cup and dish, and then the outside also will be clean.""

"Matthew 23:26!" Dwayne interjects, his sense of ignominy gone.

"And before that—Winston Churchill, June 4, 1940," I tack on.

400

"And so, Mr. Tanner and my fellow Americans out there watching on the Internet, my administration's mantra will be, first and last: ask not what your environment can do for you-- ask what you can do for your environment."

"John F. Kennedy, January 20, 1961!" inserts Mr. Tanner, an obvious connoisseur of history.

"Yes, Mr. Tanner, 'Let the word go forth from this time and place, to friend and foe alike, that the torch has been passed to a new generation of Americans... Let every nation know, whether it wishes us well or ill, that we shall pay any price, bear any burden, meet any hardship, support any friend, oppose any foe, in order to assure the survival of our environment and the success of environmental movement.'"

"Mr. Christ—on the Right, your answer, please."

The color drains out of my face, which I know must be highly visible to the viewing audience. I mean, like, I have to follow that?

It serves me right for reading little, if any, history when I had the luxury of time, back down there in Juarez. But how was I supposed to know I'd end up here tonight—performing before millions of discerning Americans, asking for their votes— and worse, be required to quote oratorical greats to keep on an equal footing with my opponent? All I ever read were the floor speeches of my all-American hero—Senator James M. Inhofe. But then again, what more did I need? He was a great, great man. Plus he knew a thing or two about climate change—the Far Left's sorry excuse of a scheme to put one over on the American public. Don't remember what he was famous for? I do. His statement on the floor of the U.S. Senate that global warming was "the greatest hoax ever perpetrated on the American people" was ahead of its time. It's still ahead of its time. Far, far ahead of its time. But right or wrong, Inhofe stood, Inhofe towered, Inhofe even teetered, on nothing if not principle. So okay, my stepbrother can quote JFK and Churchill with ease and fluidity. Well, good for him. But I bet he can't recite even a single line of Inhofe—not like I can.

So I dive in, with a quote or two tucked like a rocket in my back pocket, courtesy of James M. Inhofe, the distinguished slayer of Great American Hoaxes from the Great State of Oklahoma.

401

"'Debate predicated on fear, rather than science,' that's what Mr. Tanner's accusation is." (I go Inhofe right off the bat because, as everyone knows, the best defense is a good Inhofe.) "Make no mistake, my fellow Americans, the Hummer is the Mother of all Funners! Not the Mother of all bummers! Mr. Tanner and his green genie tribe of out-of-work ecotagers are waist-deep in conspiracy to perpetrate the Second Greatest Hoax ever on the American people—the one that paints the Hummer as a global warming amplifier, a carbon emissions magnifier, a doomsday enhancer.

"It's just not true! As noted author Dr. Michael Crichton wrote in his popular novel, 'State of Hummer,'" I bellow. "I suspect that people of 2100 will have many more Hummers than they have now, that Hummers will consume more energy than they do now, and ride them across more wilderness than they do today. I don't think we have to worry about them." That's Dr. Michael Crichton talking about Hummers!

"And so my fellow Americans, I ask you to remember the words of Senator James M. Inhofe as he spoke them on the floor of the Senate: 'The climate change debate should be based on fundamental principles of science, not religion.' Do you hear that Mr. Tanner? The Hummer debate should be based on principles of science, not the ideology of zealots, not the intolerance of SUV racists—however well intentioned they may be! Avidity and bigotry do not justify the character assassination of Hummer's good name!

"Let me simply say this, from Genesis 1:28—more or less: Let Hummers be fruitful and multiply. Let them fill the seas, and multiply on the earth. Let Hummers be Hummers, my fellow Americans!

"And may God shed His grace on them, and crown their good with brotherhood, from sea to shining sea!"

Hosannas soar from the lips of my supporters; Senator Inhofe, I know, would be so darn proud!

"That's one big No to Hummer genocide, and one big Yes for technological innovation. Of course, the most prudent course of action to prevent even the slightest chance of Hummer harm—not that there's ever been a scientific consensus about that, nor is there ever likely to be one—is to retrofit each Hummer diesel engine coming off the Shanghai assembly line with a Greasecar Vegetable Oil Conversion System.

"We do that and America runs the Mother of all Funners on vegetables, my friend! Vegetables! Take that you Left Wing Green Genies! Eat vegetables!

"Therefore, on Day One in office, I will propose legislation to Congress making it unlawful to drive Hummers anywhere in these United States unless they're fueled by 100% waste vegetable oil. My legislation will also make it mandatory for each Hummer sold in America to get 30 miles-to-the-used-vegetable-oil gallon (UVOG) in the city and 50 on the highway. That's a CAFE standards' dream for an 8,600 lb. off-road/on-road SUV, my friend!

"I will also introduce legislation expanding America's domestic vegetable drilling programs. Here I'm in complete agreement with former RNC chairman Michael Steele: We need to 'Drill, Baby, Drill!'

"Drill for used vegetable oil wherever we can find it. That means drilling in every waste oil container of every fast-food and Chinese restaurant in America! That means drilling for it in every old grease coffee can next to every stove in every kitchen in America! That means drilling for it even in Anwr, too! Yes, I said, Anwr! And I'm not afraid to say it! And neither is my friend Sarah Palin! We're soul mates about that!

"Yes, my fellow Americans, if you elect me president, I promise to be America's first recycled vegetable oil wildcatter-in-chief. Our Hummer fuel needs, can, and must be met with reprocessed vegetable oil. Why? Because it's clean, it's renewable, and it also smells pretty darn good, too.

"We must and will do this to preserve the Hummer. There has never been, nor will there ever be, a better overland drive than the Hummer! Never. Ever, ever! They're not some cheap chrome crap ghetto ride, you know. They're not some foreign terrorist fueled tin deathtrap, either! No, my fellow Americans, they're an off-road vehicle with attitude! Marine Corps drill sergeant attitude! And if it's the last thing I do, I intend to make them drivable in the fifty-one states because Hummers must be

403

driven as God intended them to be—across overland trails and on dirt back roads of America!

"So let the word go forth: Under a Christ—the Republican— Administration, I will shield, protect, and defend the Mothers of all Funners. I have taken the Save the Hummer Pledge. As it was in the beginning, is now and ever shall be, world without end. Amen."

Now it's my moment to turn pale. Exceedingly pale. My stepbrother was the clear victor there. No sweat, I can take a licking in public. And yes, I'm a little more impressed with him. Actually, I'm awfully impressed. If the Old Man's looking down, He'll be just as dazzled. Beelzebub's come a long way in no time. After listening to him, I think it's fair to say that once every millennium or two, miracles do happen in politics. Hearing him wax fluent on the imperatives of drilling for waste vegetable oil IN THE NAME OF THE ENVIRON was practically a transcendental experience.

Only Senator James M. Inhofe would be able to read anything nefarious into my stepbrother's Greasecar Vegetable Oil Conversion legislation. As for me, I'm ready to christen him the Green Genie. His own conversion is breathtaking.

"Our next question is directed toward Mr. Christ—the Republican. Our questioner is a graduate of the U.S. Army Command and General Staff College and recipient of one of its highest awards, the General George C. Marshall Award; a graduate of Princeton University, who received a Master of Public Administration; an attendee of the Woodrow Wilson School of Public and International Affairs, who also earned a Ph.D. in international relations; an Assistant Professor of International Relations at the U.S. Military Academy, who then went on to attend Georgetown University on a fellowship; and a four-star General in the Army, as well as the former Commander of the U.S. Central Command and the Multinational Force in Iraq. He makes even General George Patton look like a desperate underachiever. But our special guest questioner is the first to admit that his awards, his accomplishments and his lifetime of glory pale in comparison to his latest honor. And no, we're not talking about the Congressional Medal of Honor. No, we're referring to the Greatest Honor of Them All: His Lifetime Membership in Cub Scout Pack 6, bestowed on him by his Orange County, New York, boyhood troop.

"If you haven't guessed who our special guest questioner is yet, you haven't been paying attention, because he would be, none other, than al-Qaeda's worst nightmare: General David H. Petraeus.

"General Petraeus, where are you? Oh, there you are—the one dressed in khaki green with a chest full of medals. Please, step to the microphone...

"THAT'S AN ORDER!"

"YES, SIR! THANK YOU, SIR! AM ON MY WAY, SIR!" Petraeus salutes, before marching to the microphone stand.

"Permit me to offer my special guest questioner credentials, SIR! I am indeed Al- Qaeda's worse nightmare, SIR! And proud of it, SIR! I've also been called the 'most competitive man on earth', SIR! And proud of it, SIR! On top of that, they call me the most political general since General McArthur, SIR! and one of the brightest soldier of my generation, SIR! And proud of it, too, SIR! What's more, in certain circles I am known as a Designated Thinker, SIR! And proud of it, SIR!

"Likewise, while I've got the mic and the whole country's attention, I'd like to put in with both our candidates for the position of Secretary of Defense, SIR! I could be the smartest one ever, SIR! That much I know, SIR! But for me it's less about brains, SIR! and more about service, SIR! Service to my country, SIR! Service to the Army, SIR! Service to the fighting men and women of America's Take-No-al-Qaeda-alive Armed Forces, SIR! Service, first and last, to all my 'Petraeus guys,' SIR!

"I live to serve; they serve to live; WE ALL LIVE TO SERVE, SIR!"

"General, your question, please."

"Yes, SIR! Straight away, SIR! But it's also about the medals, SIR! I live to win more badges, more medals, SIR! Always, SIR! Permit me to illustrate my mind-boggling qualifications, SIR! Starting left to right."

"General, can you put a hold on the SIRS, please?"

"Why, YES SIR! I can, SIR! I will, SIR!

"I won fair and square the Combat Action badge, the Air Assault badge, the Expert Infantryman badge, the Ranger Tab, the Master Parachutist badge, and the Bronze Star—with 'V' Device, SIR!

"I won fair and square the Army Achievement Medal, the Gold Award of the Iraqi Order of the Date Palm, the NATO Meritorious Service Medal, the Defense Distinguished Service Medal, the Defense Superior Service Medal—with Oak Leaf Clusters, the Joint Service Achievement Medal, the Distinguished Service Medal—with Oak Leaf Clusters, the Legion of Merit—with 3 Oak Leaf Clusters, the Defense Meritorious Service Medal, the Meritorious Service Medal—with 2 Oak Leaf Clusters, the Joint Service Commendation Medal, the Army Commendation Medal—with 2 Oak Leaf Clusters, the State Department Superior Honor Award, and the Joint Chiefs of Staff Identification Badge, and Army Staff Identification Badge, SIR! SIR! SIR! SIR! SIR! SIR! SIR! SIR! SIR! SIR! SIR! SIR! SIR! SIR!

"Oh, and I left out all my cub scout and boy scout merit badges, too, SIR!"

"GENERAL! Your question!"

"YES, SIR! THANK YOU, SIR! AM ON MY WAY, SIR!

"My question is about Iraqi and Afghanistan, SIR! I have one question and one question only for Mr. Christ on the Right. It's a question even more valuable than a first edition of my *Field Manual 3-24* on the Army's counterinsurgency doctrine, authored by Marine Lt. Gen. James F. Amos and myself. More meaningful than the Iraqi and Afghan Surges!

"My question is, Mr. Christ... Where does this end, SIR?

"Tell me where this ends! After 17 years, the 101st is still in Iraq! So tell me where this ends? We rebuilt Mosul and Nineveh Province. We used money—cold cash— as ammunition, but the war goes on and on and on. We have Sunni fighting Sunni, still. We have Shiite attacking Shiite, still. We have Sunni warring with Shiite, still. We have Shiite in conflict with al-Qaeda, still. We have al-Qaeda battling Kurds, still. We have Kurds opposing Turks, still! We have everyone at war with everyone, still.

"SO, PLEASE, TELL ME WHERE THIS ENDS, SIR!"

"Thank you, General Petraeus! At last, we have our 4 Oak Leaf Cluster question! Mr. Christ, your answer, please."

"Well, let me first congratulate you, General Petraeus, on your magnificent resume and spectacular chest full of medals. I want you to know that your *Field Manual 3-24* holds a very special place of honor in my household because I have it sitting on my bedside table right now and I read it every chance I get. There's no question that it's an anti-insurgency classic and a real page-turner to boot. Mind you, there're too few laughs for my taste, but certainly it deserves its No. 1 ranking on the U.S. Army War College's Best-seller List.

"So, yes, General Petraeus, you'll get my nod for Secretary of Defense because under no circumstances will I consider Donald Rumsfeld. The world's had enough of Rumfeldisms for one century, I should think. Besides, anyone who was quoted as saying that Osama Bin Laden was 'either alive and well or alive and not too well or not alive and just plain dead,' lacks a certain grasp of the obvious, don't you think? Especially for a Secretary of Defense."

"YES, SIR! THANK YOU, SIR!"

"Send me an autographed copy of your book and it's a done deal."

"YES, SIR! THANK YOU, SIR!"

"So where does this end, General Petraeus? I'll tell you where this ends: It ends when the 101st Airborne rolls into Iran; it ends when the 'Screaming Eagles' take over Syria; it ends when U.S. Army Special Forces nail Hezbollah; it ends when the Green Berets take out Hamas; it ends when U.S. Nuclear Forces wipe out al-Qaeda; it ends when the Secretary of Defense sticks Osama bin Laden's head on a pole on the White House North Gate. That's where it ends, my friend! It ends when we treat the entire Middle East as a counter-insurgency zone. It ends when we adopt the 'Petraeus Doctrine' from Egypt to Pakistan! It ends, General Petraeus, when this country commits all of its blood and all of its treasure to the Greatest Surge This Planet Has Ever Known!

"Sure, some will naysay it. And others will claim that it costs too much. But according to budget estimates drawn up for my campaign by the Heritage Foundation, the price tag will be very reasonable indeed. $75 trillion—max!—and require just 8.5 million troops over 32 years! It's a steal at double the dollars, triple the years, and quadruple the troop strength. Why? Because this is our moment to start to end it! This is our hour to launch the Mother of All Surges, and secure—once and for all— the largest Counter-Insurgency Zone on the face of the earth—the Middle East! Now I ask you: How much more inspiring can foreign policy get?

"So in answer to your question, General Petraeus, that's when it ends. It ends then and only then. When we've secured the Middle East. When we get to rename it America's Last Colony."

"Mr. Christ on the Left, your answer to the good general's question, please."

"'Money is ammunition.' That's what General Petraeus once said. And that's what it's all about: Making allies out of enemies. 'The wolf also shall dwell with the lamb, and the leopard shall lie down with the kid; and the calf and the young lion and the fatted calf together; and a little child shall lead them.'"

"A little child with *cash*?" an audience member blurts out skeptically.

"Yes, a little child with cash. When the world puts down $7.5 trillion in cash to transform the Middle East into an Oasis of Peace, that's where it will end. Build peace and peace will come. 'Cash is Peace.' We will do it for one-tenth the price, in one-third the time, and with zero troops. We will put down the cash. That's where it ends, General Petraeus, when we put down the cash, when the Middle East is rebuilt by a little child with fistfuls of cash."

My little stepbrother got me there. Aced me—but good. Got that right. But it won't happen again. "The wolf shall not dwell with the lamb." Isaiah 11:6. Don't think I don't know my American King James Bible, either. I've been studying up in my spare time and I'm not a bit embarrassed to say that there's some stimulating material tucked in amongst those bound pages.

"Our next question comes from Louise Lasser of St. Louis. It's on capital punishment, which is not exactly what our congressional representatives routinely do to us on Capital Hill back in Washington, but pretty close.

"Ms. Lasser is a horticulturalist by profession and grows organic hothouse roses, daisies, magnolias and medical marijuana year round. She's the president of her local PTA and is instrumental in promoting garage sales, potlucks suppers, roller skating events, Christmas Caroling, and 'All Things Green' Saturday afternoon events to raise money to pay for extra textbooks. Three mornings a week she works as a volunteer crossing guard at the corner of Ashland and Clay, near Farragut Elementary. As a mother of three, she's always on call. Her children regularly go to bed right at eight and she only has to ask them once—which is some kind of a city record.

"Recognized as a master Gin Rummy player, she's at her most commanding making melds and trashing deadwood. She once broke the bank at President Casino, located down near the St. Louis Riverfront. A second-degree Tae Kwan Do black belt, she's currently working on her third-degree. Generally speaking, nobody messes with her.

"Ms. Lasser is nationally known for her opposition to the death penalty. She will pose our next question to the candidates. As this is a fairly emotional issue, she's volunteered to maintain the peace between the candidates with combination tornado/reverse spinning hook kicks should any kind of dust-up occur.

"Ms. Lasser—oh, there you are—the pit—I mean—the floor is yours."

"Thank you, Mr. Moderator. I'd also like to point out that I'm a pretty decent pre-called bingo player, too.

"Mr. Christ, the Ten Commandments preach, 'Thou Shalt not Kill.' The Catholic Church condemns capital punishment in no uncertain terms. Yet a majority of Protestant Christians in America endorses the so-called 'moral virtues' and 'practical benefits' of state-sponsored executions. You and through you the Catholic Church says, 'Thou Shalt Love Thy Neighborhood as Thyself.' Protestants and Baptists shout, 'Thou Shalt Execute.' So I have to ask: Where's the love and what do you intend to do about it?

"They're making a travesty of your Sermon on the Mount! In the past 44 years, there have been 1,870 executions carried out in the United

410

States, 1,623 by lethal injection, 217 via electrocution, 21 in the gas chamber, 6 on the gallows, and 3 at the end of a firing squad. Each year, Texas alone administers 23 lethal injections. Since 1976, it has executed 666 persons. But it's not only the Lone Star state throwing the death switch. It's just that Texas's the worst. The South more generally carries out 80% of all executions! So, again, I have to ask: Where's the love and what do you intend to do about it?

"I ain't smokin' no dope—as Disciple Jackson says—and I'm not just hoping for hope, but this may be the time for change 1) because you've come back and 2) America as a whole is makin' progress toward banning the death penalty. Back in 2002 and 2005, the Supreme Court lumbered down a back road to Damascus, riding sidesaddle, and saw the light. They banned executions of juveniles and the mentally retarded. But still, that leaves today—right now—3,627 inmates about to do dead man walking. And 62 of them are women. And some of them are mommas—"

"We get it, we get it, Louise, your question, please."

"So again I have to ask—"

"'Where's the love and what do you intend to do about it?' Yes we know, Louise—your question, please!"

"Soon, Jim, very soon! The thing that makes me nuts is that according to surveys conducted by the American Society of Criminology and the British Society of Criminology, 87% of past and present presidents deny that the death penalty acts as a credible deterrent to murder. The southern states, for instance, which execute 80% of all death row inmates, have the highest murder rates. The northern states, which execute less than 1% of death row prisoners, has the lowest. Yet the Evangelical Right—Protestants and Baptists alike—who attend your Church and read your Scriptures—stands squarely behind throwing the switch, based on Leviticus 24:19–21. You know, all that Neanderthal

411

crap about an eye for an eye. Excuse my Midwestern English, my Lord. On the other hand, Catholics stand united in opposition to acts of human vengeance. 'Dearly beloved, avenge not yourselves, but rather give place unto wrath: for it is written, Vengeance is mine; I will repay, saith the Lord.'"

"Romans 12:19!" an audience participant jumps in.

"Exactly: 'An eye for an eye makes the whole world blind—'"

"Mahatma Gandhi!" another one blurts.

"Catholics—God's gotta love them—are adamantly opposed to the taking of any life—for any reason. Including abortion. Whether or not you can take the incense and the long liturgies, they're nothing if not consistent. In the Show-Me State, we like that. We like that a whole lot.

"So, yes, Mr. Lehrer; yes, Mr. Moderator; yes, Mr. Christ; my question is: How're you gonna make Protestants and Baptists act more like Catholics and return vengeance to the exclusive province of your Old Man?"

"Mr. Christ, your answer, please."

"Thank you, Jim, and thank *you*, Ms. Lasser for your good question. Being the only one in the room who's ever experienced the death penalty up close and personal like, and was reborn to tell about it, I—"

"Says you!" interjects my stepbrother.

"That's right, says me—"

"In your fantasies, maybe..."

"Let's not start, shall we?"

"Yes, gentlemen, please! Can't we all just get along to debate?"

"Well, I will, if he will."

"Yes, if he will, I will."

"So I want you two to shake hands."

"Okay, Jim."

"You got it, Jim."

"There. That wasn't so difficult, now was it?"

"Done worse."

"You got that right!"

"Hey, make him stop, Jim!"

"FELLOWS!"

"Okay, sorry, Jim."

"Yes, sorry, Jim."

"One more outburst and you're both doing time-outs in the corner."

My stepbrother and I immediately go quiet, because there're absolutely no votes to be had in us going to the corner.

After a considerable pause, Jim finally says, "Now that's better. Let's keep this more or less civilized, shall we fellows?"

"As I was saying," I begin again, "having experienced execution in the first-person, died and was resurrected, I've concluded—not so surprisingly—that there's really nothing whatsoever good to say about it. The truth is, it hurts something fierce. It also hasn't served as a deterrent, as the Romans hoped it would. Today, Christianity's the most popular religion in the world—more popular than the Beatles, even; the Roman Empire's toast, and I'm back doing God's work on earth, running for president. Or so I like to think. So I win; they lose. There's no deterrence in capital punishment from my point of view—and I, of all persons, should know.

"And while we're on the topic of the Beatles, I'd like to finally respond to John Lennon's long ago remark that the Beatles were 'more popular than Jesus.' Let the record show that the Beatles have sold only a 100 million plus albums, beginning with Love Me Do, in 1962, while my Bible sales, I point out as a matter of fact, not pride, are in the 3 plus billion range. So do the math. Draw your own conclusions. The truth is,

413

the Beatles never played at my level—good as they may have been—and I mean that. As for John's personal attack on my original disciples—Matthew, Luke and John, et al.—where he referred to them derisively as, and I quote, 'thick and ordinary,' I have this to say: It'd be better if you'd stuck to songwriting, John. My first disciples rocked, even though they didn't have Bono in the band."

"Is this your Sister Souljah moment?" my stepbrother snidely carps. I let that pass. I'm not about to get banished to the corner with such a jerk by snapping back. Instead, I carry on, like any smart politician would. "So how am I going make Protestants and Baptists act more like Catholics? To answer that, let's look at where the psychology of supporting public executions comes from."

"Need we bring up all these myths and memories?"

I ignore him because he's such a prick.

"Think Babylonian creation myth," I begin. "Think stealth-like infiltration of the American consciousness when it wasn't looking. Think perverted myth claiming violence saves, that brutality redeems, that a superior life rises out of chaos."

"I thought this was supposed to be a debate, Jim—not a Joseph Campbell retrospective." He's at it again.

"Say *what?*"

"You heard me."

"Did not."

"Did so."

"Did not."

Jim flings his fistful of notes to the floor, exasperated. They scatter like a bunch of wild bird feathers. "You know what fellows? As of now—right now—I'm exercising my Dean of Moderator's prerogative. You're playing by St. Louis Rules now! St. Louis Rules!"

"Never heard of them," my stepbrother unflappably remarks.

414

"And they would be?" I ask, a tad more diplomatically.

"St. Louis Rules mean that there are NO RULES! No rules whatsoever. Anything and everything goes. You got that right: You two are on your own now. Good luck, fellas!"

"Anything goes?" I inquire again, disbelieving.

"Anything."

"Anything?"

"Anything."

"But—but—but—" I stutter.

"Jesus, make a point, why don't you?"

Sometimes, it's all I can do— "My point is that a majority of Americans—54%—in fact, have bought into this confounded creation myth, at least at some level. The tragedy is that they have been deceived. Mightily deceived."

"Says you."

"Says me. I say forget the myth, read *Genesis*. There you have a good God, well, better than good—GREAT—who forges a new universe without a single act of savagery. God creates the earth and sky and sea, the animals, fish and fowl, the fruit, the trees, and man and woman and child in an act of sublime beneficence. 'And God saw every thing that He had made, and, behold, it was very good." Whereas in the original dark myth, a ruthless hotshot parvenu named Marduk slays Babylon's mother goddess Tiamat in an effort to get ahead—god climber that he was. Then, in the aftermath of the uprising, he dumps Tiamat's silent corpse on the alter of the sky where it is miraculously transformed into the whole of the universe."

"Your point being?"

"That Genesis' universe is delivered by acts of goodness, while Babylon's stems from an act of violent darkness."

"And I suppose butterflies can defeat standing armies, too… The problem with you is that you don't read enough Nietzsche to get a proper perspective on things. Real-politics is Nietzsche-politics—tragedy coming home to roost in the form of eternal reoccurrence."

"My Old Man made the Earth and called it good. The Babylonians made the Earth and called it chaos. I don't know about in your faith, but in *my* faith goodness predates the existence of evil. Evil is only a subset of a universe otherwise made of light matter. Not dark matter. The Babylonians stood the universe completely on its tush. Only from light—which in this day and age comes in the form of Compact Fluorescent bulbs—can come the better life. Which means, of course, axing the death penalty. Lord only knows, it's not about springtime picnics and blooming wildflowers. It's about death."

"So Augustine got it wrong, did he?"

"Gather your conclusions while ye may."

"Thomas Aquinas, too? Wasn't he the one who said that executions were 'tempered with mercy'—positively dripping with it—because the law conveyed to the condemned 'an opportunity which he did not grant to his victim, the opportunity to prepare to meet his God…?'

"Isn't mercy an act of goodness and light?"

"It's mercy-come-lately, come too late to do any true goodness."

"Whatever. Put me down on the side of Augustine and Aquinas. I'm all for executions—so long as we can claim they're tempered with mercy—late or not."

"Well, now I've heard *EVERYTHING!*"

"Meaning what exactly?"

"That you—Lord of Demons—believe in mercy. As I live and was reborn, well, I never!"

"$$%@$#@$#**"

"'%^#!**^&$^%$#$#!%%^%$#$%%%^$##@SS,   to   you, too!"

"Say what?"

"You heard me."

"Don't let me hear you repeat that!"

"'%^#!**^&$^%$#$#!%%^%$#$%%%^$##@SS!'"

"I warned you!"

"You're just a crock!"

"Take that back!"

"I say if the crock fits!"

"I said take that back!"

"No can do."

"Yes can do."

"Won't do!"

"Will do!"

"Look, you, read *your* Scripture! You can read, can't you?— *Deuteronomy* 22:25; *Leviticus* 18:22, 20:9, 21:9; *Zechariah 5:3*, 5:4; *Exodus* 21:16, 22:18; *Deuteronomy* 21:18-21; *Zechariah* 5:3: Permission is granted: Stone rapists; blow away fornicators; execute perjurers; decapitate kidnappers; burn witches; snuff out children who curse their parents; disappear disobedient daughters; zap thieves; give cursing neighbor rope neckties. Read your Scripture! It's pro-death penalty beginning to end. As pro-death penalty as the Great State of Texas!"

"I repeat: 'And God saw every thing that He had made....'"

"I repeat: Put me down as pro-death penalty."

"Hmmm, come to think about, you may have convinced me."

"Really?"

"Really. Why? Because there is one person I could support the death penalty for."

"Really? And who might that be?"

417

"YOU!"

"Hypocrite! 'JUDGE AND YOU SHALL BE JUDGED!' Luke: 6:37!"

"You got that wrong! It's 'JUDGE NOT, THAT YOU BE JUDGED!' you moron! If you're going to quote me, at least get it right!"

"Did you hear what he just called me, Jim? He called me a moron on public TV!"

"St. Louis Rules. My hands are tied."

"No one says that to a Texas Republican and gets away with it!"

It's then that I belt my stupid, little stepbrother. It's understandable really. My sensitive soul won't stand for it.

"HEY—THAT REALLY HURT! MAKE HIM STOP THAT, JIM! MAKE HIM STOP!"

"Like I said, fellas—"

"But I can't fight back with fisticuffs on PBS, Jim, because—"

"Because you're a god damn pacifist! A pacifist! And the last thing this country needs is a pacifist sitting in the Oval Office! The American public will back me up on that!"

Just to provoke me, my crummy big stepbrother belts me again, this time in the gut. He knocks the wind clear out of me. Now that really, really hurt!

Still, I try to remain calm. Stay very, very calm. Try counting slowly to ten while I do my level best to forgive him, even attempt to just forget it. I do all these things in good faith, in an extreme effort to control my temper, as I was raised to do. But I fail. I fail to override my basic training because, well, now, I'm a politician, for Heaven's sakes! And I'm running for president of the United States! I mean, who's going to believe that I'm capable of defending the United States from, let's say, al-Qaeda, if I take it without responding?

418

My stepbrother's right, pacifism is for Christ, not for PRESIDENT CHRIST!

So I forgive myself in advance and do what any Commander-in-Priest would be compelled to do. Right there and then, before God and the public, I treat my stepbrother like a Joe Bazooka punching bag.

And miracles of sunshine, he goes down. Down, down, down.

So typical: My Beelzebub's gotta a glass jaw.

Then I hear Mr. Moderator cry out, "PLEASE, SOMEBODY, FETCH SOME ICE! And a towel, too! Hurry! He's bleeding, for goodness sakes!"

Meanwhile, Jim recalls his St. Louis Rules. That is, he starts to count. Standing over my stepbrother lying there unconscious on the floor, and resembling an angel sleeping, he assumes the role of referee: "ONE, TWO, THREE, FOUR, FIVE, SIX, SEVEN, EIGHT, NINE, AND TEN! AND IT'S CHRIST—THE DEMOCRAT—LADIES AND GENTLEMEN—IN A KNOCKOUT!"

I hear it, but I can't quite believe it. Am I ever glad we reverted to St. Louis Rules now! Who knows who would have won this debate otherwise? I'm serious. I had my doubts. The outcome was that much in question.

Jim grabs my right wrist and then raises my arm above my head. He holds it there like a flying flag, sailing in the breeze. You better believe I can feel the glory, the glory of Joe Louis, Rocky Marciano, Jack Dempsey, Sugar Ray Robinson, and Mohammad Ali. I can also feel their pain. My fist's swelling up like a ruby red grapefruit. It's screaming. But otherwise I don't mind telling you I'm feeling fine. After everything that louse has done, I feel just fine about putting him down. It's not as if he hadn't been asking for it—forever.

Violence and intolerance—I still can't stand, of course—and I do so apologize for this one uncharacteristic act of barbarity—but what can I say? I'm not wrong. And as every politician knows, it's necessary—sometimes vital even—to throw an elbow once in a while. That's if you want to win, which I do.

"Is there a doctor in the house?" I hear Jim call, as he sets free my arm.

I lower it and look down at poor old Beelzebub sprawled out there on the floor. Oh dear. What have I done? He's lying there looking so peaceful, so calm. Frankly, he appears five hundred years younger, maybe more. Which is never a bad thing. Come to think of it, it's something of a miracle. Beyond miracle, actually. Who would have ever thought that Beelzebub and I—cosmic opposites and nouveau political desperadoes—would ever get to go mano-a-mano here on PBS? Of all places in the home of the Muppets.

CHAPTER TWELVE

"**H**ear ye! Hear ye! The Supreme Court of the United States is now in session. Chief Justice Clarence Thomas presiding."

Neither I, nor my little stepbrother, can get our minds around this idea. Neither can the courtroom spectators. A wave of cough, coughs, cough, coughs cross the public seating area, like wind across low grass.

"I heard that. Don't think I didn't hear that. And don't think I don't know exactly what the subtext of your cough, coughing is all about, either. I'm quite aware of what you courtroom spectators think of me being appointed Chief Justice of these United States, after the sad—but not too sad—departure of Chief Justice John Roberts, due to the onset of epilepsy. You see, I've read every single opinion poll; I've pored over all the lies printed in the liberal press about me; I've scanned the editorials and burned my New York Times; I've even skimmed through Anita Hill's statement about my presidential appointment, which in my opinion was a whole lot nicer than what she said about me at my Senate confirmation hearings before I was originally appointed to this bench, making reference to the fact that under no circumstance are Coke bottles or the use of sexually suggestive language permitted in or within a 300-yard radius of my chambers. Possession of said Coke bottles or expression of said sexually suggestive language—whether intended to harass or not—is subject to a 30-day jail sentence and $500 fine. There is no judicial immunity—not even for the Chief Justice, who just so happens to be me. That said, have any of you detractors ever even once considered that that bastion of insight, the Wall Street Journal, might have gotten it right when it christened me the Great Black Hope of Strict Constructionism in its endorsement of me as Chief? You better believe I have fans. And plenty of them. They're just not assembled in this courtroom today—or any other day, unfortunately.

"But it's like this my mocking coughing sidebar commentators: You're in *my* courtroom now and I AM THE CHIEF JUSTICE. This is me you see sitting in the center seat of the courtroom seating chart. This is me wearing the long black flowing robes that in the right light make me look like a Roman Catholic priest. This is me presiding before the red velvet curtains and at the same time the great judicial wizard pulling the strings of this court behind them. This is me in the big leather swivel chair. Nobody else.

"So let's get this right from the start, shall we? Starting today this courtroom is a Zero Tolerance Zone for any and all you mocking coughers, disparaging sub-texters, and denigrator mutters. That's right: You are hereby served judicial notice that this court will not countenance—under risk of being cited for contempt—any editorial comments in the form of stealth megaphones camouflaged as any or all

421

of the above. Please, no more surreptitious expressions of awed incredulity, shocked stupefaction and confounded bewilderment at me—Clarence Thomas—being confirmed by the Senate to preside over All Matters, Right or Wrong, Left or Right!

"Now before we hear oral arguments on the instant case, there is one more declarative I am compelled to state: Courtroom spectators, members of the assembled liberal press: GET OVER IT! That's right, GET OVER IT!

"I earned this seat! OH, HAVE I EVER! Decade in, decade out, I was made to sit and listen uncomplainingly—I might add—to my distinguished but dotty colleagues unmercifully carry on about pro-abortion rights this, anti-guns-and-ammo rights that, both in conference and in open court! Oh, did I ever! I was even made to suffer the indignity of standing silently by while the president and Senate evaluated my suspect class qualifications by using the higher standard of strict scrutiny instead of the lower standard, based on the rational basis test.

"The fact is, court spectators, I earned this job the old-fashioned way—by biting my tongue, digging deep and absorbing a Library of Congress-full of public humiliation. Punishing, I tell you, punishing. Anita Hill's hearings had *nada* on this last one!

"Regardless, you're stuck with me now; whether due to strict scrutiny or rational basis, it matters little to me because I am the Chief Justice of Everything, supreme or incidental. So I have to ask, I have to plead, with the words of Rodney King, 'Can we all get along?'"

"Cough, cough."

"I'll let that one go—just this once and only this once."

"So let's go. This morning we'll hear argument on No. 20-222, *Jesus v. Jesus,* on the question of which of you two presidential candidates are entitled to receive California's 54 contested electoral votes.

"This cause of action was brought by one Christ, claiming to be the true Christ, against the other Christ, also claiming to be the true Christ. All of which is more than a little preposterous because, as I've proclaimed from time to time from this seat on this bench before these red velvet curtains, the Christ of Christs is, in fact, not some honky invention borne of Eurocentric wishful thinking, but rather, as God is my witness, was and always shall be, black. Black, blacker than my Georgian ass!"

Not a few eyebrows in the courtroom rise and fall.

"Saw that!" the Chief Justice barks like a fierce Doberman on a frayed leash. His voice is rife with frosty irritation, soaring indignation. He's a force to be reckoned with, a volcano on the dais. Even I'm unnerved—and I'm the kosher Christ, honky though I am.

"Listen up you white bread spectators," he intones, his bearing magisterial. "I'm here to advise you further that my courtroom rules governing comportment and demeanor apply to subtle acts of eyebrow raising, as well as to coughing and muttering. So hear me from high atop Mount Supreme: Your contempt citation won't be a pretty sight for any of us to see. That you better believe."

I keep my eyebrows as level as I possibly can.

"And on the matter of the color of Christ, I side with Albert Cleage, founder of the Shrine of the Black Madonna Church, God rest his merry black soul, who argued persuasively that the real-life Christ was no honky—no indeed. That he was and always will be black as the night sky without stars—regardless of how many white bread priests think otherwise or how many children's Bibles limn Him white as egg whites.

"I digress from the case at hand, I know, but not so much really. Consider the tribes of Israel. Weren't they virtually black? Consider Exhibit A, the Arabs. Weren't they virtually black? Consider Exhibit C,

423

the Chaldeans. Weren't they virtually black? Consider Exhibit E, the Egyptians. Weren't they virtually black? Consider Exhibit E2, the Ethiopians. Weren't they virtually black? Consider Exhibit K, the Kushites. Weren't they virtually black? Consider Exhibit M, the Midianites. Weren't they virtually black? They answer to all of the above is, yes, they were virtually black. Which makes Christianity comprehensible to me because black represents the integration of all colors, whereas white is the absence of all colors. Black draws colors together; white separates them, which is the perfect metaphor for what Christ is about: Integrating through love the holistic colors of the human family."

Hmmm, dere. Clarence makes a good point—even I must admit that. And what he says is quite correct. My skin tones were considerably darker back when my stomping grounds included Judea and Samaria. They've definitely faded since I was last in Jerusalem. Why? Well, I should think that was obvious. There are no tanning salons up in Heaven.

"Ergo, I hereby call for an investigation by the UN Special Rapporteur on Racial Discrimination to look into this matter of the authentic skin color of the original Christ, which shall also include additional DNA testing on the Shroud of Turin to identify fresh evidence, and anything we can get on the Black Madonna would be good, too. I'll expect to see that report on this bench within six months!"

"I'm afraid you don't have the authority to order the UN to do anything, sir," Justice Kagan intones in slow monotones from seat No. 2 on the courtroom seating chart.

"No? Well, I'll just have to see to that!" blusters Clarence right back.

"Can we all get GOING?" Justice Ginsburg importunes, from seat No. 6.

"Of course," replies Thomas, "it's just these two pretenders to the sacred womb of the Black Madonna burn me more than listening to Anita Hill ream me at my first confirmation hearings. But anything for you—my leftist Sandinista Associate Supreme Court Justice."

"*Gracias*, my rightist Contra Mr. Chief Justice."

"Just so long as you call me—"

"CHIEF JUSTICE!" courtroom spectators and Associate Justices roar.

"—I don't mind whatever else! Because never in the history of the world were there two more drop-dead gorgeous words than those—with the possible exception, of course, of the appellation of my dear Black Lord—Jesus Christ.

"Allow me to summarize the case. In *Jesus v. Jesus,* plaintiff, Jesus Christ—the Democrat—asserts, among other things, that yet uncounted and contested ballots cast in Orange, Riverside, and San Diego counties cannot be counted for the purposes of awarding California's 54 electoral votes because any such recount—no matter how many ballots possess hanging and partially hanging chads—would violate his constitutional right to equal protection under the 14th Amendment. Winner of California's electoral votes will become president-elect of these United States—I regret to say not just a little.

"But before we begin consideration, this Court wishes to commend all parties on their exemplary briefing which, to a greater or lesser degree, had a cornucopia of nuanced references to both Catholicism and Seventh-day Adventists— which I'm assuming was not unplanned because they just happen to be my favorites—to earn counsel, my respect, and enduring affection. I especially appreciated your footnotes relating Catholicism to the question of 14th Amendment

425

equal protection. Come Judgment Day, I'm counting on the ever-mounting stack of new case law, arising in both common law and federal common law, based on briefs like yours and opinions like mine, to weigh heavily in my favor for expedited admittance into the law libraries of Heaven.

"I would like to particularly thank both parties for their really rather touching footnotes referencing the theology of the Seventh-day Adventists and its relevance to California election law. As you know, my dear grandmother, who brung me up by hand, and raised me as a Seventh-day Adventist, predicted the return of Christ was in the more or less immediate offing. Though I don't for a second believe that White makes Christ, she might have been convinced, and I'm actually okay with that. I'm sorry she didn't live to see this day. She herself wouldn't have minded if Christ was black or not.

"We also appreciate plaintiff severing from these proceedings his cross-complaint appealing the assault-and-battery charges brought by him against his opponent Mr. Christ—the Democrat. Those charges pertain to the alleged assault against him, which took place during the PBS presidential debate before an audience of millions. While we most certainly would not have granted certiorari on that petition, since we saw no federal jurisdiction there, plaintiff's relief is appreciated and will win him special consideration in the instant case if for no other reason than we Justices of this Supreme Court are chafing at the gavel to do some last minute seasonal shopping!

"I, for one, still haven't had the time to order online all my gifts for my law clerks on Amazon dot com. Just so you know, I'm buying them each the Collector's Edition of the 2020 Christ v. Christ Presidential Debates—probably the most celebrated debates since the 1858 Lincoln-Douglas debates. In case anyone else in this Court is still searching for that special gift for that Special Somebody, the DVD includes post-fight interviews with the Dean of Moderators himself—Jim Lehrer—as well as frontline audience questioners, including most notably, Louise Lasser and General David Petraeus. As you'll recall, Ms. Lasser's key question on the death penalty helped cause the brawl, which ended in Christ—the Republican—being rushed to the hospital with a broken nose and a bloody lip. Happily, this Special Edition DVD also has on it supplementary footage of Christ being escorted to the Emergency-Trauma Center of St. Louis University Hospital as well as an interview with orthopedic surgeon Dr. Stanley Willis, who performed the complex nose reconstruction. It also includes two post-operation interviews with his room nurses that aren't to be missed."

"Mr. Chief Justice, if you don't hurry this along, I'm going to have to call for a recess to run to the little girls' room," Associate Justice Ginsburg inserts into the record.

"Yes, my leftist Sandinista Associate Justice. I'm right on it.

"The matter before this Court boils down to three pertinent questions: (1) What was the intent of the uncounted votes in the three contested California counties? (2) What are the recount sub-standards by which the contested votes would be counted, should this court permit such a recount during the contest period? And (3) Will the recount sub-standards be at such variance with counting standards applied in other state counties as to render them violations of equal protection standards?

"Was that close enough for legal work, counselors?"

"Yes, Mr. Chief Justice," I answer, happy at least one person up there understands my Gospel and brief.

"Got that right, Mr. Chief Justice," I follow on, adjusting the white strip of adhesive tape Dr. Willis placed over my aluminum splint, which presently occupies a prominent place on the ridge of my recently reconstructed nose.

"Sweetest five syllables in the English language those—" smiles the Chief.

"Let the record show that plaintiff and defendant are acting *pro se,* and have voluntarily waived their right to court-appointed counsel. Despite this court's reservations about them representing themselves, it has allowed them special dispensation just this once because of who they claim to be. Cough, cough, cough, cough. You won't let us down, now will ya, boys?"

"No, sir, we won't, Mr. Chief Justice," my big stepbrother and I reply exactly in sync.

"I imagine there's not much I could say or do in this courtroom today that you two would find objectionable, am I right?"

"Yes, sir!"

"Couldn't quite hear that fellas…"

"YES SIR, MR. CHIEF JUSTICE!" we again reply in sync.

"Now that's better. Could listen to those succulent syllables everyday forever…

"We'll hear first from Jesus Christ—the Democrat. Counselor, get your thin white butt up here in a fat hurry because Kwanzaa shopping calls—pardon my Chatham County, Georgia English, sir."

"Thank you, Mr. Chief Justice. And may it please the Court.

"It may and then again it may not."

"Yes sir, Mr. Chief Justice."

"Gotta love that—'Mr. Chief Justice!'"

"Yes, Mr. Chief Justice. Just one week ago, this Court vacated the California Supreme Court's November 21 revision of the state's election code, which abolished the sacred writ of statutory deadlines, usurped the numinous authority of California's chief election officer, and presided over the transmutation of such consecrated words as 'shall'

428

and 'may,' transmogrifying them into ungodly opposites, such as 'shall not' and 'may not.'

"But the most unforgivable sin of all, your honor—the transgression that condemns the California Supreme Court in this world and the next one, if it is allowed to stand—is its irreverent, if not depraved, sanctioning of standard-less manual ballot recounts in selected California counties. In an election recount, there can be no greater equal protection violation—no greater ballot counting desecration!

"Myself, I'm all for forgiving poor judicial transgressions; I even stand ready to forgive legions of politicians their indiscretions. I'm just not ready to let the California Supreme Court commit voter suppression in my home state!"

"Says you."

"Says me!"

"Say—I like spunk in my *pro se* lawyers! Even ones who forget to call me—"

"Mr. Chief Justice!"

"Thank you. Now Mr. Christ, you can start by telling us where you think the federal question lies. Why should we Supremes be made to parse California's election code when we could be off Kwanzaa shopping?"

"Or singing 'O, Chanukah, Oh Chanukah,'" offers Justice Kagan from seat No. 2 on the courtroom seating chart.

"Or lighting the Menorah," adds Justice Ginsburg from seat No. 6.

"Or spinning dreydlekh," continues Justice Breyer from seat No. 7.

"I'd be happy to answer that question, sir."

"*Come again?*"

"I'd be happy to answer that question, Mr. Chief Justice."

"That's what I thought you said."

"If it please the Court…"

"And so it does."

"The federal question arises because the California Supreme Court violated Article 1, Section 1 of the Constitution."

"Do tell."

"But it gets worse, because it also violated Section 5 of Title II of Federal Law."

"Does anyone on this bench remember what's in Section 5 of Title II?"

"Title what?" asks Justice Breyer, scratching his head.

"Title II," Chief Justice Thomas barks.

"Which?" inquires Justice Kagan, straining to hear and cupping his ear.

"Title II. Title II."

"Not likely," Justice Ginsburg mutters beneath her breath.

"No clue," Justice Alito answers from seat No. 8.

From seat No. 9 Justice Kondo shakes his head back and forth, back and forth.

"We'll have to get back to you on that," Justice Scalia snaps from seat No. 3.

From seat No. 5, Justice Sotomayor just shrugs. "It's a mystery, *amigo.*"

"We may ask you to give us a refresher course on what's in Title II down the line, counselor."

"I'd be honored, Mr. Chief Justice."

"Well, we'll be embarrassed, but what can we do?"

"Not too much…"

"*Say what?*"

"Not too much, your Chief Honor."

"You think you've got us right where you want us, don't you counselor?"

"Yes, I do."

"*Say what?*"

"Yes, I do, your Chief Honor."

"You may now proceed. And wipe that smile off your face!"

"Yes, your Chief Honor. Just four days after this Court vacated the California Supreme Court's erroneous, and in my opinion, reviled revision of California's election code, the state court again disemboweled its election law, committing an iniquitous transgression against this Court by expanding its original November 21 judgment which incorporated the original sin of sanctioning the contest period counting to proceed, despite this Court having earlier rendered it a nullity."

"*A WHAT?*"

"A nullity."

"*COME AGAIN?*"

"A nullity—a nullity."

"Where's my *Black's Legal Dictionary* when I really need it?" asks Clarence Thomas.

"It means void of legal effect," Kagan intones, not a little impatiently.

The Chief Justice snaps his fingers. "I *knew* that's what it meant! I was only testing you!"

"Yes, of course, you were," replies Justice Kagan, rolling her eyes.

"So as I understand your position, counselor, you're not exactly lovin' thy California Supreme Court justices as thyself these days, are you?"

"No, sir, Mr. Chief Justice, I'm not."

"Which is just one more evidence that you're not my grandma's Seventh-day Adventist Christ—the one she was waiting for."

"And why may I ask is that, your Chief Honor?"

"Because grandma's Christ would love them California Supremes no matter what opinion they handed down. The honest-to-legit Christ would love them come crucifixion or resurrection. But it's clear that you're not lovin' those California Supremes now and that's how I know that you're impersonating one-third of the Holy Trinity—the Big C. Because, in my Book—the Black Book—once you stop lovin' 24/7, you might as well be masquerading at the Mardi Gras Ball. That is to say, without The Love, you're just an ordinary politician, sonny!"

"Who're you calling, sonny?"

"I mean, counselor, counselor."

"That's better."

"Better, *who?*"

"Better, Mr. Chief Justice."

"Now we're even."

"Yes, Mr. Chief Justice."

"Moreover, the real Christ would never stoop to running for high office, let alone take up *pro se* lawyering. Which, in my expert opinion, is a good thing, because, as every high school history student knows, those of us lording it over everyone are mindful of a little doctrine we call SEPARATION OF CHURCH AND STATE. And there's a damn good reason for that. We don't want our politicians—and Heaven forbid our *pro se* lawyers—believing they're the private voice boxes of God."

"I agree with you, Mr. Chief Justice."

"Ah—the ten sweetest syllables in the English language those.

"And why is it we don't want our politicians claiming to be the voices boxes of Jehovah?"

432

"Oh, do tell, Mr. Chief Justice."

"Because none of us knows, with the possible exception of some of the more senior Catholics on this bench, precisely what the Almighty is saying to us, now do we? No matter how hard we pray or how long we pray, there's just no tangible evidence to back up what He has in mind—no WeTube videos, no text messages, no Gmails—nothing to conclusively prove what transpired in that very private communication."

"I agree with you, Mr. Chief Justice. Even I get it wrong."

"Says you."

"Says me, Mr. Chief Justice."

"I like you better now, counselor. A little humor goes a long way in this job."

"I like you better, too, Mr. Chief Justice."

"Just can't hear those dear sweet syllables often enough, counselor."

"Yes, I know, Mr. Chief Justice, which is why I say them every chance I get."

"I like you even better now! So listen up, counselor: This Court would like to know what counting standard you would use to recount thousands of invalid California ballots?"

"None, Mr. Chief Justice, none at all, because the law is clear: Thou shalt not count unclean ballots, neither those with hanging or partially hanging chads, nor those dimpled or partially dimpled, either. So sayeth the Good Book U.S. Constitution."

"Do say."

"Do say, Mr. Chief Justice. I do say it because counting unclean ballots in Orange, Riverside and San Diego counties—but not in the fifty-five other counties—would violate the equal protection clause of the 14th Amendment and transmogrify our the Bill of Rights into the Bill of Wrongs."

"As the ghost of Chief Justice John Marshall is our witness, we certainly wouldn't want to be accused of doing that, now would we, my fellow Associates Justices?"

A spat of coughing and muttering passes from one end of the bench to the other.

"So the question this Court is stuck with is whether it will rise to protect all counties in California equally or fall to protect three counties unequally?"

"Hmmm, dere, makes sense to me."

"Exactly. I'm reminded of the turn of phrase my Old Man often used when standing at the Pearly Gates overseeing the General Admission with St. Peter: 'Every judgment gotta make sense and every decision gotta be right.' Which is to say, there are no Do-Overs on Judgment Day.

"This brings me to my final point. If the voters of Orange, Riverside and San Diego counties can't be bothered to put down their bongs, set aside their margaritas and sunglasses long enough to punch their ballots through and through in order to ensure that their votes are correctly counted, then why—Mr. Chief Justice—why should this Court grant them a do-over? As on Judgment Day, there are no Do-Overs in politics, either, Mr. Chief Justice."

"Hmmm, dere, point well taken, counselor."

"I'll close with this—a little something I picked up from former Solicitor General Ted Olson who, as you'll undoubtedly recall—"

"Who?"

"Ted Olson, Ted Olson, Mr. Chief Justice. He represented George W. in *Bush v. Gore* and delivered oral arguments in this very chamber twenty years ago today. To paraphrase Mr. Olson—an equal protection defender of the Right: 'Thou shalt not give Do-Overs to bong smokers and margarita drinkers.' Those words are as valid in 2020 as they were in 2000.

"Thank you, your Chief Honor."

"And thank you, counselor. For a white bread impostor, you turned out to be way cool. Now let's hear from our next white bread masquerader and *pro se*, Christ—the Republican. Let's hope he's way cool, too, which would be quite an accomplishment considering he's a Republican, who don't generally speaking, do cool. But hey, where there's Obama, there's hope. That's what I always say, anyway."

"Thank you, Mr. Chief Justice. May it please the Court..."

"Hopefully—but in the event it doesn't, we'll stop you when we've heard enough."

"You're all soul, Mr. Chief Justice. Allow me to lead with *Bush v. Gore*.

"As you'll recall the U.S. Supreme Court based its decision to deny a recount of undervotes in three Florida counties because any such recount, other than a statewide recount, would have constituted a violation of the Equal Protection Clause."

"We said that?"

"The Rehnquist Court said that, Mr. Chief Justice, and you sided with the majority. As you'll recall that decision brought on the Dark Ages of Terrible George, an era so catastrophic to the standing of America that few if any citizens—other than perhaps Dick Cheney and his daughter Elizabeth and oh yes, certain factions of the Evangelic Right—will ever want to revisit those ghastly days of pointless invasion and deplorable debt. As you once said, Mr. Chief Justice, politics is a bugaboo when combined with creed, or was it the other way around?"

"A what?"

"A bugaboo, Mr. Chief Justice."

"Where's my *Black's Legal Dictionary* when I really need it."

435

"It's a non-legal term," Justice Kagan intones from seat No. 2., "meaning an object of fear or alarm; a bugbear. ORIGIN mid 18th century: probably of Celtic origin and related to Welsh *bwci* bo 'bogey, the *Devil*,' *bwci* 'hobgoblin' and Cornish *bucca*."

"It's also the non-legal definition of what comes from inserting detonator religion into explosive C-4 politics in the name of actualizing the so-called 'will of God' in public policy," Justice Ginsburg informs quietly from seat No. 6.

"Ah—bugaboo. *Now* I remember. You've got some kind of kahoonas to antagonize the Holy Right, counselor! I love that in a *pro se* lawyer!"

"And I admire your reputation as a strict constructionist, Mr. Chief Justice. Which brings me to my opening argument: Judicial activism by this High Court is as hazardous to the national landscape as strip mining is to the natural landscape. Opposing counsel cites *Bush v. Gore*—a controversial decision viewed by many as judicial activism, plain and simple, and which resulted in the Era of Terrible George. The less said about that the better, except to say: Never again. Never again will America be bankrupt and dishonored by the unintended consequences of this Court's judicial activism."

"Back then we didn't call it judicial activism, sonny; we called it equal protection."

"But most everyone else saw it as judicial activism, Mr. Chief Justice. By staying the Florida Supreme Court's December 8, 2000 order for a statewide manual recount, and ignoring your colleagues arguments that 1) 'counting every legally cast vote cannot constitute irreparable harm' and 2) 'preventing the recount from being completed will inevitably cast a cloud on the legitimacy of the election,' this Court went above and beyond strict constructionism.

"Moreover, by stopping the recount, this Court violated 'Three Truths of Judicial Restraint;' that is to say, 1) showing due consideration for state supreme court decisions, 2) carefully exercising jurisdiction in light of 'another branch of the Federal Government' having primary responsibility to settle the matter, and 3) refraining from 'issuing irreversible presumptions about federal constitutional law before a full presentation on the issues can be heard.'

"In other words, the Rehnquist Court, in which you were a conservative pillar (some likened you to a pillar of salt), ignored these fundamental Truths and, as a result, stepped into the No-Fly Zone of Judicial Activism. Not that you didn't have the best of intentions— regardless of the Court's injudicious and reckless opinion—to get your Man Bush into the White House. And well I can relate to your desire to push George W. through the North Gate because I, too, was once a Kool-Aid-drinking supporter of his. But more than enough time has passed for both of us to own up to our electoral and judicial indiscretions. The fact is: We were all hoodwinked by that presidential impostor! (Just saying that out loud makes me feel a whale of a lot better! It's like psychotherapy—but a whole lot cheaper!) You should try it, Mr. Chief Justice! Just say it!"

"Maybe later, counselor."

"You'll feel fresh as flowers, your Honor, I guarantee you!"

"I said later, counselor."

"Yes, Mr. Chief Justice. Have it your way, but it's going to be a default judgment against America, if you don't."

"Your argument, counselor—please."

"May it please the Court..."

"Not so far, counselor, but as I always say, where there's hope there's Obama."

"Huh? The Fourth Truth of Judicial Restraint is that the U.S. Supreme Court, like God, doesn't—mustn't—play dice. By that I mean this Court shouldn't—mustn't—dance down the activist path in the name of equal protection and what not and end at a Junction of Equal Destruction. If history is prologue, it will only result in more invasions in more lands in more ways than you have ever dreamed possible. Picture invasions as far as the eye can see. A national debt as high as the moon—what comes after trillions, anyway?"

"Got me, counselor. If it's not in *Black's Law Dictionary*, I don't know it!"

"In other words, such a roll of the dice may well lead to the Coming of the Great White Anti-Christ."

"I object, your Chief Honor!"

"Objection sustained! Counsel will rephrase the accusation."

"Brought on by Christ—the Democrat!"

"That's better."

"By not counting all of the hanging chads and partially hanging chads and dimpled and partially dimpled ballots in Orange, Riverside and San Diego counties only—there will be no Middle East peace, there will be no end to al-Qaeda and the Taliban, there will be no end to war at all—no hope at all, even where there's Obama.

"Therefore, I entreat you, Mr. Chief Justice, Associates Justices all, do not make the same mistake twice. Grant yourselves a do-over in the instant case. Let the California Supreme Court recount order stand. Get out and do your Kwanza, Christmas, and Hanukkah shopping now. Embrace the fact—the only facts that count—that I—Christ—the Republican—won the popular vote; that I—Christ—the Republican—am within striking distance of making a fairly decent argument for why this Court should fork over all those beautiful Electoral College votes to me which will put me right over the top and into White House Situation Room without a hard pass any time I want."

"And that argument would be?"

"That Article II presupposes judicial review and the interpretation of state statutes, and that the California Supreme Court simply invoked those basic principles of statutory construction in reaching its—and if I might use a non-legal term, Mr. Chief Justice—righteous decision ordering recounts in three California counties, where I was most likely to win. And win big. But as God is my witness, and so I will believe until my dying day, the California court did not make any new law in its interpretation of California's election law; no, sir, Mr. Chief Justice, it merely massaged—and gently massaged at that—sunny California's election law, interpreting it in a very positive and very friendly fashion, which just so happened to inure to my benefit. If that don't beat the moon with a stick!"

"You almost had me at Article II, counselor. You almost had me at Article II... But may I be perfectly frank, counselor?"

"By all means."

"*Say what?*"

"By all means, Mr. Chief Justice!"

"That's better. What I fear more than having an Anti-Christ in the White House is having ANY kind of Christ in the White House! Black or White! No, counselor, I've lived long enough and hard enough to know that the last thing this country needs is one more God-talking George W. delivering declarations of war against al-Qaeda or whomever from the pulpit of the Washington Cathedral in the name of Christianity! No we don't. We don't want any more George W.s delivering the State of the Union armed with a hidden agenda hatched in private conversations with the Lord Almighty Creator Maker that no one else is privy to! We don't want any more George W.s invoking the will of the

439

One and Only Heavenly Shaker without conclusive proof admissible in a court of law detailing what precisely the Chief Justice, the Greatest Chief Justice of Them All, had to say about the future of America!

"And why is that, my Associate Justices?" Clarence asks rhetorically.

"BECAUSE 'IN GOD WE TRUST,' BUT IN POLITICS SEPARATION OF CHURCH AND STATE IS A MUST!" the Justices intone in unison, like a chorus line.

Then from seat No. 2, Justice Kagan finally gets a question in edgewise. "Would you kindly tell this Court which standard you'd use to count the contested votes, counselor?"

"Yes, Justice Kennedy, I'd be happy to."

"I'm Justice Kennedy—She's Justice Kagan," Kennedy observes from seat No. 4, noticeably annoyed, and pointing to Justice Kagan sitting in the chair next to him.

"That's why they tell you never to do that—"

"Whoever said that, definitely got that right."

"It won't happen again, Mr. Chief Justice."

"I'm one of eight Associate Justices! He's the Chief Justice— astonishing as that may be."

"I heard that!"

"To answer your question, your Honor, the correct counting standard comes from Section 166 of the California code. That provision becomes operative when hand-counting machine-damaged ballots in the protest phase of contested elections. It applies only to machine-damaged ballots; but there are inferences to be drawn in the instant case."

"But that's not my question, counselor. My question is, what standard would you use to count the undercounted ballots in Orange, Riverside and San Diego counties? How would you tally up all those muddled votes?"

"Justice Kennedy—"

"*I'm* Justice Kennedy! *She's* Justice Kagan!"

"I don't know why I can't get that right, your Honor! So sorry!"

"White Christ not necessarily *right* Christ," Associate Justice Kondo decrees, smiling like a Buddha, one forefinger lifted toward the celestial Heavens.

"My counting method is as simple, your Honor. I would count them in my favor."

"That's a refreshingly honest answer, Mr. Christ. You're the Democrat, right?"

"No, *I'm* the Republican! *He's* the Democrat."

"Whatever, as much as I love judicial activism of any kind, I like equal protection better."

"But, your Honor, by finding for me, this Court has the unique opportunity to make up for how it ruled in *Bush v. Gore*! This is your chance to do a Do-Over! It's a once in a generation shot at balancing the proverbial scales of justice!"

That's when my little stepbrother elbows his way into the conversation and takes an unscheduled shot at me. How dare he.

"May it please the court—there are no Do-Overs in politics! How many times do I have to say it! Do-Overs are for the Great Unwashed; ballot counting is for secularists. And the business of this Court is about upholding the joys of us secularists!"

"Correct!" the Chief Justice proclaims, grasping his gavel. "There are no Do-Overs in politics—like the white man said!" To emphasize his legal point, he slams down the gavel, rendering his initial judgment in the instant case. Which makes me furious because I thought the Supreme Court was supposed to be about the administration of supreme and abiding justice. Boy, did I ever get that wrong.

Now usually I'm cool; and customarily I'm very calm; but for the Chief Justice of the United States Supreme Court to turn his back on justice—well—I'm—there's just no word for it. And right when I was starting to have faith in going straight and siding with the Establishment! Now my soul feels crushed by concrete! Good grief, Charlie Brown. It's a tragedy.

And now everybody's starting to be unfriendly to me: The U.S. Supremes, judicial history, and the worse kind of legal precedent—*Bush v. Gore*. All the things that matter in a court of law.

I can see the handwriting on the courtroom wall. "In the matter of *Christ v. Christ*—CASE CLOSED! THERE ARE NO DO-OVERS IN POLITICS!" Okay, I get it, the Supremes aren't going to buy my argument.

"Mr. Christ—the Democrat," inquires Justice Ginsburg, "Could you—"

"I'm Christ—the Republican. He's Christ—the Democrat. Get it right, you leftist Sandinista Associate Justice!"

"Hey, that's my pal you're talkin' about!" interjects the Chief Justice.

"Don't care, you rightist Contra Chief Justice! There are TOO DO-OVERS in politics! ARE TOO!"

"Hey—Watch it, buster! That just so happens to be my soul brother you're talkin' to!" Ginsburg vents like a steam pipe.

That's the moment I lose it and drive my campaign bus right off the cliff. That's when I know this election is lost and, ironically, that's the first time in my campaign life that I can relate to Reverend Al and how he must have felt when the Supreme Court handed down *Bush v.*

Gore. Poor guy. And above and beyond all of the above, that's the precise moment in recorded history that I know with scientific certainty that I'm not—repeat—not going to have a great day.

I don't know about you, but I utterly detest that phrase. It always makes me feel like one in a billion Starbucks customer. Or whatever.

In any event, I've had it. Had it. And proceed to torpedo any last chance I ever might have had to score with the U.S. Supremes.

"You're nothing but a rat pack of strict constructionists!" I shout.

"Are not!"

"Are too!"

Justice Ginsburg and I go at it.

"Am not!"

"Are too!"

"AM TOO AND OH SO VERY PROUD OF IT!" the Chief Justice chimes in from the bench, as if he was singing hallelujahs on Easter.

"Strict constructionist?" Justice Sotomayor jumps in, "*Usted es loco, hombre!*"

"STRICT CONSTRUCTIONISTS—EACH AND EVERYONE OF YOU!" I howl, having unreservedly had it with all things U.S. Supreme.

"That may not be your best argument, counselor," he offers gently, hoping to lower the courtroom temperature a notch.

"Even the Great Litigator David Boies, Esq. couldn't pry open your minds. They're clamped shut tight like the jaws of an Alligator Snapping Turtle! No sunlight gets in there because you've already made up your minds to put the Anti-Christ of the Returned Christ into the White House!"

"Now let's be calm, shall we, sonny?"

443

"Who're you calling, *sonny*? I'm the titular head of the REPUBLICAN PARTY and a reborn democrat in the small d sense of the word, of course. Beside, Charles Krauthammer predicted that this would be my Unipolar Moment and that once in office I'd establish the Christ Doctrine. But because of you and your thirst for equal protection and your blatant disregard for Do-Overs, nothing's turning out the way it's supposed to! Not for me, not for Krauthammer. Only for my stepbrother!"

"It wouldn't be the first time old Krauthammer got it wrong."

"But Charles has seen the writing in the sands: Democratize the Middle East anyway we can! I'm for that! It's been a wreck for a century!"

"Keep it down, sonny! This is a court of law, not some Pittsburg political convention."

"Could have fooled me."

"*SAID WHAT?*"

"Said, in case you didn't get it, 'Could have fooled me!'"

"Why, I have half a mind to hold you in contempt!"

"Yes, that would be more than max!"

"BAILIFF! WHERE'S THE DAMN BAILIFF? IF THERE'S A BAILIFF IN THE HOUSE TAKE THIS WHITE MONKEY OUTA HERE. I HEREBY DECREE HE'S IN CONTEMPT OF WE U.S. SUPREMES AND ESPECIALLY ME!"

"You'll pay on Judgment Day!"

"THAT'S BETWEEN ME AND MY BLACK JESUS—AND YOU'LL NEVER GET ME BELIEVING OTHERWISE BECAUSE HE'S ALLOWED ME TO GO UP TO THE MOUNTAIN. AND I'VE LOOKED OVER. AND I'VE SEEN THE PROMISED LAND.

AND BELIEVE ME, THERE AIN'T NO WHITE JESUS UP THERE NO WAY, NO HOW, NOT EVER!

"Cuff him, bailiff."

"Oh no need, no need. I'll go peaceably. I'm about as nonviolent as Mahatma Gandhi these days. Truly. And I'm really okay with my defeat. I won't hold a grudge like Al. But before I go, I'd just like to say one little last thing—on the record."

"It's a free country. Especially now that George W.'s gone back to Texas. So be my guest. But quickly, because Kwanza shopping calls."

"Well, it's like this, Mr. Chief Justice: NO WAY, NO HOW, NOT EVER YOU'RE CHIEF JUSTICE JOHN MARSHALL!"

"Sticks and stones... Sticks and stones..."

Then the real Chief Justice Clarence Thomas proclaims:

"Now take this white bread Christ from my courtroom and take him down to the courthouse cafeteria and serve him up for toast because I, CHIEF JUSTICE CLARENCE THOMAS, do decree that in the matter of *Christ v. Christ*, He and a majority of the Associate Justices of this Court, finds for the poor put-upon Plaintiff—Christ—the Democrat. If *Bush v. Gore* has taught us anything—anything at all—it's that the right is not a little iffish in America and that voters who can't put down their bongs or stop their margarita swigging long enough to punch holes from one side of their ballots to another will never ever ever have those votes counted by this U.S. Supreme Court, so long as I'm CHIEF JUSTICE!

"ACCORDINGLY, AND HEARING NO OBJECTION FROM MY FELLOW JURISTS—JUDICIAL ACTIVISTS AND STRICT CONSTRUCTIONISTS UNITED IN COMMON CAUSE— THIS COURT STANDS ADJOURNED!

"HAPPY KWANZA EVERYONE!"

Then down comes the Gavel of Chief Justice Clarence Thomas.

If that's not a kick in the ass, I don't know what is. Disbelieving, believing, I'm swarmed by courtroom spectators. They slap me on the back. Some want to take me out to dance. I really wouldn't mind. I've just scooped up California's 55 electoral votes, which puts me at 271 electoral votes. Enough to win. How 'bout that Clarence Thomas? How 'bout those Supremes! Let's just say I'm pretty sure this is a make-up call. One which the Republicans will be griping about for the next hundred years.

I myself am overcome with joy and jubilation. That's because I've been to the mountaintop myself and seen the miracle. No, not the miracle of winning a presidential election. That's good and everything, but the miracle I'm talking about is the miraculous transformation of my older stepbrother. If nothing else, the marvel is that he's turned into one helluva democrat.

Then when the hubbub dies down, and I'm out on the courthouse white marble front steps on a bright, sparkling winter's afternoon, thousands of people chanting, cheering, more press than I've ever seen, I get on my satellite cell phone.

This is the one call I've been waiting to make.

At first the damn phone just rings and rings and rings. Then finally—someone answers.

"Hey, Dad, is that you?" I ask. "Yeah, it's me—your son, your son Jesus. I'm just calling to let you know—

"What's that? You can't hear me? Hold on, wait a second, let me move over here for better reception. How's that? Better now? Oh, good... Great... I can hear you just fine now, too. Yes, dad, like I said, I can hear you just fine, too...

"Dad, I have some news. I said I have some news, dad. U-uh. Well, I'm just calling to let you know that I've been elected the 47th

446

President of the United States. Yes, that's right! I'm over the top with 272 Electoral College votes. And come January 20th, believe it or not, I'm moving into the family quarters of the White House. Yes, that, too, the Oval Office. Yes, that's right, dad, the big white house at 1600 Pennsylvania Avenue.

"What's that? Say it again... How do I feel? Good question.

"I'm going to have to get back to you on that."

CHAPTER THIRTEEN

This is the day Chief Justice Clarence Thomas hath made: Inauguration Day, January 20, 2020. I'm lying in a king-bedded suite at Blair House across from the White House, soon to be My House, wiping sleepy dust from my eyes. Out my window I glimpse the columns and contours of the North Portico, suffused in early morning light. I'm swaddled in 1500 thread count Egyptian cotton organic sheets. Last night my head lay on 800 Fill Hypodown pillows, which gave me the dream of dreams because I dreamt Beelzebub ran for mayor of San Antonio and won by a ten-point margin. I woke up happy for him. He deserves to win public office, somewhere, somehow. The country will be better off with him contributing constructively. Besides, a little executive experience couldn't hurt him. And we certainly don't want him going back to his grizzled ways, so as long as the San Antonio Express-News or some such other newspaper keeps a close eye on him in whatever city he lands in, we should be okay. God love the fourth estate. We could think of it as a probation period. And if he made good in a West Texas small town or a place like San Antonio, he could eventually consider making the leap to the governorship and from there who knows? Although you can bet that if I flub up during my first term, he'll consider going at me again in 2024. Which gives me powerful incentive to do my job as president as well as Abraham Lincoln, FDR and Obama put together.

A 100% organic Turkish cotton luxury bathrobe cloaking my shoulders, I sit up in bed and admire the delicate golden light cascading over the naked, gray branches of the ghostly forest of winter oaks and elms framing the big white house sitting like a wedding cake across the street while sipping English breakfast tea from an impeccable Eternity Round Fine Bone Wedgewood China cup. I couldn't be more calm in the face of success. After all of the hardships on the campaign trail, the bum lunches and brutal hours, the indignity of delivering the near identical stump speech thousands of times and those last few demeaning months when I had to heavy-up on negative ad buys and hurtle negative negatives like lightning bolts at my opponent, I'm content to slowly wake on this, my big day, and nurse a cup of delicious orange-pekoe tea because, my fellow Americans, this is the day Chief Justice Clarence Thomas hath made, and I shall rejoice and be glad in it and return to the realm of the uniquely positive, except of course when I have to crack heads on Capitol Hill. I never claimed I'd bring an end to bipartisanship. If Obama couldn't do it, I don't know why I should be expected to.

But I'm going to enjoy this moment, milk it for everything it's worth, because this may be the last chance I get to zone out before the roar of new responsibilities occupies my head. It may also be time to offer up a farewell prayer to my pre-presidential candidate ways since as of 12:02 PM Eastern Standard Time today, I can pretty much blow off any last traces of my Lord-of-the-Streets, humbler-than-thou profile, for the next four years at least—and conceivably eight—because from here on out, when going to Milwaukee, I'll be riding at 40,000 feet in a fiery cloud bubble, otherwise known as Air Force One, wearing, if I choose

448

to, a soft-touch, peached finish Presidential Windbreaker embroidered with gold and blue Presidential Seal on left chest—in my opinion the perfect in-the-skies throw-on, like President Bartlett wore on *West Wing*. I always did like that show. It may also have given me some pointers on how to conduct myself as president.

And while down on the ground and in town, I'll be whizzing about in a bomb-proof Prezmobile, courtesy of the American taxpayer, and shepherded about by a mobile army of black, armor-plated, Secret Service Suburban SUVs, made as tough as Abrams Main Battle Tanks, and occupied front and rear with a gaggle of crew-cut Secret Service agents wearing wrap-around shades, who never ever smile, and are armed with Uzis. We'll come and go soundlessly, like cool black clouds blown across low asphalt streets, followed within spitting distance by my very own private Magen David Adom ambulance, outfitted with mobile intensive case unit, emergency medical and blood bank service—mobile operating room also included. We crash; I bump my head; no sweat. I'm in surgery, just like that. Far ahead of the pack, running interference of sorts, will be what every modern-day president needs—a nuclear, biological, chemical reconnaissance vehicle (UNBCRV), modified for action in da hood, if necessary, and equipped with stand off detectors, capable of sensing any kind of toxins, from Ricin to Anthrax, with sensors so finely trained that they compare favorably with the wet nose of a German Shepherd sniffing about at Customs. Naturally, protecting my flanks will be legions of motorcycle policemen sitting astride idling Harley-Davidsons that pulled up at the ends of neighborhood streets quasi-mysteriously, temporarily shutting them down, as if for a block party. Then the streets will magically reopen after my cavalcade rolls by; the Harleys will vanish, like rabbits from hats under the wand of a conjuror.

To be sure, my days of going it alone on donkey back and getting about as best I can over cobblestones and asphalt, let alone concrete, will be donkey ears over.

However, this much I pledge—regardless of transport upgrade. I pledge that I will attempt in all good faith to maintain as modest a personal profile as is practicable and that my Secret Service detail permits, including, but not limited to: Ironing my own dress shirts and silk ties, doing my own washing and drying, and polishing my pairs of Tony Lama cowboy boots. You can bet I'll still be wearing them to work each day. And at all State dinners and on the night of the State of the Union address, too—notwithstanding the ridicule I've had to endure from those Reliable Source writers at the *Washington Post*. But, hey, I like myself just fine. Can they say the same about themselves? And while we're on the subject, let's have a look at their shoes, why don't we!

Besides, I feel ten-feet tall in them. What's more, they're a secret source of something powerful. When I polish them, which I do religiously, if not obsessively, the act of polishing is actually clinical therapy. Scent of Kiwi boot polish; polish applied to dull and tarnished leather; brush strokes back and forth; the dull disappearing, the shine emerging. It helped keep my equilibrium, and also gave me quality think time, allowing me to contemplate creative ways in which I could be of service to my nation. In other words, it opened up a whole new sweet space for me, one where I could chew over campaign strategies and difficult policy decisions in a quasi-sacred, Zen-like place of contemplation. Moreover—and I kid you not—there were times when it brought me closer to God; not that I can necessarily explain all that, but it may have had something to do with the fusion of sound and scent and shine.

So I highly recommend that everyone shine their own shoes or boots or high heels or whatever, whenever they have time. Of course,

I'm not staking out that idea as one of my 100-day policy initiatives that I'll be laying out in my Inaugural Speech. And certainly I'm not in favor of putting anyone employed in the shoeshine industry out of work. Lord only knows, this economy can't afford to lose any more jobs. Nevertheless, there's something soul informing about engaging in the practice that counts for more than just dollars and cents.

Through the lacy winter trees, snowflakes fall, as in a C.S. Lewis story. They blanket Pennsylvania Avenue, coating the seats of the bleachers set up for my parade in a fine, snowy, white powder. It's a scene from a childhood dream, a white dream dreamt under white sheets. It's something very special, which I haven't seen in forever and that brings to mind one particular gripe about my days in Heaven. And that gripe is, it never snowed. Perhaps not altogether unexpected considering the mean temperature hovers at a tropical 82°. I was always in favor of the Old Man lowering the thermostat, but He wouldn't stand for it. His arthritis kept everyone warm. So you'll have some sympathy for me when I divulge that there's nothing more I'd rather do today than go out in the falling snow, pack the perfect snowball, and let loose. Come to think of it, it should also help prepare me for my looming battles up on Capitol Hill.

A soft tapping at the bedroom door…

That would be breakfast.

After waffles and strawberries, I shower but do not shave. I comb my beard and moustache, but not too much. I like that lived in look and people expect it. I blow-dry my hair. Freshly shampooed, it glistens under the bathroom lights. More or less, I look like Johnny Depp. Or rather Johnny Depp looks like me. I study my face in the mirror: The face of the next Commander-in-Peace.

I go over my speech, which comes in at 236 words, one word shy of George Washington's second inaugural address, and 8,310 fewer than William Henry Harrison's 1841 humongous classic. He delivered his in inclement weather, without topcoat or hat or gloves, and four weeks later he was dead from pneumonia, just like that. So you can bet that I'll be wearing triple layering today. All day. I can't be too careful at my age. As for William Henry Harrison, he should have known better. A little common sense in a president is a basic necessity, don't you think?

My cell phone rings. That would be Disciple Pelosi. She's calling to inform me that my disciples have gathered outside the Jackson Place Conference Room door downstairs. I want my Cabinet up and running the moment I get sworn in, so I'll be choosing my Cabinet secretaries this morning. My administration's going to hit the ground running as soon as I'm in because this much I pledge: We'll begin addressing the problems of our nation and the crises of this world right after today's Inaugural parade. I have nothing but Obama-size hope that a Christ Administration can bring down the national debt and make peace with our Middle East enemies, including but not limited to al Qaeda, the Taliban, the Yemenites and the Iranians, all in my First 100 Days in office. Now that my stepbrother has been democratized and his toxic days are behind him, anything's possible. And I'm not just referring to his coke-dazed days down in Juarez; we're talking Golden Age of Genocide here. All of which means, my fellow Americans, we may finally be in with a chance to get the country back on track and set the world right. As J.P. wistfully whispers in *Angels in the Outfield*, "It could happen."

You bet it can.

Down empty corridors and into an awaiting elevator, I go, accompanied by wall-to-wall Secret Service agents. They whisper my new codename into their sleeves as I flit past: "Godhead One's on the move." I like it; I like it a lot. It's snappy and cool, even outrageous.

452

Everything you'd ever want in a Secret Service codename, in my opinion.

I'm escorted into the Jackson Place Conference room. Whoa. Sitting under the English mid-19th century, ballroom-size cut-crystal gasolier, now electrified, are my 21st Century disciples. They're bunched about a mahogany oval dining table—late 19th, early 20th century—shining with gorgeous ebony piano finish. As I walk in, they stand and applaud. Naturally, I owe them everything because definitely I'd be back in L.A., watching my stepbrother take the oath of office today, if not for them. They pulled me through the wastelands: through the Iowa Caucuses, the New Hampshire Primary, Super Tuesday, the L.A. Convention, and the General Election. They even put an icepack on my hand after I clobbered my stepbrother during my infamous Jim Lehrer's debate. That I will never forget because I was in pain, let me tell you. I ached. So as I enter the conference room, spiffed up for the day, and looking as respectable as Barak Obama, I applaud them, too. It's a joyous mood because we all know what we're about to do: We're about to end hunger in castoff places like Haiti and Africa. We're about to cure all sorts of incurable diseases from AIDS—yes AIDS in Africa, too!—to Guinea worm. We're about to put a stop to, if not reversing down to 350 ppm, global warming because if nothing else, we must and we will make the Arctic and the Antarctic safe again and fun again for polar bears, penguins, and Lindblad Expeditions. (Okay, that last crack was supposed to be a joke, a little Inauguration Day humor. I want it known from the get-go that my presidency will not be, well, entirely humorless—not like that other J.C.—Jimmy Carter.

Not, of course, that we'll be able to accomplish all this in my First 100 Days. But by the end of my first year, there's always an Obama hope and a Hail Mary prayer that we can, so long as I'm sitting at the table with Reverend-Go Green-V.P. Al.

Which is where he is now, seated at the far end of the table. I love Al. He's my political Messiah. But he's struggling to remove himself from the embrace of the older Chippendale-style chair. He has that polar bear look about him, even though there's a gold medallion dangling from his neck, looped about his starched white minister's collar. I know what that medallion is. Everyone knows what it is. On it is engraved the profile image of Alfred Nobel, and around the edges are written these good words, *"Pro pace et fraternitate gentium."* For those who cut first-year Latin class, they mean, "For the peace and brotherhood of men." Naturally, on seeing this, I can't help but have Obama-size hope that the Noble Norwegian Committee will hand over one of those medals to me before the end of my first year in office, too. I mean, if Obama got one—why not me? It's not that I require any kind of special validation for my work. It's not that at all. I'm way beyond that. But as a matter of course I'll be making "extraordinary efforts to strengthen international diplomacy and cooperation between peoples," as the peace prize committee noted in its praise of Obama when it handed over the award. So you bet, just like 'bama, I'll take a couple of quick trips across the pond—not too many, but not too few either—deliver a handful of stump speeches on global peace and reconciliation, and presto! Nobel Peace Prize, here I come!

In any event, I've always been happy that Al got his award. He deserved it. And earned it the old-fashioned way. By working for it. He looks just great in it, regal, too, like King Harald V of Norway, only considerably more rotund. Al finally frees himself from the grip of the embrace of his Chippendale chair. He greets me with a polar bear hug. "Jesus! Jesus!" he bleats, his reverential Reverend Al-side showing. It's actually quite gratifying to think of myself as *Al's* savior. Though, as everyone knows, Al requires no saving. His global warming work alone gets him through the Pearly Gates. For sure, Al's got nothing to worry about in that department. His weight, however, may be another matter. But that's not my department. Of course, none of us, especially me, want to see him arrive prematurely at St. Peter's Golden Gate because everyone, everywhere, needs the Great, Good Al.

Having said all that, there's really no further need for me to consider my first important just-about-to-be president decision. Since my goal, like Al's, is to cap Carbon Dioxide equivalent concentrations at 650 parts per million while lowering temperature rise to 2.5 degrees C— ambitious I know—but that's Al, that's me, and then reverse Carbon Dioxide concentrations down to 350 parts per million and slash temperatures to 1.5 degrees C, I ask Al to be my Light Bulb Gladiator, our nation's Energy Star CFL guy. His mission: To light up the nation and then the world, CFL-style. No job for the feint hearted, to be sure; one for the lighthearted only. Get it? Which is Al. At least Al knows how to laugh at himself, which is something you want in any kind of gladiator. So I hereby appoint Al as this Christ Administration's Gladiator-in-Chief-in-Charge-of-Reversing-Global-Warming-CFL-style because if anyone can, Al can. He's the Man.

But don't think I don't know Al's none too happy about this change, because he knows and I know that he's been there, done that before. And don't think I don't know Al was really looking forward to leading prayers and reading text at showcase dignitary funerals in distant lands as Reverend Al. But, Al's a real trooper, and he's willing to let go of that job for the Sake of the Nation. Sometimes we all have to make sacrifices for the sake of things greater than ourselves, especially when destiny calls. Going Green has and forever will be Al's global destiny.

The truth is a wise and thoughtful president has to know when and how to allocate his most precious resources. First among equals, that's Al.

So how am I doing so far?

I take it from your silence all's well.

"I will be your Gladiator-in-Chief-in-Charge-of-Reversing-Global-Warming," V.P.-elect decrees oh so humbly. Then we shake on it as real tears come to Al's moist eyes.

"What is it?" I ask, worried.

At first, Al can't speak. He tries but can't force his words. But his actions say it all. Slowly, he peels away his starch white clerical collar. Without sign or fanfare, he slides it into his jacket pocket, puts it away for another day. I try to console him, naturally; I feel his pain. But what can I do? The buck stops with me, and I need to show results. That's what the American people elected me to do and what I get paid for.

Al waddles back to the far end of the table and attempts to re-insert himself into the older Chippendale-style chair. It's a bit like trying to put a popped cork back in a bottle—hard work. But Al succeeds—as he succeeds with everything. He finally drops down, creating a sound of muffled thunder and causing the room to shake, but it's hardly anything to worry about on the Richter scale. I take my seat at the head of the table, and am struck by a sudden sense of history. To think that Winston Churchill and Nelson Mandela and even Barack Obama once sat here! Their asses—large and small—in this same chair. I'm overcome with humility. Giant men. Giant footsteps to fill. Leaders of great nations, no small thing. Obviously, I'm suffering from great leader envy.

My disciples are seated six to a side. Everyone's present. Everyone's engaged. Their eyes smile with Obama-like hope, which is what you'd expect on Inauguration Day, I know, but this is a very special kind of luminosity they show, like sunshine shooting through sheets of falling rain.

That's because they know and I know that this is their moment, our moment, America's moment, Earth's moment. And like Al and his Nobel Peace Prize, we earned it the old-fashioned way. We earned it.

We earned it by kicking Beelzebub down the cellar steps or out into the outhouse or wherever it is defeated politicians go to review their sorry exit polls.

So let the Cabinet appointments begin!

First up is my choice for Secretary of State. I need a class act, a seasoned choice, someone with an iron hand in a velvet glove. Lord knows, some frontline experience would be just great, too. Let's see... There's Arnold, there's Jesse, and Nancy. There's Madonna, too. But a Christ Administration can't afford to have the Vatican snubbing its Secretary of State. No way. And we all know that the Vatican has a long institutional memory. It's not likely to forget her mock-execution on my cross any millennium soon.

Hmmm, then there's Oprah. She's universally loved, for sure, and the very definition of a goodwill ambassador. Oprah's angels and all. Or Bono? That's a thought. He could be quite good—and he has experience at lobbying heads of states and yes, even the pope! Plus I did like some of his guest columns published in the *New York Times*. I read them online up above. Given his assets, I could definitely overlook the fact that he's more Irish than American, as I'm still more Heaven than Earth. Hmmm, then again, maybe not. But having U2 accompany Bono on his overseas missions, which I know he'd insist on, just because Bono's Bono, might be more trouble than it's worth. On the other hand, music *is* the universal language...

So many choices; so little time.

That's when I'm touched by sunshine. I get all warm and woozy inside—whatever that means. It's like I'm walking in a glowing field of wheat. I turn to my first and only choice, seated on my right. That would be "America must be a light to the world—not just a missile" Nancy Pelosi.

"Your country needs you," I pronounce. "Will you be my Secretary of State?"

Before she has a chance to respond, the sunshine disappears from Arnold's kind Austrian smile. He leaps up from his seat, first chair on my left, and launches into an uncharacteristic, un-disciple-like rage. "But, Mr. President-elect, I already told my Maria dat you'd make da two-terminator governator—dat's me—da next Secretary of Stater!" Arnold sinks to his knees. "Please, Mr. President-elect, please! You gotta do this for me or my Maria will never get over it!" I pat Arnold on the head like a panting golden Lab, and tell him that everything's going to be all right. I'm not sure he believes me.

Then I turn back to Nancy.

"Well, Disciple Pelosi?"

"It would be my honor to be your Secretary of State—my About-To-Be-Inaugurated Mr. President, because we San Francisco Liberals and former House Speakers make the best Secretary of States, Arnold."

"Do not!" Arnold protests.

"Do, too!"

"Do not!"

"Do, too!"

"Do not!"

"Arnold!" I intervene, "it's going to be all right!"

"Okay, okay, I believe you, sorry," Arnold says, pulling himself somewhat together.

Then I turn back to Nancy.

"Effective 12:02 p.m. today, I appoint you my Secretary of State... Now tell us your plans for your First 100 Days."

"I intend to tear down the wall dividing Palestinians and Israelis by settling all outstanding issues regarding Palestinians' right of return, settlement freezes in the West Bank and Jerusalem, and oversee the transformation of Jerusalem into a two-sate capital of Peace, Reconciliation and Religious Freedom, with your help, my About-To-Be-Inaugurated Mr. President.

"Then I'll set out to resolve the conflict between North and South Korea, so we can pull our troops out of the DMZ in time for the 70th anniversary of the conflict, with your help, my About-To-Be-Inaugurated Mr. President.

"After that, I'll settle all wars and low-intensity conflicts in Africa. That would include those in Cote d'Ivoire, Guinea, Liberia, Nigeria, Sierra Leone, and Togo, Eritrea, Ethiopia, Somalia, Sudan, Uganda, Burundi, Democratic Republic of the Congo, Rwanda, Algeria, Angola and Zimbabwe. If I left out a war or two, it's understandable, given their soaring numbers, but I promise to settle those, too, with your help, my About-To-Be-Inaugurated Mr. President.

Thereafter, I have in mind to bring off a global consensus on democratic governance in all countries, including China, Burma, and Singapore. And yes, even in Cuba. It's going to be tough because of the bad rap democracy got during the terrible Reign of Terrible George, but I'll do my very best, with your help, my About-To-Be-Inaugurated Mr. President.

"Then in my remaining time, I'll negotiate multilateral agreements on world denuclearization. I'll see to it that every nuclear weapon is scrapped in the United States, Russia, the United Kingdom, Brazil, France, China, North Korea, India, Pakistan, Iran, and Israel, and oh, yes, those few in Papua New Guinea, too. In under sixty days, give or take, with your help, my About-To-Be-Inaugurated Mr. President.

"I also plan to win a global consensus on banning all landmines, using first my considerable San Francisco charms and my husband's deep, deep Apple stock pockets to woo the U.S. Senate, with

459

strawberries and white wine, and Bourbon, if need be, into signing the landmines treaty, together with those other prickly landmine-loving governments, including but not limited to China, India, Pakistan, Myanmar, Russia, North Korea, and Greenland. I can do that, with your help, my About-To-Be-Inaugurated Mr. President.

"Human trafficking? I'm on it. We simply inflate the price of prostitution 5000% worldwide by imposing a global value-added tax to be applied to retraining *filles de joie* in green technology. A regressive tax, to be sure, but our plan won't be treated seriously without one. Under this plan, nobody anywhere will be able to afford them! *Voilà*! End of global human trafficking, with your help, my About-To-Be-Inaugurated Mr. President.

"Finally, I'll also organize much needed relief to draught-stricken people in Sudan, Zimbabwe, Mauritania, Egypt, Ceylon, Afghanistan, Pakistan, and Haiti. I can do all that if I work Saturdays and Sundays, on top of 16 hour days during the workweek, which I'd already planned to do, and so long as my dear husband Paul doesn't mind, which he won't, because he's a prince. So consider that a given, with your help, my About-To-Be-Inaugurated Mr. President."

"But what about making time to advance international women's issues?" I ask, not so unreasonably, I think, in light of Nancy's legendary talents.

"Yes, that, too, with your help, my About-To-Be-Inaugurated Mr. President. Sorry I let that slip my mind. I'll begin by corralling the governments of the world and encouraging them to mandate 50% participation of women in their national legislatures. Beyond all of the above, that'll have to be it, I'm afraid, for my First 100 Days in office."

"That's *it*?" Arnold carps at my elbow.

"There's only so much a girl can do in limited time, Arnold," Nancy responds, diplomatically.

"Dis disciple could bench press twice dat much in half da time, Nancy."

"Put a barbell in it, Arnie," she strikes back.

"Let's not start, you two!"

My mind turns to who's going to be my Secretary of Defense? Naturally, the American people deserve a SecDef who's no candy-ass, but also one who's capable of running the Defense Department in a fashion that's consistent with their Commander-in-Peace's "Love Your Neighbor as Yourself Because They're All You've Got" philosophy. In other words, the likes of Donald Rumsfeld and Melvin Laird, et al. need not apply. Who among my disciples could fit this job description? Bono? No chance. No one wants a singing Secretary of Defense with a rock band that has the same name as the U-2 spy plane shot down, together with its pilot Gary Powers, over the Soviet Union in 1960. That doesn't inspire confidence, which is a must in a Secretary of Defense. Martha Stewart? She's tough as nails, but it's unlikely she'd pass a FBI background check in order for her to get her security clearance—not with her conviction for obstructing justice and lying to investigators. Felonious stock sales don't go down with the Federal Bureau of Investigation. Arnold? No, not Arnold. The last one I'd want in charge of the United States Armed Forces is the Terminator, for obvious reasons.

So many choices; so little time.

Fourteen more cabinet posts to fill before my swearing-in and my inaugural ride down Constitution Avenue on the back of a jackass.

That's when once again I'm touched by sunshine. Yet again, I get all warm and woozy inside—whatever that means. I feel as though I'm walking through a wonderful field of winter wheat. It glows; it shines; it sways in waves. Then I turn to my first and only choice for

461

Secretary of Defense, seated two seats down on my right. That would be Disciple Jesse Jackson, who never saw a war he ever liked.

"Your country needs you," I pronounce. "Will you be my Secretary of Defense?"

He springs; he leaps; he bounds from his seat: "Praise be the baby Jesus! Praise be my Commander-in-Peace! I will be your Secretary of Defense because I'm a man of action and always have a sensible reaction to any kind of chain-reaction 'cause my name's Jesse Jackson!"

Kneeling at my elbow, Disciple Schwarzenegger puts on a childish pout, "Everyone knows I'd make a betta SecDef dan Jesse ever would. Dat's 'cause I'm da pumping-iron-man-three-time Terminator dat I am and have absolute total recall, except about where I'm always putting my damn reading glasses!"

Again I pat Arnold on the head, like a panting Golden Lab. "There, there," I say. "Everything's going to be all right."

Arnie tries to force a smile, but he really is just a big Godzilla baby.

I turn back to Jesse, who's reported in for duty, and standing next to me.

"Effective 12:02 p.m. today, I appoint you my Secretary of Defense because there never was a war you ever loved... Now tell us your plans for your First 100 Days."

Jesse drops to one knee and clasps my hand "Thank you, baby Jesus; thank you, my soon-to-be Commander-in-Peace. I won't let you down; I won't let the country down! I won't let Dr. King down!"

He then stands, salutes. His eyes shine with fire, like distant meteorites.

"First, I'll rename the Department of Defense the Department of Compassion, or DOC, for short, because I think that name rocks, which may not come as a shock, but when you hear my vision for how I will maintain this country's freedom from distant dangers, I hope you'll agree that thus it must be, even though it may sound partially inane and surely won't bring me no fame. Nevertheless, there can be no shame, because I'm in a whole new game, and a man of action who always has a sensible reaction to any kind of interstate-reaction, 'cause my name's SecDef Jesse Jackson.

"It is thus, because we must.

"Second, I'll shut down the whole darn Military-industrial complex, or MIC, for short, because I'm just so sick and tired of being sick and tired about all those defense contractors getting rich off weapons that do more harm than sow charm. Sure, all those top execs at Lockheed Martin, Northrop Grumman and Raytheon may go apoplectic and try to put a lien on my corner E Ring office over at the Pentagon; but it's my job to make sure our country's secure as well as pure, because I'm a man of action who always has a sensible reaction to any kind of interstate-reaction, 'cause my name's SecDef Jesse Jackson.

"It is thus because we must.

"Third, I shall not rest until we are blessed with an emergency replacement for 'Mutually Assured Destruction' or MAD, for short, and I will propose and shall not dose until Congress coughs up the non-negotiable budget appropriation in the form of hard cash so we can make a big splash with a brand new strategic deterrence I will dub, 'Mutually Assured Construction,' or MAC, which will be based on logarithms even the Chinese can't hack, because I'm a man of action who always has a sensible reaction to any kind of interstate-reaction, 'cause my name's SecDef Jesse Jackson.

"It is thus because we must.

"And regarding the development of an urgently needed new generation of stealth weapons systems required to stave off al-Qaeda and the Taliban, and probably those pesky Iranians, too, I plan to

463

announce our first MAC attack on my first day in office that will be intended not to do harm, but rather to utterly charm, and win over hearts and minds. With a little assist from our DOC Lepidopterologists, we'll deploy on your order down there in the Situation Room a barrage of aerial artillery, the likes of which the world has never seen or dreamed. We'll launch hundreds of millions of Silver Hairstreak butterflies, 100% organic and as sustainable as they are naturally obtainable, into the mountains of Afghanistan and Pakistan. And if the winds are just right, I will show you might, because we'll have about a better than fifty-fifty chance of making all those bad boys in al-Qaeda and the Taliban smile for the first time in their miserable lifetimes. And the more butterflies we send in, the more they'll likely to grin because rainbows of butterflies are the most beautiful things, and soon our sworn enemies will be singing and dancing and no longer ranting. Then we know, because we're not slow, that they'll come down with a bad case of warrior's remorse because we'll have our sources. And one by one they'll lay down their arms and vow to end all the harms because of the butterfly charms. There will be no more crying, an end will come to all the dying up in the Hindu Kush, and that ain't no mush. And then at your behest, I'll do my level best to sign them up for a permanent armistice, because I have a gift, like Arnold says, for just dis kind of ding.

"Those butterfly charms are more powerful than any MQ-1 Predator harms, and I believe because I do not deceive, that they can and will induce, if not permanently seduce, all those so-called freedom fighters' up in those old cold mountains into making nice with the West, so we can all invest in reconciliation and harmonization and even contemplation, because I'm a man of action who always has a sensible reaction to any kind of interstate-reaction, 'cause my name's SecDef Jesse Jackson.

"It is thus because we must.

On that note of hope, SecDef and I shake: He's going to make the Military-industrial Complex quake. I can hardly wait to see the look on all those top dog exec faces at Lockheed-Martin, Northrop Grumman and Raytheon.

SecDef Jackson drops to one knee and clasps my hand again. "I do hereby swear, my Commander-in-Peace, that I will always be one step ahead of all manner of havoc and destruction that threatens the United States, and will be ready, willing and able to perform any kind of Mutually Assured Construction in the name of my soul spiritual inspiration, my President Baby Jesus!"

But my mind has already turned.

Next. My Secretary of Homeland Security.

So many choices; so little time.

Thirteen more cabinet posts to fill before my swearing-in and my inaugural ride down Constitution Avenue on the back of a jackass.

That would be one choice. One man. One legend of the DVD and silver screen. That would be 'Everything's going to be all right' Arnie. Who better to protect our ass from al-Qaeda than the lead actor from *Hercules in New York* may I ask?

I turn to the pumping iron man, still squatting at my elbow.

But for the asking, it's a done ding.

"Your country needs you," I pronounce. "Will you be my Secretary of Homeland Security?"

Gone is the pout; absent are the teary eyes. Arnold's back.

He rises, rises like the 'Austrian Oak' he is and ever will be. Dat's my Arnold. Now he towers and broadcasts, no, radiates, security. Homeland security. Even in a tux. His biceps bulge, big as Colorado mountain boulders. He's definitely da Man for Dis Job.

And there's not a naysayer against him in da room, either.

465

"Effective 12:02 p.m. today, I appoint you, Arnold 'de Conan and Never been no Girlie-Man' Schwarzenegger, as my Secretary of Homeland Security... Now tell us your plans for your First 100 Days."

"As your Secretary of Homeland Security—you better believe it—I promise to do anyding and everyding in my pumping iron man powers to fortify our national defenses so to protect our porous shores from all dose al-Qaeda and Taliban Girlie-Men. On my oath of honor as a Non-Girlie Man, I swear dat dere will be no more surprise attacks within our four borders by dose good for nothin' rock eaters and goat herders, 'cause my name's Conan de Barbarian of Homeland Security!

"You better believe it—Prez Jesus—I'll make dem run and I'll make dem hide and if dey come nearby I'll make dem feel very, very sorry for what dey done, or about to do, 'cause I got da Coast Guard, da Federal Protective Service, da Border Patrol, da Secret Service, and dat FEMA by my side. On top of dat, I'll have access to da CIA and will do my best to coordinate intelligence with da NSA, da FBI and dat Office of Naval Intelligence. I want to be damn sure dat everyone connects de dots and does not disconnect all da dots dat I connect! In my First 100 Days, I will connect all da dots, no matter how many dots they got. I will I safeguard da future for all Americans, for all da bench-pressers and hairdressers and cross-dressers, for all dem moms and pops and body builder kids growin' up in da land of da free and da home of da brave, 'cause my name's Conan de Barbarian of Homeland Security!

"And you better believe it, if any of dem terrorists out dere wants a piece of me, I say, 'Bring on da Girlie-Men!' Meet me on de North Jersey Shore! Meet me on de Golden Gate Bridge! Meet me in de middle of any Iowa cornfield! I'm not afraid of all you Taliban, al-Qaeda Girlie-Men! I'm not afraid of ANY GIRLIE-MEN, 'cause my name's Conan de Barbarian of Homeland Security!

"I promise you, Prez Jesus, dere won't be no attacks on America in my First 100 Days, not in my second hundred days, not in my three hundred days, not in our entire two-terms in office, 'cause my name's Conan de Barbarian of Homeland Security!

"So dat's all I got to say othder than it's gonna be an action-packed First 100 Days 'cause I promise to pump up all our national defenses and make dem as muscle bound as any pumping iron man out dere. I'll pump 'em up so dat da national bod will look just like mine. You better believe it, Prez Jesus, I'm gonna make dis country so safe dat even George W.'s former V.P. Dick Cheney will say dat it's even safe enough to stop torturing all dem Girlie-Men terrorists!

"Da Guinness Book of World Records called me 'da most perfectly developed man in da history of da world.' Wid me as your Conan de Barbarian of Homeland Security I swear, I will make dis country de most perfectly secure country in de world. Dat's my 100-day promise, Prez Jesus. Dat's a Conan de Barbarian-Arnold Schwarzenegger promise—so you better believe it."

Well, dat's dat. No one could ask for more dan dat.

America will be in good hands with dat no Girlie-Man.

Next. My Secretary of Energy.

So many choices; so little time.

Twelve more cabinet posts to fill before my swearing-in and my inaugural ride down Constitution Avenue on the back of a jackass.

My eyes comb the profiles at the table. They come to rest—a shrieking halt in fact—on Madonna, otherwise known to me as Madonna, the Magnificent and Magnetic; Madonna, the Beautiful and Beguiling; Madonna—and I'm only half afraid to admit it—Madonna, the Towering and Tempting. She's that appetizing, like a ripe pear mid-winter. She exudes, emits a spectacular radiance. Marilyn Monroe, move over. I once had her glow, her bubbling charisma; but that was a year

467

ago, before all the stumping, the lunching, the fundraising and speechmaking. Now? Now, I'll admit it: Put me next to Madonna and my charismatic candlepower doesn't hold a lumen next to hers. She shines like a Klieg eye. But what would you expect? I'm a politician now; I drained my haloed luminosity bank to become president of the United States. But not Madonna; her electric lumens are only now just peaking. And she's just what this nation needs—undiluted, unalloyed, unrefined and, most of all, uncensored ENERGY!

I pop the question.

"Your country needs you," I pronounce. "Will you be my Secretary of Energy?"

By way of issuing a definitive Madonna response, the Queen of Energy flips on her Ipod Orchestra tabletop boom box, leaps atop the oval conference table with ebony piano finish, accompanied by the introductory sounds of hot guitar and cool brass, and starts performing, as only Madonna can, by singing, "Energy Girl," her title air from her CD-in-the-works, *DOE*, which is most assuredly not an acronym for Department of Energy. More like Department of Eroticism—if you want my good guess.

Here it comes; here it is, the Inaugural performance of "Energy Girl."

What's in it for a Material Girl like Me?
Renewable, sustainable forms of Energy!
What's in it for a Material Girl like Me?
Being Secretary of Energy!
What gives me tons of erotic fantasies?
Thoughts of renewable, sustainable energy!
Which makes me, what else?
Your quintessential choice for Secretary of Energy!
What's in it for a Material Girl like Me?

Renewable, sustainable forms of Energy!
What's in it for a Material Girl like Me?
Being your Secretary of Energy!
What gives me tons of erotic fantasies?
Thoughts of renewable, sustainable energy!
So take me!
Slake me!
Make me your Secretary of Energy!
On the grave of my dear Mother,
I promise, I swear,
To provide this country with more organic energy!
Wind, solar, geothermal, biomass, cold fusion, too! (Well, maybe not so organic!)
And just so there's no confusion, or illusion, as Jesse would say,
In my First 100 Days, I intend to invent even more forms of alternative energy
Because I'm no Material Girl living in a material world, not anymore!
I'm an Energy Girl living in an energy world
As your kick-ass Secretary of Energy
Who's inspired by erotic thoughts of renewable, sustainable energy!

Madonna concludes with a right split, right there on the mahogany table, and right in front of me, which is fairly impressive, especially for a sixty-two-year-old songster turned disciple dressed in top hat and tails. So I'm pleased to announce, "Effective 12:02 p.m. today, I appoint you my Secretary of Energy."

"And I accept, Mr. President-elect, in the name of Madonna Louise Ciccone, my dear mother. Bless her sacred heart."

She says it with a quiet, understated earnestness that I actually find quite moving.

About Madonna: She will always be a marvel. Because she moves from strength to strength, as the Book of Psalms says: From musical maverick to religious iconoclast to dedicated disciple to senior

469

presidential advisor. Madonna reassumes her seat at the mahogany table, looking way more maverick-like than she ever did, even while wearing her crown of thorns on her mirrored cross singing "Live to Tell" during the Confessions Tour. Madonna was a maverick long before Sarah Palin and John McCain ever were.

Next. My Secretary of Secretary of Housing and Urban Development, or HUD, for all you Beltway outsiders.

Still plenty of choices; could use more time.

The perfect choice in absolutely no time.

Eleven more cabinet posts to fill before my swearing-in and my inaugural ride down Constitution Avenue on the back of a jackass.

Think Martha, decorous Mother Earth. Think Martha & Co., Mother Hen of Zu-Zu and Paw-Paw and Chin-Chin and Empress Wu, too. Think Martha, Inc., esprit queen of seasonal trimmings and Entrepreneur of Industries borne of glitter. You'd be correct if you were thinking Disciple Stewart, doyen *magnifico* of all holiday frippery, finery and frou-frou, to say nothing of bells and whistles. The Grand Dame of Gingerbread Empires, who never met a pinecone she couldn't make sparkle like Frosty the Snowman, from start to scratch, in under two hours and thirty minutes.

Now I ask you: Who better to dress up America's slums than Martha?

"Your country needs you," I pronounce. "Will you, Martha Stewart, be my Secretary of HUD?" I inquire respectfully.

Never one to miss her next ship coming in, Martha comes to stand before me, holding Mont Blanc pen in hand. "Where do I sign?" she asks, in search of her official U.S. government contract.

"No need," I answer with a dismissive wave of my hand.

"But I like to have everything down in writing," Martha counters. "And, of course, I was so looking forward to using my Greta Garbo Mont Blanc fountain pen again!"

"My word is my compact," I gently insist.

Martha wisely puts her pen right back in her handbag.

"So effective 12:02 p.m. today," I announce, "I appoint you my Secretary of HUD... Now tell us your plans for your First 100 Days."

"Like my idol Lady Bird Johnson used to say, Mr. President-elect, 'Ugliness is so grim!' So I intend to 'clean-up, fix-up, paint-up and plant-up' America's black ghettos and Hispanic shantytowns, its sorry poor folk hovels and dilapidated No Man's Land rat holes, wherever I may find them, consistent with my legal obligations as Secretary of HUD under the New Fair Housing Act. For obvious reasons, I take legal matters very seriously these days.

"You can also count on me to steer HUD clear of any federal court citations for not addressing the severe segregation it was responsible for and for consigning poor black people to unsightly and plug-ugly urban shack towns in Baltimore, unlike George's W.'s stone-walling HUD. No sir, District Judge Marvin Garbis will never fault my HUD for treating black folks in Baltimore as 'an island reservation for use as a container for all of the poor of a contiguous region.' Quote, unquote. Not in a Christ Administration; a Christ Administration will live up to its statutory mandate. No sir, I will remedy that kind of wrong by beautifying every aesthetically challenged neighborhood in America because I'm a down-in-the-glitter, thinking pink, and painting in delicious pastels kind of gal, who was born to transform the drab and dreary, the ram-shackle and the run-down, the decaying and the decrepit, as best she can, and remaking urban, segregated America into many Martha Stewart-like oases, the kind of tasteful paradisiacal getaways that tend to congregate at the leafy edge of shady, green woodlands and

471

boast meandering moss paths leading up to natural sea sponge painted Robin's Egg Blue or Red Miso front doors—using Martha Stewart Signature Colors, as you would expect—with copper satin bows hanging from polished brass lion door knockers. Special places where one should always arrive, when possible, while being pushed in a vintage Smith & Hawken wheelbarrow—pre-Target, Inc. takeover—it goes without saying—under dappled shade in the sweet, drifting hours of a long and lazy, summery afternoon.

"How am I going to accomplish such uncompromising levels of urban aesthetics during a time of national austerity and in such a brief time? Well, Mr. President-elect, I intend to recruit and mobilize thousands of junior high school students from shore to shore in order to paint all the slums and all the available wall spaces on skid row in Martha Stewart Skyland™ colors, both interiors and exteriors, because I can get a super duper discounted rate from Sherwin-Williams. Needless to say, everything will be done consistent with my strict but, I'm not afraid to admit, inspired aesthetic principles laid down in exacting detail in my *Martha Stewart's Homekeeping Handbook,* which I'm only too glad to make available on MarthaStwart.Com free of charge to every wanting American citizen, urban or otherwise, at the click of a mouse by PDF download. That is, every American who takes the Martha Stewart pledge to eschew the tacky and take up the tasteful in order to live like the chic and highly cultured. It's not ONLY about the money for me, Mr. President-elect! It's about the pure, unadulterated beauty of life as seen through Martha Stewart's eyes! About the privilege of Martha Stewart Living which I am giving gratis to the masses as your Secretary of HUD!

"And I'm fairly certain that we won't need to pass any special congressional legislation to accomplish all that in my First 100 Days, but I'll check in with your soon-to-be-named Attorney General about it, just to be on the safe side, because one things for sure: This country can ill-afford another all-expenses-paid vacation to Camp Cupcake for the likes of yours truly and I definitely cannot afford to loose another billion due to a second incarceration, especially now that I'll be living more or less hand-to-mouth on a cabinet secretary's salary."

Of Martha, I am so very, very proud. Unquestionably, no better Secretary of HUD could there be. So uncompromisingly passionate about her in-perfect-good-taste-we-shall-all-be, whether in suburban or urban housing concerns, Martha has more than atoned for offending her neighbors. The thing is, I may know how lucky I am to have her on Team Christ, but America really hasn't gotten its mind wrapped around it yet. Despite that I have this to say to all those clueless souls: Just hold onto your porch stenciled rocking chairs! You ain't seen nothing yet!

Martha, Inc. has come to save the cheerless ghettoes!

Next. My Secretary of Health and Human Services.

Still a few choices; barely enough time.

Ten more cabinet posts to fill before my swearing-in and my inaugural ride down Constitution Avenue on the back of a jackass.

So let's see. Possibilities. Mel, Oprah, Sparrow, Bono... Bono. I look down the right-hand side of the table. And there he is: Bono the Miraculous. Wraparound Armani shades tinted red, white and blue stripes; Jesus-length hair down tumbling down past his shoulders; borrowed, boring, brown, baggy suit—too long in the sleeves; crocodile cowboy boots. Across his naked barrel chest, the slogan, END AIDS, hand painted in decidedly non-Martha Stewart Signature Colors over the contours of a map of Africa. Precisely the cool style attitude you'd expect from Bono. He sits there with that special look on his face—you know the one I'm talking about—that look of sterling Bono Attitude that telegraphs ever so diplomatically but resolutely to every head-of-state on the planet with available financial resources to possibly spare, "Make Your Discretionary Funds available for my Good Purposes."

473

He's everything an about-to-be unconventional president could ever hope for in a Secretary of Health and Human Services. Really he is.

So I signal Bono that he's up for a political Grammy. I do it by smiling with my eyes, just like the Dalia Lama. He signals me back that he's ready to accept. He does it by adjusting his patriotic shades as only Bono Vox can. It's fusion time at Blair House: Rock 'n' roll meets Health and Human Services. Or put another way, the face of fusion philanthropy meets the face of fusion health and human services.

"Your new country needs you, Bono," I pronounce. "Will you be my Secretary of Health and Human Services?"

I don't know what you were expecting, but I was expecting just exactly this.

Bono, like Madonna before him, sings a song to convey his enthusiasm for his prospective new job. It's called "Inoperable Day." He knocks it out a cappella.

The heart is doomed, tries to find an operating room.
There's no room, no affordable space in this hospital I'll assume
You're out of luck and the reason is nobody cares
You're stuck and you're not gonna be operated on anywhere
You thought you had the right to all the necessary repairs
Someone you could pay at a reasonable rate in return for no cares
It's an inoperable *day, the ceiling falls*
And you feel like it's an inoperable *day*
Let it go away

You're on the skids but you've got no health insurance
You're in the poor house, in the maze of medical self-reliance
You'd love a comprehensive health care policy even though you can't afford one
You've been all over and now you're done
It's an inoperable *day*

474

Let it go away
It's an inoperable *day*
Let it go away

Touch me, take me to that Canadian health care system
Teach me, I know I can learn about lacto-vegetarianism

See health care in black and white as a fundamental human right too
See universal health care right in front of you
See the population broken by health care costs
See the doctors and pharmaceutical companies ignoring their loss
See the health care fires at night
See the patient bankruptcies at first light
And see the banker with your deed in her mouth
After the bills come in you have to move out
It was an inoperable day
Inoperable day
Let it go away

Touch me, take me to the Canadian health care system
Teach me, I know I can learn about lacto-vegetarianism

What you don't have you could die without
What you don't know is docs don't care if you shout
What you don't have you could die without
You need it now, you need it now,

Inoperable day...

I think we can now all agree. Never ask a pop artist to answer a simple, straightforward question unless, of course, you don't mind listening to their latest tune. That last one of Bono's makes it more or less conclusive: He's the Raphael of pop song writing, although to my tin ear "Inoperable Day" sounds suspiciously like a variation on his grand old classic "Beautiful Day." You know, the one with the soaring sound and soaring lyrics that he sang live in Slane Castle, Ireland in 2001. "It's a beautiful day, Don't let it get away." It went something like that, if memory serves, which customarily it doesn't these days, for understandable reasons, relating to my substantial age.

Bono senses my need for an encore, so he disappears his hand-held radio mic and assumes his new cabinet secretary's hat. As if addressing the National Constitution Center Award's dinner after being honored with its distinguished Philadelphia Liberty Medal for his Christ-like deeds, he finally gets back to my question. "When you are trapped by bad health, you are not free. When hospitals prevent you from getting the health care you need, you are not free. And when you are a child in America or Africa or the Antarctic this very week, barred from getting treatment for HIV/AIDS or some such other disease because you don't have access to universal health insurance, well, then none of us are truly free. So yes, I accept your nomination as Secretary of Health and Human Services, even though you must have a pretty terrific sense of humor to put me in charge of it. Then again, there's much work left to be done to be a part of God's ongoing purposes, so who's not to say, all hands on deck."

I quickly interject, "The *president's* ongoing purposes, you mean…"

"Yes, just that—separation of church and state, and all that."

That's good enough for me. Having Bono in my cabinet is even better than having the Beatles in my basement.

"Effective 12:02 p.m. today," I pronounce, "I appoint you my Secretary of HHS… Now tell us your plans for your First 100 Days."

As if I didn't know. But before he can say it, I say it for him: "End AIDS all over, right?"

We clasp hands in solidarity, as rock stars do, except I don't have a brass ring piercing the lobe of my left ear like Bono does. So understandably, my handshake doesn't have the same rock culture gravitas as his, but what the hell. Bono doesn't care. I'm one with him and he's one with me. He smiles his conquering smile, and I smile mine right back. For sure, our winning smiles, together with his righteous band, will change the world.

"Beautiful Day!" he exclaims, unable to resist the virtuous temptation of the truly triumphant.

That and "We've ended AIDS" is all Bono ever needs to say to me as cabinet secretary. The rest he can articulate in lyrics and put to music any time he wants.

Next. My Secretary of the Interior.

Just a few choices; less and less time.

Nine more cabinet posts to fill before my swearing-in and my inaugural ride down Constitution Avenue on the back of a jackass.

I don't know about you, but I'm thinkin' JLo.

What d'you say?

I turn to JLo, seated opposite Bono, and ask the charged question, even as I smell her seductive perfume, a sampling from her recent Black-footed Ferret Collection, I have no doubt. The scent's to lay down your life for, but since I've already done that comparatively recently I don't intend to offer myself up for sacrifice any time soon. Nevertheless, it calls to me, like open prairies after a storm or great lakes in summer or distant alpine mountains practically any time. She's a matchless choice for top administrator of the U.S. Fish and Wildlife Service, for sure; possessing the perfect scent to make both man of the

477

prairie and prairie dog go hog-wild. "Your country needs you, JLo. Will you be my Secretary of the Interior?"

I wouldn't have asked if I'd thought she'd decline. On the other hand, you just never know about JLo because as I recall her parents insisted on her being a lawyer and look what happened; she slammed the door on that. And cabinet secretary is much closer to being a lawyer than either singer or disciple. So it's not as though I'm not taking a chance.

JLo offers me her considered response.

"*Thank you,* Commander-in-Padre; *gracias, el capitaine Gloria in Excelsis Deo; merci, presidente in terra pax hominibus bonae voluntatis.* I accept on behalf of my parents, with one piddling reservation. It's this: Frankly, I'm just terrified I might burst out singing in one of your cabinet meetings, much to my and everyone else's embarrassment! But if you can wrap your mind around that, and be prepared for that all but certain eventuality, then I'm your Secretary of Interior!"

You see? JLo's easy. Not difficult to work with at all. She's disproven her naysayers who originally predicted that she'd be a volatile disciple and a hotheaded cabinet secretary. I've always had faith in her, so it's all good. JLo, it is.

"Singing will never be discouraged in any of my meetings, JLo," I answer back.

"So effective 12:02 p.m. today," I pronounce, "I appoint you my Secretary of the Interior... Now tell us your plans for your First 100 Days."

This should be rich.

"'Cause I still feel just terrible about my contributing to the extinction of all manner and kinds of living things, especially those cute, big and little, furry things, I swear on the success of my next line of non-animal tested perfumes and associated products and in 100%

478

compliance with the Animal Welfare Act, to do whatever's necessary, and I do mean whatever's necessary, to repopulate our sixty-two national parks with every adorable creature on the U.S. Fish and Wildlife Service's list of endangered and threatened species. Everyone of them, including but not limited to the gray bat, Hawaiian hoary bat, Indiana bat, lesser long-nosed bat, little Mariana fruit bat, Mariana fruit bat or Mariana flying fox, Mexican long-nosed bat, Ozark big-eared bat, Virginia big-eared bat, American black bear, grizzly bear, Louisiana black bear, polar bear, wood bison, woodland caribou, Columbian white-tailed deer, key deer, black-footed ferret, San Joaquin kit fox, San Miguel island fox, Santa Catalina Island fox, Santa Cruz Island fox, Santa Rosa Island fox, jaguar, Gulf Coast jaguarundi, Sinaloan jaguarundi, Fresno, kangaroo rat, giant kangaroo rat, Morro Bay kangaroo rat, San Bernardino Merriam's kangaroo rat, Stephens' kangaroo rat, Tipton kangaroo rat, Canada lynx, West Indian Manatee, Point Arena Mountain beaver, Alabama beach mouse, Anastasia Island beach mouse, Choctawhatchee beach mouse, Key Largo cotton mouse, Pacific pocket mouse, Perdido Key beach mouse, Preble's meadow jumping mouse, sal marsh harvest mouse, southeastern beach mouse, St. Andrew beach mouse, ocelot, Northern Sea Otter, Southern Sea otter, Florida panther, Utah prairie dog, Sonoran pronghorn, eastern puma, Lower Keys marsh rabbit, pygmy rabbit, riparian rabbit, rice rat, Stellar sea-lion, Caribbean monk seal, Guadalupe fur seal, Hawaiian monk seal, Peninsular bighorn sheep, Sierra Nevada bighorn sheep, Buena Vista Lake ornate shrew, Carolina northern flying squirrel, Delmarva Peninsula fox squirrel, Mount Graham red squirrel, Amargosa vole, Florida salt marsh vole, Hualapai Mexican vole, blue whale, bowhead whale, finback whale, humpback whale, killer whale, right whale, Sei whale, sperm whale, gray wolf, red wolf, Key Largo woodrat, and San Joaquin woodrat.

"And that's just for starters. Extinction is not an option. Aren't I exactly right, V.P. Al?"

"As God made night, you are exactly right, Madam Secretary."

What more could a president possibly ask for in a Secretary of the Interior?

Next. My Secretary of Veterans Affairs.

Hardly any choices; far too little time.

Eight more cabinet posts to fill before my swearing-in and my inaugural ride down Constitution Avenue on the back of a jackass.

Again, I'm touched by sunshine because—and let's be perfectly frank here—there's only one man with the right kind of credentials to do this job justice and I don't mean Disciple Dago or Mel, capable and righteous as they are. I mean the original Maverick himself, Mr. Top Gun, whose F-14 Tomcat fighter jet just came in.

I look at him and he looks at me, with reaching green eyes. Tom's never met a look he couldn't match, especially when he's in generic Tom Cruise character mode and in his CWU-27/P flight suit, without, of course, standard aviator HGU-33/P Aircrew Helmet and MBU-12/P oxygen mask.

"Your country needs you, Tom," I pronounce. "Will you be my Secretary of Veterans Affairs?"

Tom Cruise stands and salutes, as if I were the chairman of the Joint Chiefs of Staff. That's a good sign and just one more illustration of how my life has changed in oh so many ways since Chief Justice Clarence Thomas delivered the goods on Mount Supreme Court, which I knew he would, because practicing Catholics know how to really stick it to Beelzebub types. To think that in a few short hours I'll be able to take some potshots at the military industrial complex! Don't worry,

Dwight! I'll do you proud! The truth is, Christmas came early last year and Clarence's gift was as good as it gets.

"Secretary of Veterans Affairs Tom Cruise reporting for duty, Sir! Thank you for this earned opportunity, Sir! You have my pledge as a reformed Scientologist and an informed Hollywood Christian, that I'll always stand by our vets, just as agent Jerry McGuire always stood by his veteran wide receiver Rod Tidwell of the Arizona Sun Devils in 'Jerry McGuire,' Sir! You have my word, Mr. President-elect. I'll treat each of my vets every bit as well as Jerry handled wide receiver Tidwell, Sir! I'll give each and every one of them the individual attention they deserve, Sir, as if they were my one and only client! It's all part of my mission statement, Sir! 'The Things We Dream but Never Do!' Which, of course, is based on Jerry's mission statement: 'The Things We Think and Do Not Say,' Sir! You know the one Jerry wrote in the middle of the night calling on his company of sports agents to give their clients *more* personal attention, not less. Make *less* money, not more. Accordingly, it's personal attention I intend to give to them, Sir! Just like Dicky Fox tells Jerry in the movie: 'The secret to this job is personal relationships.' And so I intend to honor the philosophy of Dicky Fox, Sir! I intend to follow the Gospel According to Dicky Fox, Sir! I swear that I'll develop personal relationships with each and every one of my vets, Sir! I didn't play Ron Kovic in 'Born on the Fourth of July' for nothing, Sir!"

"That's one inspiring memo, Tom!"

"Mission statement, Sir! Not a memo! Sir!"

Mission statement, memo—whatever. What counts is that Tom's both right and righteous and just the man for this job.

So...

"Effective 12:02 p.m. today," I pronounce, "I appoint you my Secretary of Veterans Affairs... Now tell us your plans for your First 100 Days."

481

Tom double salutes in his aviator suit. He's got authority, that one. Living authority. If the Academy won't give him an Academy Award, I will. This will be his finest performance ever. Of that I'm sure.

"I will visit all 1,593 VA facilities in my First 100 Days, Sir! From Guam to Georgia, Sir! Because the secret to this job is..."

I fill in the blank. "Personal relationships."

"But that's just the start, Sir! Because I intend to write or email all 24.6 million vets alive in my First 100 Days to thank them for their service to their country, Sir! I won't use spam, either, no Sir! Each one will be individually addressed!

"And I will ask each vet to help me help them, Sir! In the name of Jerry McGuire, who begged Rod Tidwell to do the same, Sir! 'Help me, help you!' he said. Of course, Tidwell was no vet! The closest he ever came to being one was as a fictional veteran wide receiver in the movie, as portrayed by Cuba Gooding, Jr., Sir! Which is not to take anything away from my good buddy, either, Sir! No, never! If not for him, I could never be what I intend to be, starting in my First 100 Days—the Ambassador of Kwan for Veterans Affairs, Sir! because Cuba as Tidwell was the original Ambassador of Kwan in 'Jerry McGuire,' Sir. In fact, he became the Ambassador of Kwan for the Academy of Arts and Sciences, too, long before you came back to Earth, Sir! On and off screen, he earned that title, Sir! Because he embodies Kwan, Sir!"

"And Kwan conquers All! So I'll recommend to all my veterans that the first thing they can do to develop our personal relation is to go to WeTube and punch in www.Kwan.bliss and watch Cuba give his Best Supporting Actor acceptance speech at the 69th annual Academy Awards for his role as Rod Tidwell, Sir! His 84 seconds of stream of consciousness thank-yous is an Academy classic, Sir! Especially the part where he says, 'Tom Cruise! I love you, brother! I love you, man!' Which

482

is Cuba's kind of Kwan. Also your kind of Kwan! And now my kind of Kwan! Sir!

"So in my First 100 Days, I'll deliver Cuba's kind of Kwan and your kind of Kwan to every vet alive, because in the world of the Kwan, Kwan conquers All!"

For a second I worry that Tom will get up on the tabletop and jump up and down like on Oprah on her couch, but then he doesn't and all's swell. He simply double salutes in his aviator suit and then resumes his proper seat, while assuming the new generic Tom Cruise character: Veterans' Man of Kwan.

Now I ask you, spectators of Kwan? What more could a Commander-in-Kwan ask for in a Secretary of Kwan?

Next. My Attorney General.

Barely any choices; way too little time.

Seven more cabinet posts to fill before my swearing-in and my inaugural ride down Constitution Avenue on the back of a jackass.

So let's see. For AG there's Mel—and then again there's Mel. In addition there's—well, Mel. Definitely not Dago and no way Sparrow. As for the big O, I have other plans for her. She's my hotshot in the hole.

I look to Mel. He looks at me. We mind meld. We can do that because he was the original true believer. He believed I was coming back. And, as anyone who knows Mel knows, he made that pretty great film about me dying on the cross. But he, above all others, believed in his Mel heart that I was coming back. And indeed I did. And now look at me. I'm flourishing, against all odds. More than flourishing, actually. Dominating. I struck a vital blow for democracy against my tyrannical stepbrother. And now in a few short hours, everyone but everyone will be calling me Mr. President. And who will be sitting behind the Resolute Desk in a chair painted with a sun on its back? Me, that's who. And I'll be able to report to the American people in my first Saturday morning radio address this weekend that the sun is rising again—not setting. Mr. Franklin will be very happy to know that.

"Your country needs you, Mel," I pronounce. "Will you be my Attorney General?"

Naturally, Mel springs up and over, delivering to me a koala bear-type hug. He moves faster than a kangaroo bounding across the Outback. Now I feel truly loved. Sure, I felt the love after receiving 72 million popular votes, I sure did. But one hug from Mel, well, that gets me to a whole new level. "Oh, you big beautiful bastard you," he exclaims, using Aussie slang only Mel can get away with. "Thanks heaps for giving me a fair go!"

Mel assumes the prayer position. Of course, it's all kinds of embarrassing because I'm done doing the divine, at least for now, or so long as I'm sitting with my feet up on my desk in the Oval Office. But Mel, well, there's just no getting the Mel out of Mel, let's face it; so in just this one instance you can expect me to be there for Mel as his very own personal Savior, regardless of the broad line between Church and State I'm drawing down Pennsylvania Avenue, separating the White House and St. John's Episcopal Church on H St. But believe me, that's as far as it goes: Everyone else is just going to have to wait to get saved by yours truly the old-fashioned way—when I resume my traditional role as you-know-who, after I retire or get run out of office, because, my fellow Americans, I'm here to govern and govern well, and not to grant divine deliverance to anyone, other than my Mel, owing to the fact that Mel's, well, Mel.

Let me repeat: I'm Mr. Governance now, and no one else. My disciple feet washing days are kaput, *finis*—at least until January 2025. But if I do a particularly good job, which I'm obviously aiming to do, and get myself re-elected in the process, you can count on me sticking around until January 2029, too. As I hear the incumbents tell it, once you land this job, it's pretty near impossible to let it go—at least voluntarily, what with all the freebies and taxpayer subsidies, such as unlimited Secret Service protection, which God only knows a person like myself could use in spades. And then there's God Force One on the tarmac at Andrews, practically idling while awaiting my go-fly order to anywhere in the world I want. Not even the pre-crucifixion Christ could resist those kinds of temptations, let alone a poor political wretch like me.

"She'll be apples!" Mel exclaims, his big blues calling out to me, too. So trusting, so admiring, they are. Now I can well understand why Oksana Grigorieva found herself surprised with his child... At times such as these, Mel's as irresistible as the proverbial Garden of Eden apple.

"It's all happening too fast," he continues, sounding like the Mel of pre-disciple days. "I've got to put the brakes on or I'll smack into something. However, it you truly need me, Mr. President-Christ, I'll be your AG, even without a law degree, because maybe I'm a genius, and can do it with only a Diploma of Dramatic Art from the National Institute of Dramatic Art, my alma mater Down Under. But it shouldn't be that difficult, not anything compared with directing *The Passion* in two dead languages. Not that I'm trying to up myself, but I know and you know that the Holy Ghost will be working through me in this job and I'll just be traffic direction. So reckon! I'll be as good an AG as Ramsey Clarke, not that I'm under the illusion that everything's just going to be hunky-dory work wise forever. I've never been under that illusion. Things could go awry tomorrow. Take for instance, feminists. Feminists don't like me and I don't like them, so they'll be watching me. But I promise to uphold every anti-sexual discrimination statute on the books. Prosecute intolerance against feminists period, wherever I may find it.

485

What I did need to learn was tolerance, and as head of Justice I'll have been actually given a daily opportunity to practice it, and I know that that sounds almost like a backhanded slap, and it is in a way because I haven't been too successful yet, but my Justice department is going to be about faith, hope, love and forgiveness—themes that are as important now as they were in Jesus` time—your time, Mr. President-Christ.

"I'm not a preacher, and I'm not a pastor, but I really feel my career has been leading me to be Attorney General. I hope my position at the Department of Justice has the power to evangelize, even though I know you'll be a stickler about dividing up the province of Church and State. Maybe with me you'll make an exception because as I've said before, there is no salvation for those outside the Church... and I believe it. Put it this way. My wife is a saint. She's a much better person than I am. Honestly. She's like, Episcopalian, Church of England. She prays, she believes in God, she knows Jesus—you—she believes in that stuff. And it's just not fair if she doesn't make it; she's better than I am. But that is a pronouncement from the chair. I go with it. As I go with your pronouncement that I should be your Attorney General, Mr. President-Christ.

"Besides, I come to it honestly. I played the role of Martin Riggs in *Lethal Weapon I-IV*. Martin was one ace of a cop with a bunch of street smarts and I learned a lot from him. That's just the kind of experience America wants in its top cop. And in my days in Oz, my role on *Cop Shop and Punishment* won't be no tits on a bull, either. It'll help me just as much as my Martin Riggs' role to do what's right at Justice.

"Now after about 20 years of waiting for you and finally being with you this past year, I'm finally starting to scratch the surface of what you want from people like me and from people like you. And I don't think the answer lies somewhere between conversation and chocolate. If you ask me, you want to better understand man to help him. Like Jerry

McGuire said, 'Help me, help you." Sure, I'll catch it from the feminists for using 'man' instead of 'person,' but like I said, they don't like me and I don't like them.

"One more thing: I won't put on the wobbly boot on the job. At least not after one big going off tonight to celebrate your election. You won't ever catch me as cross as a frog in a sock spewing out anti-Semitic garbage at the other end of a Maryland State Trooper's flashlight just 'cause I happened to get rotten down in Georgetown one night! There's no more hittin' the turps for me. My screamer days are officially over. It's London to a brick that won't happen while I'm the top cop at Justice. I won't be off my face as long as I serve at the pleasure of Mr. President-Christ.

"And you have my word that I'll do my level-headed best to keep my nutty father's views on the Holocaust off the front page of the *Washington Post*. You know that I know the Holocaust happened, but my father—well, there's no excuse for him. His opinions are his and his alone, not mine and certainly never the policy of a Christ Administration."

I'm sold. Mel's the top cop for the job, though I expect his term will not be without incident, so long as his Holocaust denier father's within a block of the press.

But these are the chances I must take as America's Commander-in-Justice.

"Effective 12:02 p.m. today," I pronounce, "I appoint you my Attorney General... Now tell us your plans for your First 100 Days."

"First, I might go and go somewhere no one can find me. You know where that is? You know where the place is no one can find you? I was thinking of pitching my tent right next to the weapons of mass destruction. Then no one would find me."

I look down at Mel as though he was—

"Fair suck of the sav, Mr. President-Christ! I'm only *teasing* you!

"Take a squizz at this. As your head kangaroo at DOJ, I'll be busier than a cat burying shit in my First 100 Days showing everyone that I know law enforcement like Bushrangers know robbery under arms. No brag, just fact.

"So let the police car radio call go forth from this time and place: In my First 100 Days, I'll show all those criminals a thing or two. They don't know Christmas from Bourke Street. So you better listen up you bushrangers. You know who you are!

"You better watch out, you better not cry, you better not pout, I'm telling you why. Martin Riggs is coming to town.

"He's making a Ten Most Wanted list, and checking it twice, gonna find out, who's naughty and villainous. Martin Riggs is coming to town.

"He sees you when you're thieving. He knows when you're embezzling, he knows if you've been bad or reprobate, so be good for goodness sake.

"Oh, you better watch out, you better not cry, you better not pout, I'm telling you why. Martin Riggs is coming to town. Martin Riggs is coming to town."

It amazes me, but my cabinet secretaries always seem to have a song at the ready.

"Not that I'm trying to big-note myself, Mr. President-Christ, it's just that I know law enforcement like Bushrangers know robbery under arms. No brag, just fact. So in my First 100 Days I'll partner with the FBI to arrest and prosecute every bushranger on America's Ten Most Wanted list. No murderer, no burglar, not even a lousy drug dealer, to say nothing of no kidnapper, blackmailer, human trafficker, embezzler, and sex offender, and obviously no terrorist, arsonist, extortionist, or fugitive from justice, will escape the magisterial wrath of Martin Riggs Returned, a.k.a. your AG, Mr. President-Christ. No brag, just fact.

"So let the police car radio call go forth from this time and place: In my First 100 Days, I'll be arresting and prosecuting every kind of bushranger on every mean street in America. Starting at 12:02 pm today.

"Scratch that. Starting *tomorrow*, Mr. President-elect, starting tomorrow, 'cause I won't be able to resist—nor should I—one last big inaugural Going Off tonight! But after that, I'll be flat out like a lizard drinking doing my cop shop and punishment job.

"No brag, just fact."

If you ask me, that pretty much cinches it for Mel. Not only does he get eternal life—guaranteed—but also this country's top law enforcement job.

Ramsey Clark, move over, 'cause Martin Riggs is coming to town.

No brag, just fact.

Next. My Secretary of Department of Transportation.

So few choices; almost out of time.

Six more cabinet posts to fill before my swearing-in and my inaugural ride down Constitution Avenue on the back of a jackass.

Now I ask you, what better Secretary of Transportation could there be than a former Hells Angel? Who better to understand America's highway transportation system than one who's done the open road, one Harley mile at a time?

"Your country needs you, Dago," I pronounce. "Will you be my Secretary of Transportation?"

Dago gets up, pushing back his antique chair at the far end of the table, sitting next to Sparrow. At first glance, he's a Hells Angels fashion plate—no less. White carnation pinned to a wide lapel, cut from shiny black leather, and made into a tuxedo. The distance Dago has

489

come since his road hog days is the perfect substance for a Hallmark Card made-for-television movie, if you ask me. From Hells to Mel's Angel, from loyal campaign disciple to Washington-insider is a journey few will ever make. What a long, strange trip it must have been for him, to paraphrase the lyrics of the Grateful Dead—just in case there're any non-Deadheads out there who don't recognize the words of their all-time greatest hits songs. Strictly speaking, for these purposes, it should be from a song called "Bikin'", not "Truckin'", but I'm countin' on you not to raise a fuss.

"Gonzo wow, Mr. Transportation-in-Chief, gonzo wild. I accept in the name of the late-great Hunter Thompson—the gonzo-man, who inspired me to team up with my first Hells Angels, long before I ever became one of Mel's Angels. I accept in his name because gonzo is as gonzo does. He was nothin' if not gonzo wild. He was the Gonzo Man, the journalist who made gonzo journalism what it was and turned my Hells Angels into an American icon. And though I can't exactly prove it—not in a court of law, that is—I believe his chronicles about them inspired Steppenwolf to write "Born to be Wild," which went all the way to No. 2 on the Billboard Hot 100 singles charts in 1968 and is still one of my favorites! Except for "O Little Town of Bethlehem" and "Rock Around the Clock," that is. The latter's my all-time sentimental favorite cuz Sparrow and I used to listen to it while waiting for you to return to Earth and come to Mel's. So I accept this position with pride and joy in the name of Hunter S. Thompson—and Steppenwolf, too. How gonzo wow, how gonzo wild it is, Mr. Transportation-in-Chief."

"Yes, how gonzo wild it is," I respond affirmatively, demonstrating quite convincingly I think that I am, in fact, a big fan of Hunter Thompson's edgy brand of journalism. My only regret is that I didn't come back to Earth in time to attend his memorial service in Colorado, watch his ashes shot out of a cannon perched on top of a

150-foot tower, his trademark emblem of a red fist and two thumbs framed by bursting fireworks. That would have been something. I might have even clinked a glass of ice and whiskey to him, even though, as you know, I drink only red communion wine. He was that gonzo wow, that gonzo wild.

So it's gonzo great that Dago's willing to be my Secretary of Transportation. I'm as gonzo wild about Dago saying yes as Dago was born to be wild about Hunter S. Thompson and his gonzo journalism.

"Effective 12:02 p.m. today," I pronounce, "I appoint you my Secretary of Transportation... Now tell us your plans for your First 100 Days."

"Gonzo great, Mr. Transportation-in-Chief, I'll sling on my brain bucket and be gonzo gone out of town, cruisin' like a Big Dog Rider on my Big Twin Hog Heaven and inspecting America's Big Slab— all 46,926 miles of it—I mean, the Big Road, man, gonzo supreme—and if and when necessary order repairs. That is, when I find such hazards as rainbows on and tar snakes in the cracks of the road. And after each one is done, my DOT cry will go forth: 'Angels Forever, Forever Angels! Behold, the industry of the Christ Administration!'

"As we say at DOT, 'Highway, Byway, Waterway, and Skyway Safety Comes First!' That's my pledge; that's my DOT Big Dog Rider prerogative. It's all about fixin' our interstate highway infrastructure, Mr. Transportation-in-Chief."

"Your mom will be so proud," I say.

"Yes, sir. She'll be doing wheelies in the driveway! Her son— from Hells Angels to DOT's Big Dog Rider in one lifetime! How gonzo wow is that?"

"As gonzo as it gets."

"You bet. With sixty-six days left we won't be done yet! I'll fire up my DOT Road King Classic, with fuel injector, and take to the

491

nation's 150 byways. Get to know each and every rut, every last one of its washed-out places, and order them fixed. Once everything's accomplished, my DOT cry will again go forth: 'Angels Forever, Forever Angels! Behold, the industry of the Christ Administration!'

"As we say at DOT, 'Highway, Byway, Waterway, and Skyway Safety Comes First!' That's my pledge; that's my DOT Road King Classic prerogative. It's all about mendin' our byways, Mr. Transportation-in-Chief. How gonzo wild is that?"

"As gonzo wild as it gets."

"You bet. With thirty-three days left, I'll be off to survey America's 9,436 waterways on my DOT standard issue 1250cc Jetbike. Trust me to ride them all, searching for signs of trouble, such as large-scale erosion done by aquatic rodents like the Nutria, which can lead to land loss and extensive flood damage. Whatever I find and wherever I find it, I'll write it up in a DOT report, and then order my staff to put it right. Once everything's good, my DOT cry will again go forth: 'Angels Forever, Forever Angels! Behold, the industry of the Christ Administration!'

"As we say at DOT, 'Highway, Byway, Waterway, and Skyway Safety Comes First!' That's my pledge; that's my DOT Jetbiker's prerogative. It's all about makin' our waterways right, Mr. Transportation-in-Chief. How gonzo great is that?"

"As gonzo great as it gets."

"You bet. In my last 33 days, I'll take to the skies on my DOT standard issue 150 HP airplane motorcycle. Yes, the one that actually flies. I'll go up there to investigate all manner of air traffic congestion in every last one of our 3 million square miles of American sky. At DOT, we want every square mile of our skies to be as safe as the airspace above the White House. After I know what's what, I'll right the wrongs by staffing it out before my DOT cry goes forth one last time: 'Angels

Forever, Forever Angels! Behold, the industry of the Christ Administration!'

"As we say at DOT, 'Highway, Byway, Waterway, and Skyway Safety Comes First!' That's my pledge; that's my DOT airplane motorcycler's prerogative. It's all about keepin' our airways secure, Mr. Transportation-in-Chief. How gonzo awesome is that?"

"As gonzo awesome as it gets."

"You bet. And finally in my spare time, if you don't mind, I hope to lobby Congress to pass legislation to make Hunter Thompson's birthday—July 18th—a national holiday, sir. I'll do it on my own time. This country owes him a debt of honor, Mr. Transportation-in-Chief. He saved us from the road kill of mainstream media. In a word, he was a godsend."

"You have my permission, Gonzo Dago."

I can almost hear the sound of rolling thunder rumbling up Pennsylvania Avenue: Inaugural Angels on a roll, Big Dog Riders all.

Next. My Secretary of Agriculture.

Only two choices; almost out of time.

Five more cabinet posts to fill before my swearing-in and my inaugural ride down Constitution Avenue on the back of a jackass.

In which case I better make the right choice, right now. That would be Mel's Angel II and my Disciple Sparrow.

"Your country needs you, Sparrow," I pronounce. "Will you be my Secretary of Agriculture?"

Sparrow rises at the far end of the table. She's seated next to the incomparable Reverend V.P. Go-Green Al, who even in silence holds forth in semi-autonomous splendor, his all-knowing, Buddha-like smile glowing like California sunshine beneath the shine of the overhead chandelier. His gold medallion Noble Peace prize hangs about his neck, dangling from a long green velvet ribbon, as big as a cowbell. This much is undeniable: Every time I look at Al, I feel better. And America should, too.

"I will, Mr. Agriculture-in-Chief, because I truly believe in the nutritional values housed inside the USDA's Super Food Pyramid, which when brought to the attention of the public will help America overcome its nutritional challenges, especially obesity in African-American girls and Latino boys. Despite what bio-dictator Mansanto-bankrolled Republicans-in-Congress claimed during the campaign, the USDA's Food Pyramid under a Christ Administration is no Bernie Madoff-type, Food Ponzi scheme. And it will not—let me repeat—it will not lead citizen eaters down the slippery gastronomical slope toward the socialization of American Happy Meals. There's no need for hyperbola and hysteria. No reason for anyone anywhere to raise high the fast food flag and cry, 'Eat Free or Die!' At my USDA, we'll all be on the same side."

Pyramids remind me of Moses; Moses reminds me of Israel; Israel reminds me of the land of milk and honey; the land of milk and honey reminds me of agriculture; and agriculture reminds me of a healthy diet. So there it is: Dago's Old Lady makes good.

"Effective 12:02 p.m. today," I pronounce, "I appoint you my Secretary of Agriculture... Now tell us your plans for your First 100 Days."

"In my First 100 Days, I'll invite all American moms to take a swoop inside the USDA's Super Food Paranormal Health Pyramid with me to learn all about healthy eating habits, cuz getting America eating right is my top priority. Like I'm already there. And I'll bet you my USDA standard issue Harley that once all American moms take my cyber tour inside the USDA's Super Food Paranormal Health Pyramid and get an up close and personal look at all those nutritional goodies

494

inside, they'll be swooping down the Super Food Big Slab with me, faces to the wind, crying, 'Long Live Whole Foods!'

"For sure, it'll be a perfectly beautiful cyber tour for all American moms on Big Twin desktops and Sport Tourer laptops—one more ambitious than even our own Madonna's Blond Ambition Tour!"

"Oh, I doubt that," Madonna snaps. "Three continents, 57-shows, 114 days dressed in a drop-dead gorgeous tutu. You can match that?"

"Ah—"

"Thought so."

"Well, for sure it'll be better than tonight's Bruce Springsteen, Beyonce, Bono concert at the Lincoln Memorial! Nutritionally speaking, that is."

"Doubt that," Bono responds. "The soul needs nutrition, too, you know. As the Beach Boys sang, 'Add some music to your day,' because music is soul food, highly nutritional, too. Besides, the only thing better than Bruce, Beyonce and me lashed together at the mic at the Lincoln Memorial tonight is—*add reverb and crank up the EQ*—

ENDING AIDS IN ANTARCTICA!"

That Bono. The Old Man's gotta love him Always carrying on about ending AIDS somewhere in this world...

"Regardless," Sparrow continues, "in my First 100 Days I'll take a swoop up each of the five sides of USDA's Super Food Pyramid with America's cyber scooter trash moms, so that they can get first-hand all the essential information they'll need to achieve USDA-certified Pyramid Paranormal Health for their loved ones.

"We'll take a swoop up Side 1, into Amber Waves of Whole Grains, cuz the Super Food Pyramid Word is this: Love Whole Grains. They're the thing. One three-ounce serving of whole grain bread, pasta or rice a day is essential for USDA-certified Pyramid Paranormal Health. Why? Because whole grains make the body sing. Sing like Bruce, Beyonce, and Bono lashed together at the mic at the Lincoln Memorial. For all those moms out there who spent too many hours eating too much junk food watching too many Oprah re-runs on the couch, I'll say, behold your whole grains antidote!"

"*Say what?*" Oprah asks.

"Ah—Scratch that last part. American moms can watch Oprah re-runs day and night, just so long as they eat whole grains, cuz at my USDA, Pyramid Paranormal Health comes first. It's all gonna be good and healthy inside the tummy throughout the Christ Administration.

"Then we'll take a swoop up Side 2, into Victory Gardens of Dark Leafy Greens, cuz the Super Food Pyramid Word is this: Dark leafy greens and raw orange veggies, they're the thing. Bok choy, broccoli, collard greens. Green healthy things make the body sing. Sing like Bruce, Beyonce, and Bono lashed together at the mic at the Lincoln Memorial."

"Don't forget to tell dem to eat dem carrots, too," Arnold helpfully interjects.

"Dat's right, Arnold," says Sparrow, "I won't forget to tell dem about eating dem carrots, acorn squashes, butternut squashes, sweet potatoes and dem pumpkins, too. Veggies are da perfect antidote for eating too much junk food for too many hours watching too many Oprah re-runs on da couch!"

"*Say what?*" Oprah cracks.

"Ah—Scratch that. Sorry, I forgot. American moms can watch Oprah re-runs day and night, just so long as they eat plenty of dark leafy greens and raw orange veggies, cuz at my USDA, Pyramid Paranormal Health comes first. It's all gonna be good and healthy inside da tummy throughout da Christ Administration."

"That's better," Oprah sniffs, less miffed.

"Then we'll take a swoop up Side 3, into Gardens of Not-So Forbidden Fruits, cuz the Super Food Pyramid Word is this: Canned, dried or eaten whole, fruits are the thing. Apples, oranges, bananas. Whatever. Fruits make the body sing. Sing like Bruce, Beyonce, and Bono lashed together at the mic at the Lincoln Memorial."

"Don't forget to tell dem: Eat blueberries for da eyes," Arnold interjects again.

"Dat's right, Arnold," says Sparrow, "I won't forget to tell dem to eat dem melons, raspberries, and avocadoes. Dem pineapples and papayas, too. Not to mention plenty of dem plums and prunes. Sliced or diced or munched on whole, fruits are da perfect antidote eating too much junk food for too many hours watching too many Oprah re-runs on da couch!"

"Say what?" Oprah chomps down hard, exasperated.

"Ah—Scratch that. Sorry, sorry, forgot again. American moms can watch Oprah re-runs day and night, just so long as they eat plenty of fruit day and night, cuz at my USDA, Pyramid Paranormal Health comes first. It's all gonna be good and healthy inside the tummy throughout the Christ Administration."

"Okay, let's not go there anymore," says Oprah, still ticked. "I make good money on those re-runs."

"Then we'll take a swoop up Side 4, into Wholly Milk Cow Pastures, cuz the Super Food Pyramid Word is this: Cheese, yogurt, fluid milk and even milk-based desserts are just the thing, because they give American moms calcium. I'm right again. Milk makes the body sing. Sing like Bruce, Beyonce, and Bono lashed together at the mic at the Lincoln Memorial.

497

"You don't even need to say it, Arnold, 1% low fat milk, 2% reduced fat milk, Swiss, Vermont cheddar cheese…"

"Don't forget Stonyfield yogurt!"

"Dat's right, Arnold. Low-fat milk, cheese *and* Stonyfield yogurt, they're all da perfect food to drink or eat watching Oprah re-runs day and night on the couch! How's that, Oprah?"

"You're my Oprah angel!"

"Cuz at my USDA, Pyramid Paranormal Health comes first. It's all gonna be good and healthy inside the tummy throughout the Christ Administration.

"Then we'll take a final swoop up Side 5, into the Province of Provencal Meat and Fried Beans, cuz the Super Food Pyramid Word is this: Eat five ounces a day or else. Meat and beans make the body sing. Sing like Bruce, Beyonce, and Bono lashed together at the mic at the Lincoln Memorial."

"And what makes America great!"

"Dat's right, Arnold. As we say at USDA, 'bake it, broil it or grill it,' it's gonna turn out all right, cuz it's the American Way. Pork chop or chicken breast, beef strip lean cuts or salmon steak, we don't interfere at the USDA, just so long as American moms eat five ounces of meat a day! Or beans, like almonds, cashews, walnuts. Mixed nuts will do. Meat and beans—they're the perfect antidote for eating too much junk food for too many hours watching NOT NEARLY ENOUGH re-runs of Oprah Winfrey on the couch, cuz, like I said, at my USDA, Pyramid Paranormal Health comes first. It's all gonna be good and healthy inside the tummy throughout the Christ Administration."

I have never been hungrier in my entire life.

Next. My Secretary of Education, Commerce, Labor and Treasury.

One choice; zilch time. Four more cabinet posts to fill before my swearing-in and my inaugural ride down Constitution Avenue on the back of a jackass.

I look around. There's only one person in this room who's founded a Leadership Academy for Girls in South Africa and therefore, say what you will about her, knows a thing or two about promoting children's education. And there's only one person in this room who's built up an empire from scratch made up of TV talk shows, movie production companies, magazines, book clubs, XM satellite radio channels, and cable television networks and therefore, say what you will about her, knows a thing or two about invigorating commerce. And there's only one person in this room who's managed to run a union-free shop in the hard-nosed world of union-run show business and gets away with it and therefore, say what you will about her, understands a thing or two about manhandling labor; and there's only one person in this room who's made a $3 billion fortune on good gossip and marvelous works and therefore, say what you will about her, understands a thing or two about running a treasury with a humongous surplus. And that person is...

Trembling, I get up out of my chair and walk over to the person in the room to whom I refer and kneel on bended knee before her, assuming the supplicant position, my hands folded in fervent prayer. Then and there I utter her magnificent name.

"Oh Great Oprah," I say, my voice shaky, unnaturally faint. "Your country needs you. Will you be my Secretary of Education? Will you be my Secretary of Commerce? Will you be my Secretary of Labor? And will you be my Secretary of Treasury?"

Then I wait in ringing silence—me and everyone else in the room. We wait for Oprah's answer.

But there is no immediate answer. She beholds me in prayer and is content to leave me there.

"Bless my administration, Oprah," I whisper, rather more desperately. "Just Say Yes."

I can see that she's really enjoying this—my solicitation, my exhortation. Of course, it's only natural she wouldn't leap to any immediate conclusion. She's a very careful businesswoman. And besides, celebrities love to be needed. That's the way they are. And the greater the need of fans like me, the greater their sheer delight in being needed, understandably.

Then, after what seems like passage through the time tunnel of eternity, I may have heard her whisper her answer. But I'm not one hundred percent sure. Because I can't quite hear it. So I ask her to repeat it, to say it again, this time louder. My hearing's not what it used to be.

And then there it is. I hear it. I hear her answer.

Her beautiful answer.

"Yes... Yes, Mr. President, I will be your Secretary of Education, and I will be your Secretary of Commerce, and I will be your Secretary of Labor and I will also be your Secretary of Treasury. Because O! stands for Oh So Capable!"

Now I know that the Old Man really is a caring God, cuz He sent me Oprah.

On that uplifting note, I'm filled with exuberance, dare I say, confidence? Now that the Great Oprah has consented to fill the last of my four cabinet posts, my hopes for the welfare of the American nation go elastic, stretching boundlessly beyond where they have ever been before. My only regret is that Dr. Phil won't be joining us. He won't because, well, you know, Oprah's still a little miffed at him for pressuring Britney Spears to do an on-television Dr. Phil intervention when he was still under contract with Harpo Productions and Britney was recovering from whatever it was she was in Cedars-Sinai Medical Center for, such a long time ago.

Oh, those celebrities. Can't live with them; can't live without them.

Quite enough said.

I adjourn the cabinet meeting. The mood in the room is exuberance unbound, not seen or heard on Pennsylvania Avenue since Barack Obama signed his Health Reform Bill in the East Room. As much as I'd like to stay and work the crowd and celebrate, my desire for food—any kind of food—has reached a whole new level. Which is code for I don't mind climbing down off the USDA Super Food Pyramid to grab a bite before I give my big address. I'll settle for fast food, which is an occupational hazard for campaigning politicians and even presidents. Take Bill Clinton. He ran his campaigns and presidency on McNuggets and Quarter Pounders. It's just done.

And besides, what else can I do? I've got only thirty-eight minutes to get my tail up to Capitol Hill for the swearing-in. And forty-one minutes before I'll stand before an awaiting nation and deliver my inaugural address, in which, not incidentally, I fully intend to answer—well, fess up, actually, because I've never been completely forthcoming about why—why I waited two thousand years or so to get my butt back to planet Earth, in light of all the Troubles. So I will, to the best of my ability, answer Mel's percipient question, the one he posed long ago back at Mel's Diner, back in my pre-candidate, pre-primary days when, and let's be mercilessly frank about this, I didn't know the difference between an Iowa Caucus and the Iowa Cattlemen's Association.

Why the hell did I wait so long to get my ass back down here when there was so much goddamn genocide going on? A consequential question, for sure—and one deserving a crackerjack answer, which I intend to deliver in a voice loud and clear voice soon after my

501

motorcade does a secret detour en route to Capitol Hill. That is, does a five minute layover at my favorite McDonalds on 13th Street, where I'm intent on ordering a Quarter Pounder with cheese; golden McNuggets slathered in sweet and sour sauce; a hot apple pie, very brown and crispy; and a large diet Coke—no ice. I like it best with no ice. I certainly hope my future Secretary of Agriculture doesn't find out. She'll banish me to walk the halls of the USDA's Super Food Pyramid for eternity, if she does. But she should look at it from my perspective, and make allowances. Time's short and I'm gonna need all the white sugar high I can get. I'm the one who's got to step up to JFK-level rhetoric, "Ask not what your country can do for you..." and all that. Come to think of it, I wonder what JFK ate right before he was sworn-in and belted out his classic? Whatever it was, it did the trick.

In any event, en route to the Capitol, McDonalds it is. And while I'm out getting some grub, I recommend you land a good sightline on the west side of the Capitol and listen up. You won't want to miss the confessions of the Christ Child turned Commander-in-Chief. You won't want to miss the reason why I spaced out in Heaven when the world down here was falling apart.

I have Nancy to thank for writing what I consider to be a very decent speech. No brag, just fact. It could be a classic; alternatively, it'll definitely be a hoot, at least in part. It'll also be serious because in politics balance is a many splendored thing. That is, solemnity and humor go hand in hand. Take this line from Nancy's address: "Ask not what your country can do for you—ask what you can do to make your country laugh."

There it is, proof positive that I don't intend to be the kind of president-politician who takes himself too seriously, even when I'm all about doing, saying, explaining very serious things—like why I went missing in action.

502

V.P. Al and I float up the final hill to Capitol Hill seated in the back of Bubble One, a 2010 Cadillac DTS stretch sedan with bullet proof glass and tinted windows. Outside, passing by like images from the Frank Capra film, *Mr. Smith Goes to Washington,* is the Capitol dome—neoclassical stateliness in abundance—as it emerges from the snowy embrace of winter trees as we ride and climb. I believe I counted as many as 40-some odd cars in my motorcade, not that I ever took a day of grade school math. That includes of course the standard decoy pair of limos, adding just that extra layer of security that gives a president peace of mind. But you better believe it—as my Secretary of Homeland Security likes to say—my motorcade today is no dummy, designed to confound potential assassins. It's the real thing, and is equipped with a bunch of bomb sweep police cars at the head, followed by HazMat detection vehicles, SUVs occupied by counterassault teams armed with FN P90s—state-of-the-art Secret Service automatic personal defense weapons—and SWAT teams. Don't mess with these guys. Don't even think about it. Then immediately in front and behind me is another set of black noiseless vehicles, as clean as dining room silverware, which compose my secure package. At the first sign of trouble—even the slightest sidewalk disturbance—they'll whisk me off to a pre-arranged location. Imagine that. I'm the most secure person on the planet. At the end of the motorcade come the stranglers, local patrol cars, press vans, staff vehicles and, of course, my very own ambulance trails at the last. I only wish Pontius Pilate could see me riding by. He tries to lay a finger on me again and—bam! Bam! Bam! He's history.

I lick sweet and sour sauce off my fingertips. I dap the two corners of my mouth with paper napkin. I slurp my diet Coke through the end of a striped, plastic straw, making a sucking noise, which is so un-presidential that V.P. Al turns to me and says, "I can't take you anywhere, can I?"

Now you can understand why the world needs Al. Humor is his second language.

That was one good Happy Meal.

The Capitol nears. Al and I are on our way to change the nation, if not the world. Or at the least make America safe again for rank-and-file Democrats. They were once on the endangered species list, you'll recall.

Snow falls. Each little flake reminds me of angel eyes. Inside Bubble One, it's a balmy 78 degrees, and rising. Outside, it's a frosty 28 degrees, and falling, and to tell the truth I'm having second thoughts about my endearing but possibly foolish decision to ride down Constitution Avenue on the back of a jackass in the inaugural parade, for reasons understandable, given temperatures outside. I don't want to pull a William Henry Harrison. So in a moment of candor, because I find that with a guy like Al you can talk about most anything without fear of judgment, I freely admit that I'm not so much relishing mounting a jackass today; that I must be careful not to catch cold, especially in light of President Harrison's experience; that it won't mean anything like it meant back riding the dry, warm streets of Jerusalem in order to express my spiritual connection and oneness with the people since I have more modern means at my disposal—like the Internet; and that for sure it would be a terrific headache for my Secret Service detail to expose myself like that. Besides, I argue, riding a jackass was Nowhereville compared to climate-controlled travel in Cadillac stretch sedan called Bubble One.

I know I'm changing, but. Well, there is no but. I'm changing. But it's a presidential prerogative.

"On the contrary," Al rejoins to my surprise, "your jackass riding days have only just begun."

"Huh?"

504

"Once you're sworn in, Mr. President-elect, you'll be trying to ride 535 jackasses in Congress every day and night of your administration."

Ah—Al makes another funny, providing us with yet another example of why I—America and the world—need and appreciate Al.

On the west front terrace of the Capitol, in the light, sweet snow, Tipper stands next to her Al as he places his hand on the *Bible* and raises his right hand before Chief Justice Clarence Thomas. Of course, without Tipper, Al would have made a perfectly acceptable prep school dormitory head or unquestionably a fairly decent TV meteorologist—but certainly not a used-to-be next president of the United States. We're all just so proud of him.

"I, Albert Gore," he says in a voice bursting with the confidence of a man who's a better bet for godhead than I am, "do solemnly swear that I will support and defend the Constitution of the United States.... and faithfully discharge the duties of the office on which I am about to enter for a second—count 'em—second time: So help me God."

Mark my words, the whole world's gonna sleep more soundly tonight.

Now it's my turn. Naturally, I'm a bachelor, like President James Buchanan, so I don't have a Tipper Gore watching over me, which pretty much sucks, especially for a man of my age, but what can I do? There's only just so far I can push the outer limits of my on earth evolution without stepping over the edge. Running for president and winning is one thing; but getting hitched is another. The public just won't tolerate it.

On the other hand, there could be certain other compensating advantages, which we won't go into at this time.

505

My guy on the bench will administer the oath of office. You know whom I'm talking about. But instead of placing my left hand on the *Bible,* like Al, I put my hand on a rare leather-bound edition of Hugo Grotius's *The Laws of War and Peace,* which automatically emphasizes my political priorities. And you know reporters they're capable of making a story out of anything—including Hugo Grotius. I know I shouldn't always be trying to make political hay out of every little thing, particularly during my swearing-in, but then again I'm the one taking the oath of office, so who here's going to argue?

I raise my right hand and repeat after Clarence: "I, Jesus Christ, do solemnly swear that I will faithfully execute the Office of President of the United States, and will to the best of my ability, preserve, protect and defend the Constitution of the United States. So help me, my Old Man."

That said and done, I'm legal. Not barely legal, but perfectly legal. I'm the President of the United States: President Jesus Christ. Or Mr. President to you. Not that I'm not still a God of the people.

Naturally, Tipper and Al hug me; I survive Al's big embrace. And my guy Clarence gives me a wink and we all know what that's about. Believe me, I won't forget Clarence for what he did for me, he and his Supremes.

I step up on the podium and look down out at the multitudes gathered in the snow. They're clapping and cheering along the length of the entire Mall. Then it hits me then, the reality of what has happened to little old me, what I've managed to accomplish in just under thirteen months. I have done what no other god has done before me. Those Greek gods have nothing on me. Still, my main ambition was to have made my mom and pop proud of me, which is what any self-respecting son would want to do. But if not, if I have disappointed them by the actions I have taken on behalf of the human race, in some small or large

506

way, I can't have any regrets because a god like me has to do what a god's got to do. That's how I see it and what the Old Man taught me to do. What makes my success as a campaigning politician even more incredible, fantastic really, is the fact that I survived all those shrimp cocktail fundraisers, fried chicken lunches and tens of thousands of fast food snacks with my 32-inch waistline still intact. Miracles do happen. Christ can become president and Beelzebub beaten. So I ask you, what's next, the certifiable survival of the human race?

It could happen, you know.

Below, the sprawling Mall. Obama-size hope gathers under showering snowflakes. Hope's keenest supporters—good Democrats, Independents, and not an inconsiderable number of Republicans—stand shoulder to shoulder, come to see me off on my maiden voyage into the deep waters of the U.S. presidency. I also note the presence of a fairly healthy outpouring of illegal immigrants, but only a tiny sampling of the more than 15 million undocumented aliens residing here today, and who, criminally, are often denied fair wages, safe conditions and protections in the work place, and who may not vote, and are subject to arrest and deportation at the push of a speed-dial button or because their name is Juan and they cannot get a Green Card. So you bet, I intend to do something about immigration and get those vigilantes on the Texas border real jobs.

Much to my embarrassment, they call my name, as if I was a star Laker's player. But it's all good, as they say, because for one brief moment under the falling snowflakes national unity is not just another campaign slogan.

There really is something going on down there.

"Jesus! Jesus! President Jesus!"

Naturally, I'm terrified that I'll somehow disappoint them—particularly my base. I can only hope that I'll be as good a governor as I

507

was a campaigner. Nevertheless, and I know it's too late to fret about this now, but it might have been somewhat helpful if I had served a term or two as a city council member somewhere and got some executive experience in under my belt before jumping right in and getting myself elected president. I've always been a jumper-into-the-deep-water kind of guy so I suppose there's nothing new here. Once again I find myself in over my head, but what can I do? I'm too old to change my ways. Which in my case I consider to be a good thing.

"Jesus! Jesus! President Jesus!"

There really is something going on down there.

I do a quick head count of the crowd that stretches out to the Washington Monument. We're talkin' gargantuan here. The Million Man March? No contest. The March for Women's Lives? Somewhat closer. Pope John Paul's on the Mall ministry? Dream on, dear saint. My Sermon on the Mount? Let's not even go there. The Mall's rockin' like a sock hop on a Saturday night. (Though I've never been to one, I've always liked the sound of them.)

More snowflakes fall. It's icy cold up here overlooking the snow-white expanse of the Mall. Just looking at it, never the mind the nippy January temperatures, I get a hankering for a cup of Starbucks soy hot chocolate—no whip. But what I honestly want is this: For Rush Limbaugh & Co. to be tuning into me right about now because, Rush, this one's for you—my full disclosure about why I came back to Earth when I did and why it relates to them. So to Rush and all his radio talk-show disciples who dance all night with the Christian Right and claim to speak with my level of authority and oftentimes in my name, listen up.

Here beginneth the speech I was born to give, starting with the answer to the question everyone's been waiting for: What took me so bloody long to get my ass back here?

508

And my answer is this, my fellow Americans: I timed my return to coincide with the looming Clash of Civilizations, so that I might intervene and avert the titanic collision of titan faiths, the Really Big One, the ultimate showdown between Christianity and Islam, otherwise known as the Holy War of Holy Wars that, if allowed to happen, would engulf the planet in genocides heretofore unimaginable, plunging the Earth back into the Darkest of the Dark Ages. Yes, my fellow Americans, I timed my reprise performance to prevent two mighty religions from going thermonuclear. And which, if they did, would make the Golden Age of Genocide look like just so much slaughter at a local meat packing plant.

Those three little sentences certainly capture everyone's attention, including that of a very tall man cloaked in a hooded robe the color of desert sand and standing just behind the rope line at the base of the Capitol grounds.

So okay, I finally divulge my excuse. It took me long enough, for sure. I hope America and the Christian world can live with it. It's all I have to give. I came back when the stakes were at their highest.

Then, to hammer my logic, I deliver the line I've most been waiting to give, the one Nancy thinks is as close to divine as it gets and which, of course, we couldn't have realized without a considerable rhetorical assist from our inspiration, JFK. I lift my face to the drifting veil of snowflakes dancing like angels in the white sky, and say in a voice clear and strong, and a fairly decent imitation of JFK's own sterling delivery: "And so my fellow Americans: Ask not what you can do to dominate the world with your religion—ask what you can do to stave off the coming Clash of Civilizations."

Now you may find this difficult to believe but right then and there I feel fairly certain that I hear Rush blow a casket somewhere, if

509

not his entire listening audience. Still, it could have been my imagination, but I'm not so sure.

After that line, which goes over mighty well, I can tell, I declare that I will soon be introducing legislation in Congress calling for the swift passage of the so-called Christ Doctrine, a.k.a, the Atheism in American Politics Act, or AAPA, for short. (Acronyms—they make life for us Washington insiders so much more tolerable.)

That's when I'm generally convinced I hear Rush & Co. pop like rivets on the deck of a mothballed destroyer. But what can I do, I mean really? I may or may not be the best and the brightest in Washington, D.C., but it doesn't take the genius of Edward Teller to foresee the catastrophic consequences of supporting Rush Limbaugh & Co's Religion in American Politics Act, or RAPA, for short, especially with the likes of Osama bin Laden and his listening audience round about town.

Anyway, that's my opinion, and I just so happen to be President of the United States these days. And I ask you, if you can't trust the word of the Lord Jesus Christ, whose word can you? It's a little bit ironic, isn't it? Me coming back to Earth after all this time and trying to end the role of religion in American politics. Who would've ever dreamed that one up, certainly not the author of Revelations. St. John wasn't even close.

Naturally, I have no idea what the Old Man's going to think about AAPA, but then this is my call because I'm the one who got himself elected, not Him. If He wants to go through all that campaigning to be able to press His own agenda, I say, all the more power to Him. So I say this: "Father, do not forgive me, for I know exactly what I do."

Before God and country and on CNN, I next invoke the wisdom of some highly regarded philosophers to back up my new policy position. So if you quarrel with it, take it up with them, Rush, because I am a mere vessel for their thinking. Take it up with the likes of Tacitus, Justus Lipsius, Hugo Grotius, Michel de Montaigne, Thomas Hobbes, and Francis Bacon, if you dare.

I now instruct my national audience to turn to page 43 of their philosophical hymnals, and quote Francis Bacon, with attribution, of course: "Atheism leaves a man to sense, to philosophy, to natural piety, to laws, to reputation; all which may be guides to an outward moral virtue, though religion were not."

And then—sound trumpet, pound kettledrums—the line that needs to be said: "The times inclined to atheism [are] civil times."

And comity among people and nations cannot be but a fairly good thing and consistent with my Gospels.

I'm positive I hear the rivets of the USS Rush Limbaugh pop off. And you better believe that I'm in hot water now with the Christian Right. One millennium it's the Romans, the next it's the Christians. It just goes to show that you can't please everyone all of the time.

Across the snowy Mall, there's a smattering of applause. Down below, the ghostly figure of a tall, hooded man captures my attention. He's wearing the colors of sand. His figure commands. He's clapping vigorously. Perhaps he's had one too many espressos this morning—a Starbucks fan. No matter; I take my allies where I can find them. Still, his Muslim garb intrigues, as do the shadows within, because I cannot see him clearly. Only his large, aristocratic nose protrudes from the eerie shadows of the shelter of his hood, the bristly edges of his salt and pepper beard. Nothing more...

But then the figure loosens his head covering, as if responding to a silent request for him to reveal himself more fully. He permits his hood to fall. It cascades about his shoulders under the tumbling snowflakes. And for the very first time I can actually make out his

511

phantom face, pale and gray and translucent. It's the face of a dead man, returned. It's the face of the ghost of Osama bin Laden.

We look upon each other: President Jesus and Muslim terrorist. He's come back to spook my inauguration, it seems.

CNN follows my gaze. They zoom in on that phantasmic face, the face of the unholy wraith. Sensing his moment under the stare of the world media attention, as always, bin Laden, the specter of terrorism come back to haunt, offers up a prayer in a voice clear and strong. "All praise is due to Allah, who built the heavens and earth in justice, and created man as a favor and grace from Him. And from His ways is that the days rotate between the people, and from His Law is peace in kind: a heart for a heart, love for love. Love is divine. Christians love; Muslims love. And all praise is due to Allah, who awakened His people's peaceful desire for the Garden, and all of them will enter it except those who would do war. And whoever obeys the word of peace in all of his affairs will enter the Garden, and whoever refuses will no longer know the joy of mirth and laughter."

For a ghost gone for a decade, he really is quite impressive. Then he says more.

"People of America, I am speaking to you on an important topic, which concerns you, so lend me your ears." His voice is a whisper, unearthly. "Mr. President, I commend you, and congratulate you on your presidency. And I say that I am in agreement with you. We must put an end to this unholy Holy War, which I started twenty years ago, in the name of Allah and God, the Father. I was mistaken; I was wrong. And now I beg your forgiveness."

Now that's some kind of inaugural miracle.

And though Osama's interrupted my address and even stolen my thunder, I don't mind, not a bit. I take it with a degree of equanimity because he's articulated some of the sweetest words in the English language. Not in Latin, perhaps, not even in Aramaic, but most definitely in English. "I was mistaken; I was wrong. And now I beg your forgiveness."

So—even though I swore off doing miracles during the course of my campaign, for understandable reasons, I have no objections whatsoever to accepting this brand of miracle: Osama's ghostly call for ending Holy War.

So I'm obliged to return the courtesy. And I do so in a voice bursting with joy, "May peace be with you, Osama, and so with us all..."

Then, live on Fox Television, he reciprocates: "As-Salāmu `Alaykum," he says, as he lifts his smiling, ghostly face to a sky full of snowflakes before vanishing, leaving only the stain of his sandy cloak on the snowy ground.

It could happen, you know, the end of jihad—triumph over Holy War—even the separation of church and state in all things politic—because there's really, really something great going on down there...

The Evening After

A gooseneck lamp with a burnt-out, 100-watt bulb stood beside McClellan's green velvet chair, looking dejected and inept. It was sunless and lightless in the reading room and McClellan could barely make out the last words of the last sentence on the last page of the novel. As far as he was concerned, he'd read the perfect book for an improbably imperfect day. And though he'd eaten it up—like soup and crackers—he was left with a perplexing sense of regret. Why couldn't *his* presidential candidate have been more like Christ? What the Democrats had needed was a moral values animal, capable of setting the Bible Beaters right. Next time around—which he knew wasn't ever going to happen in this lifetime—he was going to land a live wire with a hammerlock on moral values: Exactly the kind of candidate that even Karl Rove—the master of political sabotage—couldn't sink. Frankly speaking, only Jesus Christ Himself would be capable of making Karl Rove & Co. beg for mercy. Rove was that good, not that McClellan harbored any Christian feelings toward him today or any other day for that matter. In fact, if he could, he'd like to strangle him with his bare hands.

Despite the humiliation and the trauma of the last 24 hours, he had had a beautiful few hours. He'd read a book. He'd watched the sunlight shift throughout the afternoon. It had almost been a victory of sorts—just to find a place to be alone and distract himself completely from the trauma of a thousand things. He had found peace in his bookstore quarantine.

McClellan closed his book and gently rubbed the corner crease, trying unsuccessfully to smooth it out. He still had no desire to go anywhere. Anywhere at all. Besides, he laid claim to the green velvet chair beside the window. Putting the novel down on the arm of the chair, he gazed out the window. The day was no more. Only the streetlamps gave off much light, making the *Acer saccharums* glow all the more in the dark. And so he held onto his peace, recalling the gentle, shifting moods of the day: the afternoon light spilling across the arms of his chair, sweeping over it like bursts of sunlight over French green fields. It had gone from the color of autumn gold to rich rose to steel-gray blue, until it was completely subsumed by night. He couldn't remember when he had last watched the light.

McClellan looked down at his wristwatch. It was 6:06 P.M. Grand Dame's voice rattled the walls of his pleasure dome. "Closing

514

time, Mr. McClellan. And we know you don't want to be locked in for the night with all those Richard Nixon biographies..."

Appreciating a good threat when he heard one, McClellan promptly answered, "Be right down."

But McClellan wasn't going anywhere—not this minute, anyway. As he tried to rise, he realized that his thigh muscles had become re-bars locked in Sakrete. His trip to the gym was the stupidest thing he'd done since getting himself elected chairman of the DNC. There was no question about it: He had become a creature of his own indulgence.

His predicament had, however, provided him with the perfect excuse to check his cell phone messages, something he'd against all odds successfully resisted all afternoon—a fact that he was more than a little proud of. "You have 93 messages" the automated, pre-recorded drone of a voice ground out. But as how he was on a higher plane, he was able to resist the temptation to listen to even one of them. This pleased him enormously. Clearly, he was well on his way to being a new and improved person, capable of existing without electronics for an entire afternoon. They should have Olympics for such tests of endurance, he mused.

"Mr. McClellan?" the voice again called from downstairs.

"Coming!" he answered in a state of embarrassed panic. He was genuinely concerned that he wouldn't ever make it out of his chair. Rallying his pathetic excuse for a body, he seized the sides of the chair, preparing to leverage himself up and out, using brute arm strength, which was a joke because they, too, had solidified and wouldn't cooperate. The pain was too, too, too. Only when for no good reason but good fortune he flashed something Karl Rove had said in a recent *New York Times* news which indirectly ridiculed him did he manage to endure the unendurable and climb out of his chair one hundred percent certain that the howls in his heads would be heard all the way down to the Watergate Hotel.

He collected his trove of used books, plucking one more off the fiction shelf— *Eden's Lost* by Sumner Locke Ellicot—on his way out. He couldn't resist. Besides, he liked feeling just this side of paperback wealthy. He also wanted to assuage his guilt for monopolizing the upstairs today and consuming a whooping number of kilowatt-hours of baseboard heat.

"Win or lose… we always appreciate your patronage, Mr. McClellan…" She expressed her sentiment with such expression and conviction she could have been playing a Katharine Hepburn movie role. McClellan was deeply moved. In fact his reaction caught him by complete surprise. He left speechless, and feeling not a little hollow inside—more hollow than a Trojan horse. He hadn't seen much kindness on the campaign trail or in national politics in the last twenty years… And what was the high altitude ride of national presidential politics compared with a little common human kindness? As McClellan left The Lantern he considered this: maybe losing wasn't such a bad thing, after all.

Besides, blowing bubbles and skinny dipping and watching shooting stars and pretending to fly definitely had its upside: he wouldn't have to go toe-to-toe with Karl Rove anymore.

****

As McClellan navigated his shiny, red Mustang through the choked and fuming arteries of Georgetown's miserable rush hour traffic, he could have kicked himself for not taking a more discreet and far less congested backwater route up 35th Street to Reservoir, a right on Tunlaw, a left on New Mexico, up Cathedral Avenue, where if the light was green, he'd do an illegal left onto Wisconsin, before gunning his Mustang and making a break for the tree-lined streets of Cleveland Park, that last great bastion of Democratic liberalism where the majority of its inhabitants were no doubt still holding their heads in their hands, spilling tears on their laminated hardwood floors, and despairing in yesterday's election results...

His lack of forward movement did permit him the opportunity for ample reflection on what his nighttime agenda would be. It took some deliberation but soon enough he arrived at the more or less philosophical determination that what he wanted to do tonight—more than anything really—was to get astonishingly drunk—a riding stolen stallion bareback down M Street on Halloween night in Lone Ranger's gear kind of astonishingly drunk.

He considered dumping junk food into his system first, but he knew he'd get drunker on an empty stomach. Besides, he'd already decided that tonight he'd inaugurate a junk-less, fat-free diet. He was quite prepared now to do penance for years of unspeakable culinary abuse and he wasn't about to go off the weight-watchers reservation any time soon—well, at least not tonight, anyway.

McClellan drove past a long parade of recognizable Georgetown landmarks: the old graveyard on the mounded hill at 35th Street. Channel 50, and its rooftop satellite dish across the street. Further up, the Good Guys Bar, scruffy as can be, and still offering up strippers. The Guy Mason softball field, dark this time of year, higher up and to the right. And Calvert Street Liquor opposite it, inviting in the deepening night and the scene of many a pilgrimage, especially during his inebriated college years. He'd have pulled over to snag a six-pack, but parking, as usual, was a highly unlikely dream. And though a space miraculously opened up on the liquor store side of the street, McClellan wisely refrained from doing a U-turn. A banged-up DC police car, which

517

had seen one too many urban crimes, including its share of illegal U-turns, straddled his Mustang. The policeman had sideburns.

McClellan obliged the menacingly insistent stoplight by stopping at Calvert and Wisconsin. Up ahead, he noted the Russian Consulate, a yellow brick monolith barricaded behind high wrought-iron gates as if it was in a perennial state of imminent retreat. Without question it was the most vapid hunk of Leninist-style real estate this side of Warsaw. Over to his right, above and beyond mesmerizing clumps of fall trees, glowing sunny in the dark, stood the Gloria and Excelsior Tower of the Washington National Cathedral. It looked like a ship cast upon cloudy seas; it transcended the anchor of the night and it appeared more graceful and more welcoming than he could ever remember. So alive it was the granite almost seemed to breathe.

An hour earlier and McClellan would have considered going for a visit, as he used to do when time was virtually elastic. Which was too long ago to remember. In those pre-historic days, he'd often slip into the West End nave to sit alone and ponder the vast volume of the beautiful, open space: the vaulted ceilings, the stained-glass windows, the Gothic arches, and the intimate stone carvings. He'd look down the green, beige polished marble aisle to the Great Crossing and further on to the dark, wood choir, and then beyond the beyond to the white limestone High Altar where there sat the placid figure of Christ upon his throne of mercy and redemption.

McClellan couldn't help thinking about that outrageous novel again, and God forgive him, the fact that Christ come again would make one helluva drop dead good candidate for 2008.

But the cathedral closed thirty minutes ago, so he could forget about going there and blissing out on the sacred air.

The light turned green. A car horn blasted him from behind for not jumping off the mark. Overcompensating, his Mustang bolted forward, buck and bronco style. The cop in the driver's seat next to him looked at him askance. Illicit U-turns were definitely out now. McClellan evened out his driving and cruised up Wisconsin Avenue alongside the Metropolitan Police car, its headlight detached and spilling out of its rusty fender like a dangling human eye from its ruptured socket. They rode together to the highest point in the city—a city once so flush with mature oak and elm specimens that it was known as the City of Trees.

At Wisconsin and Massachusetts Avenues, which lay cattycorner to the awesome Washington Cathedral, glowing ever brighter, now so near in the night. McClellan momentarily considered skipping the getting drunk part of the evening and going straight to the taking a nature walk part. He was drawn to the Olmsted Woods. Situated on the cathedral close, they stood at the bottom of the Pilgrim Steps adjacent to the South Transept. It had been more than a decade since he'd taken the Olmsted Woods walk. And at the end of its quarter-mile trail loop, he used to park himself on a high wooden bridge on the edge of the woods. The bridge would sway and he would listen to it creak. He would behold the open grandness of the night. It was always very nice.

But being an infinitely fallible and wounded man, he rejected the healthier alternative in favor of the one that most immediately appealed to his rather more hedonist instincts. Getting drunk.

So he bypassed the west side entrance to the cathedral, puttering alongside his faithful driving companion, the 2nd District Metropolitan policeman with sideburns and a dangling headlight. He headed back into the enchanting embrace of Cleveland Park, with a one-way ticket to Burka's Wine & Spirits, his preferred destination of choice. At Macomb Street by the Zebra Lounge the cop car veered off, taking a back route to 2nd District Police Headquarters. McClellan felt relieved, not that he was even vaguely tempted to do another illegal U-turn any time soon. Well, not today at least.

519

He rolled past the Cactus Cantina restaurant, crammed wall-to-wall with devoted clientele chowing down on fresh yellow corn chips and sizzling hot salsa. As he drifted by, his hunger spiked—a seismic surge of hunger that only alcoholic drink—and plenty of it—could possibly abate. It felt right to be irrational, to cast off orthodox behavior. Booze first; burritos second; bath third; bed fourth. This was to be the grand order of his evening off before cruel reality came crashing down on him in the morning like the Berlin Wall at the feet of Mikhail Gorbachev.

Beside the Cactus Cantina, where the Hunan Gallery restaurant once was, Homeless Charlie's soiled blanket roof and rotting cardboard frame glowed like home sweet home in the darkened alcove. Lit from within by a hurricane lamp which also kept him somewhat warmish in winter, McClellan thought that it almost looked charming—a Salvation Army poster maybe. He wondered whether Charlie was feeling depressed, too. McClellan made a mental note to stop by Charlie's tomorrow and anonymously leave a twenty bill in a DNC envelope. McClellan couldn't stop campaigning.

Down the way, G. C. Murphy Co. convenience store, abandoned for too many years as community activists and commercial builders waged hand-to-hand combat over exact plans to expand the Giant Food store next door, looked like a long, dark, disturbing lump on the spine of a remarkably unattractive retail corridor. All in all, the block had the tawdry appearance of canary row. As a consequence of yesterday, he and Charlie might soon be neighbors.

McClellan made the light at Newark Street. He chugged ahead, passing Sullivan's Toy Store, The Kellogg Collection, Hot Yoga, and Starbucks. The Starbucks logo queen gleaming green and black and white in the window, made him feel right at home, but she wasn't enough to rope him in for a Grande Caramel Macchiato. The Starbucks queen would have to wait.

Past the Sun Trust Bank, he spotted his desired oasis: The Land of Hops— Burka's Wines & Spirits. McClellan hung a left at Idaho Avenue and miraculously found a parking spot. He knew that he was in the luck—destined to enjoy a solidly inebriated evening in Cleveland Park.

Inside Burka's, McClellan's first question was: Where's my gas mask? The joint out-gassed sweet Jim Beam Bourbon and Ron Rico Rum and Johnnie Walker Red Label Scotch. Throw in Smirnoff's Triple Distilled Vodka and the place was combustible. Light a match and the place would surely blow. Woozy as the air made him feel, he resolved that no toxic stench was ever going to stand in the way of him getting drunk. McClellan was on a mission. He was in hot pursuit of his divine right: the divine right of all writers and lifetime losers to get deliriously drunk.

He fished through stacks of stenciled wooden crates, sweeping past a well-populated wall of wine racks: Chateau Sirene 2001 looked especially nice. He slipped past well-stocked shelves of Cinzano Bianco Vermouth and Dubonnet Rouge, Grand Aperitif de France. He sidestepped a stand of Malibu Caribbean Rum, Coconut Flavor, which seemed seriously out of place. And the deeper he waded into Burka's barn of booze, the more he was laid low by the liquored air, which reeked. It stank like cheap perfume sold at CVS. But despite the lure of the liquor, he was in the mood for beer. Or ale. He repeated his new mantra as he drew nearer the glass bank of humming refrigerators at the back of the store. "Six-pack. Six-pack. Six-pack." In the dark, rear quarters of Burka's there was no oxygen to breathe—only Popov Vodka fumes—100-proof. But he was not to be deterred. This is what he had

521

come for. He took his time. He read every label. He flirted with each brand. So many beers; so little time...

There was Pilsner Urguell and Shiner Bock. There was Guinness Draught and Kaliber Buckler. There was Dos Equis and Harp Lager. There was Stella Artoise and Beck's Oktoberfest. But none of them demanded they be *his*. He trolled the American beers. As a leading Democrat, McClellan felt obligated to buy US-Made beer. And so he deliberated seriously. There was Colorado Coors and Milwaukee's Pabst Blue Ribbon. There was Budweiser and Budweiser Light. And then there was Miller. But for McClellan, now was not Miller Time. The US brews left him flat. They had about as much appeal as watching back-to-back re-runs of *Leave It To Beaver* on election night.

He stepped up to the last refrigerated vault. Inside the bottles of pale ales glowed amber and gold and dark dreamy yellow. Ale fit for kings, not losers, which is exactly why he thirsted for them. He wanted to be a winner. More than anything else he wanted to be a supreme winner. He wanted to win the Big One. The Grand Election. The Oval Office. Was that too much to ask? The sudden strength of his desire was overwhelming. That was all he wanted. To win the Big One...

In any event, how could he refuse a brew that went by the name of Dead Guy Ale? Or Wicked? Or Cut the Leash? Or Flying Day? He read their labels. These were highly distinguished ales. They looked incredibly delicious. His only question was: Which would deliver the drunk of all drunks?

He reviewed the choices. Each one as tempting as winning another electoral vote. He bent down to scan the lowest rack at considerable expense to the comfort to his back. And then he saw it. He had come upon the perfect ale—his gateway to a transcendent drunk. A higher drunk than even Falstaff could have imagined.

There was Blind Faith. The label described it as the Ale of Enlightenment. And Blessed with Hops. A brewery called Magic Hat manufactured it. McClellan snapped up a six-pack.

Enlightenment, if not election victory, would be his tonight.

At the counter, McClellan paid for the brew and bought a pack of Wrigley's Spearmint gum, too. He couldn't be too careful. Getting cited for DUI wouldn't exactly shine up the night for him or the Democratic Party. He also bought a Romeo and Juliet cigar. It was a male thing. Armed with a six-pack of enlightenment, a minty masking device and a fat, quality cigar, McClellan left Burka's. He was all set to transcend— Western style.

He drove past WGMS/WTOP Z104 radio station to the corner of Idaho and Newark. Standing across the street was the 2nd District Metropolitan Police Department—
an architecturally indistinct, cylindrical building made of dirty brick and unwashed glass. Two emaciated *Acer palatums* leaned pathetically left and right from the top of a small mound of grass, partially obscuring the white station house flagpole. In the dark, McClellan could make out the solitary figure of a uniformed police officer drawing down Old Glory for the night. The thought of the six-pack of ale on the bucket seat beside him suddenly made him irrationally nervous. He supposed it was one of those unavoidable visceral paranoid reactions that dated back to his senior high school days when he and his under-aged buddies would drive around on Saturday nights with illicit beer hidden underneath the seat and go paranoid ballistic at the sight of a police cruiser.

At Newark Street he cut left and rolled like he was driving a go-cart past Giant Food, which was as always at this time of night a hive of irritable and weary dinnertime shoppers sandwiched between aisles too narrow and destined to be sentenced to stand in choked check-out lines for twice as long as humanitarian law permits.

523

While awaiting the light at Newark and Wisconsin, McClellan drummed his fingers on the steering wheel to the tune of the Rolling Stones' "Satisfaction". He mouthed the words, "I can't get no satisfaction," imitating remembered facial expressions of Mick Jagger.

Soon the light switched to golf course green and he was good to go. But as he surged forward the Bishop of Washington—McClellan recognized him from Saturday mornings at Starbuck—stepped into the line of his low beams. Scofflaw though he was, McClellan remained circumspect about giving him the touch of a bump with his fender and jammed on his brakes. No doubt intent on ordering a Mocha Venti coffee at Starbucks, the Bishop crossed unscathed and above it all, wearing a regulation ministerial collar, a Jesus Lives! sweatshirt, too loose jogging pants and white, white, sparkling white Adidas running shoes that probably had never been run in, but made him look good. As he passed, McClellan briefly flirted with the idea of enrolling himself in divinity school. It certainly couldn't hurt to have Christ in his corner after a bruising career in politics.

The light changed; he bolted right. Another block drew him within sight of the west façade of the Gothic twin towers again. They loomed epic against the small face of the night. One block more and the gigantic building consumed the cityscape, appearing almost as incongruous as a luxury ocean liner put down in the middle of a duck pond. And as he drove past the incredible presence that seemed as vital as flesh and blood and as beautiful as sunrise over the California desert, McClellan knew where he wanted to go get drunk.

It was a place he knew well. It always smelled of English boxwoods and Cedars of Lebanon and fading pink roses and oval green lawns. And for him it was filled with memories of old romances. McClellan reveled in the knowledge that he would have it to himself. He'd hop the high stonewall and walk down the heavy stone path in the dark. He'd pass by massive American hollies and slip through a bobsled course of ancient boxwoods as he'd done hundreds of times before in his youth. It didn't matter to him how old he was, he'd hop that wall until the day he died. And though he was technically trespassing at night, McClellan viewed this minor transgression as adding little to the stiff sentence already waiting for him in the canyons of hell for a lifetime of transgressions he certainly wouldn't want the Bishop of Washington to find out about, let alone anyone else—Lone Ranger on M Street episode excluded. He wouldn't mind being remembered for that one.

At Lych Gate Road, McClellan bolted left, making an unscheduled detour onto the cathedral close. The dip in the road where the road met the drive caused his beloved Mustang to scrape bottom, possibly denting his gas tank. But that was nothing, McClellan was so intent on imbibing the Ale of Enlightenment in the Bishop's Garden. No offense intended to the Bishop of Washington, of course. (And it was measurably more dignified than tying one on in the smoky shadows of the Zebra Lounge.)

He scooted under the overhanging portico, V-shaped like B-1 bomber wings stood on their ends. The sloped portico slate roof was girded with battleship gray Gothic arches and mounted on fieldstone columns made strong enough to withstand a direct vehicular hit. He shot out the other side, sputtering past St. Alban's Parish, which was dark and empty for the night—and pregnant with memories. Layer upon layer of interlacing memories: friends' May weddings and baptisms of newborn babies and funerals for dear colleagues gone for good—a smorgasbord of life and death benchmarks, not to mention regular Sunday mornings, year after year, along with a battery of Sunday morning sermons well-scripted by the Rev. Frank Wade, who knew a thing or two about the souls of the members of his parish and how to rope in his elite upper-Northwest Washington audience. For all his

525

churchgoing, however, his faith over the years had failed to deepen and mature. Indeed, the effect was quite the opposite. Perversely, his hours in the pews had the surprising affect of opening a spiritual laundry chute somewhere inside of him through which he'd been able to make a great escape from the vise-lock of the Church.

He couldn't help himself. He was of the age when nothing—not even the power and majesty of Christ—could positively affect the dry rot of his bankrupted spirituality— a spirituality trampled down by the mounting pressure of collective compromises. Compromises he'd gladly made in the compulsive and ultimately destructive crusade to take down Christian fundamentalists like George W. and Tom DeLay. And the thing was—the dreadful thing was—as of today, as of now and forever—he was faced with the unarguable fact that his deepest, most unforgivable compromises had all been for naught. He had undermined the equilibrium of his sorry soul to profit zero. He was lost. No church could save him. No scripture, no Biblical verse had the power to reel him in. No Frank Wade sermon, no matter how artfully crafted and effectively delivered, could salvage the shipwreck of his sunken values. Crushed beneath rock and seaweed and sand and salty brine and bright sunshine somewhere off the shoal of soul, they were gone.

Which was also kind of liberating. McClellan didn't even have to pretend to tow the righteous, orthodox line. Plus he was free to hold the Church in quiet disregard for allowing itself to be hijacked by the Christian fundamentalists for political purposes. After all, Christian fundamentalists had come to dominate the American political horizon by promoting so-called Christian moral values—values he believed antithetical to the organic teachings of Christ. Indeed, in the year 2004 the Church had become a witting accomplice in the lamentable agenda of the Republican Party. Its divine purposes had been co-opted in the name of promoting an ill-conceived war and loving the death penalty and curtailing social welfare programs to provide the wealthiest 2% with additional venture capital. From McClellan's perspective, it was Christianity gone haywire.

On the other hand, it would have been fine with him if the Democrats had co-opted the Church and the moral high ground first. He'd have done almost anything to win the presidency and the House—even gone back to church.

The tall stone Norman cross conveyed a quiet elegance against the blue evening skylight. It stood eighteen feet high—maybe more—and sat indomitably on a double tier base of aggregate set on the near edge of an unbroken swath of trodden green lawn, now littered with amber and crimson fallen leaves. The face of the cross stood staring across a narrow, little road toward the Little Sanctuary and the old field stone buildings of St. Albans School for Boys. The stain-glass windows of the chapel glowed like rainbows in the night.

McClellan knew the Peace Cross well. It was the perfect perch to look upon downtown Washington. It was one of those special places in the world that—if you let it—would give you a moment of real peace. On July 4th Margaret and he would picnic there on Sutton Place with chicken salad sandwiches and Cape Cod potato chips and homemade lemonade and watch the fireworks display blooming above the distant Mall and puncturing the southern sky with boom after boom after boom.

McClellan snagged up a parking spot on the curving edge of the green, taking the place of a harried St. Albans student in tie and blue blazer peeling off in a gray, dented Audi. He collected his six-pack of ale, evacuated the bucket with considerable discomfort and went to lay claim to the Peace Cross. There was no else around.

Soon the bell in the Little Sanctuary bell tower struck seven. McClellan felt good to be outside. He almost felt grand to stand alone under the night sky, close to the stars.

He could see the sparkling necklace of city lights over the sightline of the Olmsted Woods. There was a gap between the high trees and the buildings that seemed to span the exact distance between RFK stadium in the east and the Washington Monument in the west. The lights looked like a row of fine jewels laid out in a jewelers' case. And almost dead center between the stadium and the monument sat the pearly dome of the US Capitol. A single light glowed in the middle of the dome—America's star of Bethlehem.

He twisted off a bottle cap and threw back some ale. It was definitely blessed with hops. He took another swig and then one more. It definitely lived up to its name. A student carrying a book bag, knapsack and a regulation Wilson football under his arm slipped past, head down, late for home. As he past, McClellan hid his bottle behind his back. When he was safely gone, he belted back another shot.

Each sip tasted better than the one before. Immediately, he felt better. Better and better. One by one his burdens lifted as his mind relaxed. He leaned against the stone cross and very nearly sighed. He put the flat of his shoe up against the base and took another sip. A black bird flew above the leafless branches of an ancient, weeping cherry tree nearby. A siren blew somewhere up Wisconsin Avenue. A woman laughed in the dark down in Pilgrim Road. Up in the cathedral bell tower, the Wednesday evening ringers started their peel. Their music spilled out everywhere. He loved the ringing changes. They represented the music—the changes—of his life.

He bolted back more ale. And after a while longer, life didn't seem quite so dire or so painful. He did, however, have a guilt attack. He was certain that Christ would have something rather unpleasant to say to him if he were to catch him on his monument getting stoned. But there was no chance of that.

McClellan noted an inscription carved into the stone at the base of the cross. It read: *Jesus Christ Himself being the Chief corner stone this Cross raised in the Historic year of 1898 to mark founding of Cathedral of SS Peter and Paul.* McClellan replied in kind after taking a good long swig: "Jerry McClellan Himself being the Chief corner stone of the DNC this Cross raised in the Historic year of 2004 to mark the founding of his Cathedral of Defeat."

Below the inscription he also found the following words: *"That it may please Thee to give to all Nations Unity Peace and Concord we beseech Thee to hear us Good Lord."* McClellan quipped, "That it may please Thee to give to all Democrats Unity, Victory and the Presidency we beseech Thee to hear us Good Lord."

Beaming at his own wit, he belted back another hit. He turned back around toward the low, electric skyline. It sizzled because the air was unusually clear this time of year. He chugged down even more ale. And as he did he began to feel as if he would be able to climb out of his self-made chasm—too deep to be knowable. Even his concrete thighs felt better. The taut muscles began to melt away. And as they did, McClellan's mind drifted down an easy lane. He remembered as a boy attending St. Albans School how he'd often stood on this very spot, and looked out over the fresh city lights and dreamed about his glorious life-to-be and wondering where it would lead. Now, of course, he knew. He had the whole, damn picture. Tragically, for him at least, he had come to the end of his history. It was with regret, yes, but also with a sense of emotional relief because now he could let all of his ambitions go... flow out of him like water, because there is nothing more for him to do. What was was and what would be would be and there was nothing more to be done about it. Any of it. It was over: The battle done; *la guerre perdue*.

The cruel irony was that all his life he'd been expecting to receive the grand prize—the keys to the White House. But now there would never be unrestricted access to the gates at 1600 Pennsylvania Avenue. There would be no dream-job at the top of the Mount Everest of American politics. There would only be this tormenting memory of inexpressible regret that the Heavyweight Right had out-boxed the Welterweight Left.

All of these generally un-likeable life conclusions left McClellan with the pressing need to above all else, sit down. Which he promptly did. He put his warm butt down on the top step of the Peace Cross and proceeded to polish off the final quarter of his incredibly tasty brew. And no beer—anywhere or at any time—ever tasted quite so refined. In fact, he couldn't ever remember tasting any liquid so damn righteous in his life. Not even when as a child his dear old mom served up steaming hot chocolate with whipped cream on snowy days after long hours of nonstop sledding with his friends.

Ah—the last sip was better than any before. Then for no other reason than just because he felt like it, he balanced the empty bottle upside down on the top step of the Peace Cross. There it stood. Perfectly balanced. In the city night, straight and narrow it stood—a sentinel to the benign effects of booze. And McClellan left it standing there for the whole world to denounce—if it wanted to—in the morning. Then he rose, feeling some new crazy urge to vent emotional release and threw his arms to the sky and let out a truly remarkable cry. It was Beowulf and Hound of the Baskerville combined. And there was a hint of John Lennon and Yoko Ono primal scream in there, too, which really made the thing complicated. But it helped McClellan believe, like James Cagney at the climax of *White Heat*, that he was

530

indeed "on top of the world, mom!" Even though, professionally speaking, he was well on his way down to the frozen tundra of the Antarctic of his post-election life. Still, the extraordinary thing was, the wild release gave him a sense of total completeness and a newfound control that he hadn't experienced in too many ages to count. It delivered—believe it or not—an ounce of peace. Which was wholly appropriate in light of where he was.

In the first ensuing moments after his cathartic cry, in the stunned, dumfounded silence that seemed to fill the vacuum, a dumb dog barked, somehow anticipating his reply. But McClellan wasn't going to fall for that, not even in his invigorated, tipsy state. And while beyond the confines of the cathedral close, there were the sounds of competing sirens that warned the night of tragedies en route again and again, McClellan didn't care. He was through with caring. He was as through caring as he was through with campaigning. He was only intent on one thing now: living life—and one in which he put into practice the principles of his new book in a paper bag in his Mustang: *Balance, a Guide to Life's Forgotten Pleasures.*

Intent on being true to his more enlightened mindset, McClellan picked up his six-pack—or five-pack rather—and with a fluidity of movement attributable to his consumption of high quality ale, McClellan retreated toward the open Bishop's Garden gate, ready, willing and able to attain the next level of his coming Age of Enlightenment.

He pushed back the creaky west side gate, surprised that it wasn't locked up yet for the night. Usually, it was. This was going to be his lucky night, he thought. It saved him from having to scale the north garden wall, which he easily could have done, as he prided himself on—even at his rigid age and in his semi-concretized condition, but who needed the aggravation? Though the quarter moon wouldn't rise before ten tonight and the way ahead was sprayed in deep shadows, he could

531

nevertheless make out the dim flagstone path leading down to the great green lawn of the fairytale garden that was always laced in profuse splendor and perennial bloom.

Lightheaded, peppy and uncharacteristically incautious, McClellan bounded down the grey stone slope like a child about to get on an exciting amusement park ride. Only as fate would have it, he snagged his heel on the very last step plowed forward, dropping like a kite plummeting back down to earth after losing its bed sheet tail on a windy, October day. His survival instincts heightened by his heightened state of perception, he miraculously broke his fall by latching onto an American holly branch. Not that the pinpricks of the holly leaves were significantly less painful than a direct hit on his knees. Still, as he sunk down onto his knees with resounding finality of a fastball going into a catcher's mitt, he also managed to avoid tipping out his precious cargo. Yes, McClellan had saved the booze. And in doing so, he had also succeeded in saving his night. There wasn't any question about it: This *was* his lucky night.

Ironically, for a man who'd lost the waxed wings of his faith, he found himself in proper prayer position at the edge of the great lawn, bottles of booze in one hand and a holly leaf stuck in the other. It hurt. On the other hand, his knees felt fine. It seemed somehow appropriate for him to cough up a little prayer in thanksgiving for his softer than could have been landing or for the redemption of his shriveled soul. But he wasn't into futility anymore. Not after yesterday. Instead he tapped out an email in his mind and hit Send. "Dear Lord, do what you can for the Dems."

Not that it would ever do any good.

Then he picked himself up and lit out into the garden dark with a rattling carton of ale slung down low at his side, and armed for bear. Or whatever.

532

He passed like an alley cat through the profound and lovely calm of a place large with trees and endless plants. Over the great green lawn he went, a spirit elevated. There was the hush of the lawn and the broad tapestry of nearby, hovering trees and the low knolls of century-old boxwood—as big as any he had ever seen. There were the iridescent red stems of Red-stem dogwoods, aglow in the dreamy night, mild by any standard. And over there were bursting autumn flowering cherry trees: a subtle blaze of fresh pink blooms in the silent, motionless tranquility. And sprinkled here and there—on the park benches and on every patch of lawn—were the leftover morsels of many a memory of so many lazy Sunday afternoons when he and Margaret were young and eager and victory was more or less a given...

To his left stood hundred-foot plus Cedars of Lebanon. They rose like colossal, hairy exclamation points in back of the Episcopal Church House and the cute Herb Cottage. The Herb Cottage was a round, domed building capped with a slate roof and reeked of a mystic charm. It was undoubtedly the perfect home for hobbits. It was the place where as a boy he'd venture to buy rock crystal candy for five cents a stick after school. Then he'd go with his friends to the Bishop's Garden and spend fifteen blissful minutes licking it down to the stick.

But as he walked and his perspective shifted, the cedars, though grand, became more like grace notes silhouetted against the cathedral's south face. The lower trees and plants were reduced to footnotes at the low water mark of the great granite ship of the Cathedral of St. Peter and St. Paul. The cathedral itself was caught in the scouring footlights of multiple battalions of floodlights, throwing up vast sheets of daylight from behind the garden walls. The whole body of the cathedral stood out so big and long and exuded such an abundance of architectural grace that it was hard to look at anything else. It was the living cross of Christ, all right, set against the infinity of sky. Though he still had his doubts about religion, McClellan believed in architecture. Architecture mattered.

He felt safe and at home in the glowing enchantment of the garden dark. For him, there was no safer, more familiar place. And no space more sublime. He'd considered having his ashes sprinkled among the fertile perennial beds when the time came. There were worse places to spend an eternity. Although anywhere in Paris would do, too. Tonight he made up his mind to phone his lawyer in the morning and have him put it in his will.

The city's orange crime lights ricocheted off the flimsy roof of the lower sky, coloring the octagonal Gazebo, which sat regally across the rolling lawn, shrouded in spiritual mystery. The downpour of macabre urban crime light wasn't exactly his idea of life-nurturing sunshine. On the contrary, it stained everything organic, everything sacred, everything truly worth something: new life. Nevertheless, the airy, stone and wood and slate Gazebo ahead seemed to summon him, beckon him like a soft bed after a 36-hour workday. He proceeded into the strange nighttime sunshine even deeper. He knew he had a rendezvous with this sacred space ahead. The night was calling; his life was calling, and it wasn't just the golden whispers of the blessed hops speaking. There was something going on in there, though precisely what he really couldn't say.

As he entered into the Gazebo, he couldn't help but notice the copper weathervane parked on top of the cone-shape, slate roof. It pointed in every direction— north, south, east and west, which wasn't much of a help in terms of pointing out a new direction for him. Curiously, once inside, that mysterious, quasi-spiritual draw vanished. What had been calling to him out on the great green lawn was gone. It vanished like mist at sunrise across an empty desert highway. He felt lost. Lost like he'd taken a wrong turn down a side street in Venice when searching every which way for the Piazza San Marco. He was not a little dispirited by this. His expectations had been high—most likely because of the ale, but high nevertheless. Then it dawned on him that his destiny had dodged him. He had not arrived in the Land of Oz at the end of the yellow brick road. Rather, he'd come to an agreeable but none un-too-familiar place that smelled like fresh loam and mulch. Not to complain. It was certainly a nicer atmosphere by light-years than hanging out in the stinky back rooms of the Zebra Lounge all alone.

There were seven benches lining the octagonal walls of the outdoor garden room. Heavy timbers framed the Gothic-shaped windows that looked like they'd been cut sometime back in Elizabethan times. Aged by inclement extremes, they gave the appearance of having been around for a long, long time and were endowed with a natural spirituality that only came from organic things. So even though McClellan felt as though he'd had the spiritual rug pulled right out from underneath him, there was one particularly gratifying aspect about his current condition: He was standing in a womb of fragrance. He closed his eyes and breathed in deeply. And got higher still. Another rung up the ladder to enlightenment.

There was the sweet confluence of dusty old roses—Damask, China, and Rugosa; and the odor of dried and dying herbs—lavender, thyme, and dill. Mingled in here and there was also the fragrance of autumn flowering cherries, and more. So much more. They converged like infinite varieties of burning incense locked in a locked-down room—Patchouli, Sandalwood, Frankincense and Myrrh, etc. McClellan took in everything there was to take in and still sought more. He was hungry for the experience of convergence. What that meant, however, he hadn't a clue.

But this much he knew: The Elysian Fields, for all their hype and mystique, couldn't possibly hold a candle to the Bishop's Garden. For

McClellan, it was greater than the Garden of the Gods. But what did he know? He was on the verge of becoming an atheist.

He plunked his five-pack of ale down on the slated wooden bench and took a seat beside it. Leaning against the rough timber sill below a Gothic arch-shaped window, he feasted his eyes on the interwoven tapestries of festooned greens beyond each window frame. Southward, for instance, there stood the still and imposing presence of the Olmstead Woods; eastward lay bundles of gigantic English boxwoods in a row that looked a bit like smooth, green snowdrifts; northward sat the imperturbable, stone shoulders of the cathedral's flying buttresses, as high as a 747's wings were long; and northeastward rose the Gloria and Excelsior tower—the granddaddy belfry that held the Borden bell. The funeral bell, which tolled very, very slowly for Kennedy, Martin Luther King, and even Ronald Reagan. Somehow this depressed him, because McClellan knew that it would never toll for him.

McClellan twisted off a cap and threw back another brew. He was intent on being happy. He refused to go down the road to morose. And his plan seemed to be working just fine. The more he drank the higher his spirits and he thought there for a moment or two at least that he felt a slight convergence with the Holy Spirit. Well, why not? It entered in through his flaccid stomach. Now he understood why the Church served communion wine. It ushered in the Holy Spirit.

By the fifth bottle of the Ale of Enlightenment the Holy Spirit was completely with him. He feared no man, not even Karl Rove. Even the likely prospect of him getting nailed to the cross tomorrow morning down at DNC headquarters hardly got a rise out of him. He was a born again drunk. But it beat being morose. It beat being glum. It beat being all by himself. And the Holy Spirit wasn't such bad company, after all. Perhaps he would reconsider his spiritual boycott of the Episcopal Church.

536

He cracked the last beer and while chugging it down had to admit that he was on the verge of feeling happy. But then, out of the blue, McClellan pictured the first line of his obituary. It read: "Jerry McClellan, age 72, died of complications resulting from his failed chairmanship of the DNC."

That kicked the Holy Spirit right out of him. It had the effect of pouring acid on his open wounds. Yet McClellan tried to valiantly fight back, groping for some modicum of self-esteem. Anything. He told himself over and over again that there was more to life than politics. But then he couldn't think of what that was. Then he went over the deep end. He swore to the oblivious night that if he had the campaign to do all over again—which he most certainly wouldn't—he'd search high and low for the perfect moral values candidate. But who was he kidding? It was over. Boy, was it ever over.

Suddenly, the floodlights showering the south side of the twin towers snapped out. Just like that. He'd never seen that happen before. The annual giving drive must have come up short this year, he thought. Or more likely it was an energy conservation thing. Whatever. Only the Gloria and Excelsior tower remained lit. Its epic scale diminished the awesome canvas of the *noir* northern sky. The very sight bucked McClellan up. It gave him permission to absolve himself of at least a miniscule fraction of his pent-up guilt for all the doom he'd brought down upon the Democrats' House. After all, wasn't he the one who'd raised $337 million for the Dems—more than even the all-time Olympic champs of fundraising, the Republicans? And wasn't he the one who was leaving the DNC coffers well endowed—even after record campaign expenditures? And wasn't he the one who'd turned out 6.8 million more Democratic voters than anyone at any time had ever done before? Surely that was worth the Borden bell at his funeral.

Momentarily, he permitted himself seething-rights, directed at all his teammates. After all, he wasn't the one who'd run for office and lost... There was only so much blame that a fellow could take, even as the head of the DNC.

The next layer of regret was setting in. Winning the DNC chairmanship, it now was clear, hadn't exactly turned out to be a genius career move. In hindsight, it would have been far better for him to have run for a seat on his local Advisory Neighborhood Commission, ANC3D. He could have at least won that election, especially because in DC Democrats outnumber Republicans by a 10-to-1 ratio. But no, he had to go great game hunting with the big boys and blow off his foot with a shotgun in the process.

The thought of all those irreplaceable years sickened him. Absolutely sickened him.

He heard a malicious whisper in his head: *It was the Moral Values Issue, stupid!*

God was he drunk. And a drunken dunce at that. He was so drunk, in fact, that he pulled out his phone and tried to dial up John Kerry to ball him out for fucking up the election. But he couldn't remember how to turn it on, so in a fit of drunken peak, he wobbled more or less over to the Gazebo doorway and threw his cell phone as far as he possibly could out across the great green rolling lawn.

"Take THAT, you loser candidate! Don't blame ME for your lack of moral values!"

The cell phone landed somewhere out beyond. He couldn't even hear it strike the grass. Accomplishing nothing, he nevertheless felt very pleased with himself for having at least tried. He stood there on the edge of the great green lawn for the longest time, listening to the lament of the dark. It was all he could do to keep from crying. He'd come to the easy realization he'd been HAD. HAD by politics. HAD by his self-absorbed, ambitious dreams. HAD by, well, the fundamentals and mechanics of LIFE!

Humiliated by his stupendous gullibility, he leaned back against what he calculated to be the timber frame of the Gazebo's doorway, only to miss by a lot. He fell like a tree in the forest, but with considerably less elegance. He landed on his ass, narrowly avoiding smacking his head on the cold, hard stone. The good thing was the booze was okay.

It wasn't too bad being down there on the Gazebo floor. He righted himself as best he could, sitting cross-legged, and staring out at the great green lawn, lost in the soup of his loose drunkenness. His Buddha-like position permitted him a moment of reflection: What had happened to that incredibly special feeling he'd had four ales ago as he traipsed across the great green lawn toward the Gazebo with such great expectations? Now he understood. It became as clear as fresh rainwater. The deal was he'd been lured by the Holy Spirit, and then double-crossed. As McClellan went in, It exited through one of the many open windows, leaving him alone, like a dumbstruck groom at the altar as his runaway bride flees down the aisle and out the church door.

The thing was, there was no such thing. There was no such thing as destiny. Not for him, anyway. Destiny was a construct of mythical fiction, borne on the twisted back of irrational hopes and intangible illusions and offered up to the gullible for consumption by dead Greek playwrights in Western literature who should have known better. Yet, incredibly, so desperate was McClellan that he was ready to be suckered all over again. So nixed was his state of mind, so frantic his circumstances, so excruciating his losses, that he made the perfect mark.

But what skewered most was that destiny's call had seemed so genuine and so real. It was as authentic as in a waking dream of pleasure, when nothing in that dreamscape could possibly make you believe that

539

the woman you had wrapped in your arms, so supremely vital and alive, was actually a fleeting figment of your most ardent desires…

Nipping at the last ounce of ale, McClellan groaned dispiritedly, before falling backwards again as he threw his empty bottle of ale over his head in a gesture of contempt for all things that had ever been and would ever be, most especially as they related to him. It landed soundlessly in the arms of an English boxwood, to be found, no doubt, in years to come by excited children playing hide-and-go-seek after service in the garden.

Hopelessly damned and defeated and pretty much doomed, he slurred his words talking to the roof, "*Fuck it*," he said. "*Not everyone gets to grow up to work down the hall from the Oval Office.*"

Nevertheless, he still wasn't done hoping yet. He closed his eyes and hoped some more.

In an empty moment, he observed that the changes had stopped. The bell tower had fallen silent. There was only a slow breathing silence about—his slow breathing, to be exact. An echo of calm drifted through the bony arms of the near trees and scented bushes. The quiet made him appreciate the fact that he was even drunker than he thought. He heard a distant splashing—a rill of running water spilling from a spout into a stone basin tucked beneath the spreading arms of the Cedars of Lebanon across the green garden lawn. Opposite, he also heard the whooshing sounds of evening traffic soaring up and down Cleveland Avenue through the stands of Olmstead trees. He heard them as clearly as if they'd been digitally amplified. *Now what?* McClellan asked himself. *Now what?* His hoping moments were over.

Now he had to pee and there was nothing to be done about it. He knew what he must do. He struggled to his feet and stumbled off in search of a clump of English boxwoods to carry out his intended purpose. Of course, he understood well that it wouldn't be very dignified or especially chairman-like, but he'd lost his dignity by the second bottle and his chairmanship days were effectively gone, and as nature was being rather insistent, there wasn't much else he could do. So he went.

Frankly, he hadn't a clue how he made it over to the boxwoods. But when at last he did, he believed that God was good.

Then came a ferocious sound—part charging rhinoceros, part stampeding boar, part hornet out to sting and die. Over the Olmsted Woods the dark noise flew, chewing up the sky. It made a whack, whack, whacking sound. Its light came on. As bright as a gigantic porch light at night. It swooped down, burning a hole in the ground. The dark mass soared across Pilgrim Road, bringing its anchor of light toward the south garden wall. McClellan finished up his business as fast as he could. The copter was on him, exposing his stealth frame in a lasso of searing, white light. He bolted for cover under the large Norman stone archway beneath the Cedars of Lebanon, while protesting in pantomime his professed innocence: *"You gotta believe me, officer. I'm innocent!"*

The forced air blew down. A tornado seemed to be ravaging the lawn. *The Republicans are after me!* McClellan thought, crazed by panic.

But no sooner had it come than it was gone.

Veering sharply west, the police copter narrowly avoided a collision with the west tower. McClellan's brush with indecent public exposure knocked the drunk right out of him. He was as sober as Florence Nightingale. The cedars rocked and swayed; the fall leaves blew every which way and battalions of startled birds flew up and away from their hiding places, frightened and confused. McClellan was no less startled and confused. He shuffled over to the water fountain still in shock. This was what he needed. He dipped his cupped hands into the water basin, and scooped up a handful of water. Holy Water. He leaned down and poured it over his face. So wet, so cold, so incredibly extreme.

541

It made him feel newly baptized. Born again to the company of Christendom.

Even at his ancient age.

Rinsed of his sins, cleansed of his failures, he recognized this transformation for what it was: a Kodak moment! He stood at the doorway to enlightenment. This was it. Well, it sure seemed like it...

Drying his face on his sleeve, he anticipated that something momentous was about to happen. He listened to the silence of Great Expectations. And lo and behold, that special sense of destiny called out to him again. This time it was coming from the center of the great green lawn.

So McClellan walked into the crime-light dark. He followed the sounds of silence. He followed the trembling call of destiny, real as never before... Something very grand was about to happen out there. The sense of it was everywhere.

The lawn was a seabed of fading summer grass and curling crimson and yellow ocher leaves that had given up the Holy Ghost weeks ago and now lay buried in the velvety dark. It was an ocean of serenity, an oasis of spirituality, and above all else a great spot to play touch football on a Saturday afternoon. McClellan entered in.

He moved as an electric current toward the lawn's center. He stood amongst the dead leaves and scattered debris. He'd arrived at Earth's center, preposterous as that seemed. And there he stayed. Transfixed and anchored. Bound to the ground. One fixed point in an incredible universe—a universe moving away from itself, and in which no anchor exists. So there it was. There he stood. Under stars that turned and a sky that moved invisibly. Waiting like an open vessel, ready to receive his destiny. And for the second time tonight his destiny appeared to be calling. *What?* Was it on *auto-dial?* Fool me once, shame on you. Fool me twice, shame on me. McClellan was prepared to be

542

taunted by that Destiny Demon all over again because a carrot of faith had been left to dangle over his head mid-lawn.

The oceanic atmosphere created by the swirl of expectations made the waiting acceptable. He was in no hurry, neither would he be rushed. McClellan maintained his alertness until about the hour of 3:00 a.m. by counting city stars through the crime-lit skies and identifying vaguely familiar constellations he dimly remembered from his days when he was hot for astronomy and by singing Broadway show tunes in his head when things went really quiet and he had to keep himself going—somehow. Then a little after three the want of sleep invaded his mind. He fell victim to a slumberous riptide that drew him foot, leg and torso into the rugged waters of his salty subconscious. He passed through many a wetland dream. Barren, treeless shores rose up and fell as he was swept along in search of sunshine. Other territories appeared as empty, lifeless islands, cloaked in sinuous, vaporous mists. They reminded him of scenes out of Sir Arthur Conan Doyle mysteries that took place on creepy English moors very late at night when baying hounds called and called and then attacked. It was not exactly the most pleasant part of his dream voyage.

But eventually these and other images gave way to sunnier ways. Soon he was transported to his old childhood haunt, as if Scotty had miraculously beamed him aboard the good ship Childhood. And there he crouched as a four-year-old mysteriously regenerated by a salute to faith at the foot of an ancient English oak tree that occupied a spot of ground beside a stacked stone wall at the edge of a grassy field that appeared to have been left un-mowed since Hadrian's wall got built.

The summer sun was fully out. In a perfectly cloudless sky that probably couldn't even recall what a cumulous cloud looked like for it had been that long since one had dared to show its face anywhere near the sky, the great tree rose. Surely, it was the tree of all trees: the

543

mythological Tree of Knowledge. Its branches, so heavy and so thick and full of summer leaves—too many to conceive of—stretched out far enough and appeared strong enough to hold up the heavenly blue mask of the bending sky, at least from the perspective of a wondrous, little boy. And so below the massive frame of the gigantic tree that appeared even taller than the Eiffel tower might look from far away, little McClellan sat in the high grass and twirled a yellow dandelion, though it had been spun one too many times. He discarded it and plucked a dandelion seedpod by his knee and twirled it, too, before blowing the feathery seeds to the endless channels of wind. The little boy beamed. He lay back in the blanket of tall grass and gazed up at seedpods blowing hither and yon in a slow motion dance. Sunshine beamed down, so clean and warm and life-affirming and held in its hands the beautiful face of a little boy as yet unharmed by the ravages of Karl Rove and a thousand, like-minded others, who'd lined up along life's way to crimp his body armor and bury his soul.

It was such an astonishingly fine day that it should have been declared unlawful to fade by the U.S. Supreme Court in a unanimous decision. Such was McClellan's suggestion. But then the dreamscape faded-out, like the ending to a good film, leaving both regret and sense of satisfaction. His bleary eyes found the dark again. Turning east, he faced first light, finishing his long night's journey across the forgotten tundra of his trampled psyche. Ending his rarified experience, both very strange and beautiful. Shutting down his night. Officially saying goodnight.

He narrowed his bleary eyes, staring at his watch dial. The big and little hands stood at rapt attention: It was six a.m. *What the hell happened?* McClellan howled inside. Baffled and confused, he shook his head. He turned due east, peering at the sky beyond the cathedral's East End. He beheld the awakening sky. It seemed to tremble with

544

expectations of a greater light to come. At the base of the sky, a Clifford Stills-type streak of pale pink light, as soft as Milton Avery pastels, brightened in a band. The new dawn was coming. Miraculously, he had slept upright all night, defying both human anatomy and gravity. How would he ever explain it to Margaret? He looked up. He took in the great web of the still sky, magnificently informed by phosphorescent oceans of starlight exponentially magnified. In his whole life, he had never seen such atmospheric clarity. Not in the Arizona desert or on a Maine lake in the deep of night. It gave off a rarified transparency that was only observable, no doubt, above Earth's thermosphere or through the space shuttle's window. It brought close to home the lights of creation—the Cosmic Singularity. He bathed in the bright and sparkling darkness; he took his early morning shower—without soap or shampoo or even water.

At last McClellan's eyes fell low, down to the western, robin's egg blue sky. They settled on an especially luminous presence a degree or two above the roofline of the Lucas Building at St. Albans School for Boys. Something told him that this was where the beam of destiny and the arc of the extraordinary would collide. How and when he couldn't say. But he knew that it was going to happen soon. He felt it in his bones. He sensed it as he'd sensed the growing awe and golden splendor of the Bishop's Garden late last night when it drew him in and in with promises of destiny in the dark.

Virgo was that luminous presence. And if McClellan remembered his high school astronomy facts even halfway right, which would be as miraculous as the Second Coming itself, it was 65 million light years away, give or take. Virgo was the Virgin or Mary Magdalene or Mother of the Son of Light—The Big Mom, so he recalled somehow. In ancient Egyptian times it was the sign of Isis, the fertility queen, and according to the *USA Today* weather page, it was the sixth sign of the

545

Zodiac. It also symbolized the Star of David and the birth of the spirit and who knew what else. How McClellan even remembered this, he really couldn't say. No doubt about it though, Virgo was one of the Grand Dames of all the constellations wheeling in the star bulge of the Milky Way—second only in size to the serpent-headed Hydra. It possessed celestial gravitas.

In the northeastern reaches of Virgo lay a pregnant field of super cluster galaxies. They were so dense, so immense and visually intense that they inspired attention. In the southern quadrant sat Spica, Virgo's single most visible star—its Broadway Star of stars, its grand performer; its ham. It showed off its blue-white first magnitude light with no modesty at all. Yet tonight, it appeared dim, pale, and weak—seriously diminished. It looked like it was about to wilt. Why? Because tonight it weighed in against first-class competition: There was a new configuration on the block and it outshone, outperformed, and simply outdid everything within its constellational limits. It was master of the Virgo sky: the Alpha and Omega of amalgamations. It shone brighter than any first magnitude starburst out there. It was the most happening thing in the sky.

Lying side by side, forming a kind of celestial gash in bluing Virgo, were two great planets: Venus and Jupiter. At this moment, incredibly, Venus, the Goddess of Love, and Jupiter, the so-called Beneficent One, were converging: The beam of destiny and the arc of the extraordinary had collided.

It was manifestly clear that the Dual Star portended something enormous. What precisely, McClellan hadn't a clue. But it felt like everything was about to blow and that he was sitting on a powder keg and the fuse was lit.

But even if he'd wanted to, which he didn't, he couldn't have turned to run. The light in the lower sky was so tantalizing—utterly

546

mesmerizing. McClellan was hooked. The Dual Star's magnitude grew and grew. Could it be, he wondered, that he was a hapless spectator to the concoction of a new Holy Alliance—a celestial union of astronomical significance?

Incredibly, the light mass kept on expanding—exponentially growing, like a laboratory experiment tumbling dangerously out of control. The Light Mass was accelerating, too. And damned if it didn't look like it was heading on a trajectory that didn't bode well for McClellan's survival: It appeared to be coming at him at the speed of light. Or was he just losing it? If so, his departure as DNC chairman couldn't come a moment too soon. He needed help! And how! A psychological makeover.

But as the light mass occupied an increasingly larger part of the sky above the Lucas Building, blinding everything in its path with a hyper, unremitting radiance, a funny but centered feeling swelled inside him. A certain rising level of spiritual volume registered within, as if he'd stopped by a gas station and filled up on high-octane. He knew he was nutty now. Could the light mass be re-fueling his depleted soul? Was *this* the Dawn of Enlightenment he'd been expecting to find last night? Had he drunk from the cup of the Holy Grail and tasted the wine of the Ages?

Something big was up. There was no question about it anymore: There were Great Powers and Principalities out and about. And they—whatever they were—were a trillion of times more powerful than any Republican Party—or Democratic Party, for that matter; and they were billions of times more potent than the Republican-controlled House of Representatives and the Senate combined; and they were millions of times more commanding than any George W. Bush in the White House. Whatever—whoever—they were, they were far beyond first magnitude material.

547

Whether or not a pre-dawn madness had struck him was beside the point. He had an uncontrollable craving—like a child for a chocolate ice cream cone—to be connected to whatever Powers and Principalities were crashing across the volcanic sky at warp speed: Destination Bishop's Garden. Instinctively bonded to it, hypnotized by its fierce and godly light, he felt this incredible urge to speak to it before it consumed him. Or blew him off the face of the earth. Whichever came first.

But one strange thing: The closer the Powers and Principalities came, the more his soul felt re-charged. Not to put too fine a point on it, but he was actually beginning to feel the balm of awe and wonder again. Which did wonders for his shredded soul.

The thought that any event, political or otherwise, could take him up the tower of hope again was, well, awesome. Being the political operator that he was he also felt the need to connect with these Powers and Principalities about to drop in on him for breakfast. No time to lose, McClellan cupped his hands together, forming them into an ad hoc megaphone, and put them to his lips. And as the sky grew increasingly volcanic and chaotic winds blew into the well-lit garden, casting a gusty hail of autumn leaves in whichever direction, he called out to the Powers and Principalities, now approaching as big and fast as the headlight of an approaching freight train at close range, beseeching them to hear his most fervent prayer:

"OH, POWERS AND PRINCIPALITIES STRONGER THAN THE REPUBLICAN PARTY, MIGHTIER THAN THE REPUBLICAN-CONTROLLED CONGRESS, AND MORE POWERFUL THAN THE PRESIDENT OF THE UNITED STATES, TAKE PITY ON US POOR DEMOCRATS!!! GRANT US THE WISDOM TO TAP INTO MAINSTREAM MORAL VALUES ISSUES AND TURN THE RED STATES BLUE!!! SHOW US THE WAY TO VICTORY IN 2008!!!"

No sooner had he said those words when the Powers and Principalities, a great mass of hurtling light, faster than a comet and as bright as any starburst, detonated above him: A spiritual neutron bomb. And as neutron bombs will do—nuclear or otherwise—it left everything standing. Including McClellan, the Gazebo, the Norman arch, and the water fountain. But instead of being contaminated with a lethal dose of uranium, he was buried in celestial radiation. Over 60,000 CPMs. Off the Geiger counter Rad charts. But instead of killing him, he instantly felt enriched, more serene than he had ever been. It was as if he'd downed a chalice of communion wine. Crank up the presses: The Holy Spirit was with him again!

It was like having divine political capital in the bank.

And as the celestial canopy of light subsided, as the grass whispered and the sky sighed and the dry leaves drifted down to the great green lawn where they belonged, everything seemed radically righteous. *What the hell happened?*

Familiar contours of the Bishop's Garden began to materialize. McClellan shaded his eye, like a Great Plains Indian scout staring at the dusty desert horizon. Emerging from the heart of the great green lawn, not more than ten yards away, stood a glorious Oriole Roman candle, shooting off an effusive rain of golden sparks. It took center stage: A sizzling shower of fireworks about twenty feet high. It was a first magnitude Independence Day display, just a few months late.

Gradually, the Oriole Roman candle sputtered out, meeting a dark and smoky fate. But when the fog of phosphate cleared, lost to the tops of trees, McClellan observed that before him stood a gentleman. In a white Panama suit and hat. And he was black, black with big funny ears and dreadlocks.

The first words of out of mouth were these: "I am Christ the Lord, come back to save the Democratic Party from oblivion, and your sorry ass, Jerry McClellan."

McClellan went weak in the knees. One thing was for sure: This was no paperback novel character. This was no tiptoe through fantasyland. This was the real thing: The Dude of Dudes! The King of Kings! The original Comeback Kid!!!

McClellan fell to his knees. What else could he do? He was overcome by divine intervention.

He looked up at his face. It was as face as fine as spun gold and Chinese silk and blooming alpine summer flowers. It was fresh like rain and clear as glass and there was about his eyes the look of supreme radiance and divine splendor—a splendor that reached down inside of him and stirred his heart, even more than when he heard a really good Bill Clinton speech.

McClellan knew that all bets were off. Anything could happen now. He had reached the outer limits of temporal experience. He was certainly *way* beyond politics. But what he couldn't get over was Christ's incredible youthful appearance. No way U.S. Immigration would mark him for a day over thirty-three. Which was saying something considering that the Comeback Kid couldn't be a day under 2,036 years old. What's more, despite his hasty travels across the light years, he gave no hint— no hint whatsoever—he was suffering from a case of galactic jetlag.

McClellan strained to say something in response. A simple "Thank you" would have done quite nicely. But for the first time in forever, words eluded him. And there came a mad rush of self-doubt and spatial confusion, too. Could this really be happening to him? Or was he actually safe and sound in bed with Margaret dreaming, dreaming, dreaming?

He desperately needed a reality check: Something—anything to confirm that his experiences were authentic. Then McClellan remembered his packet of Wrigley's Spearmint gum he'd bought the night before at Burka's. He rooted around for it in his jacket pocket. Ah—There it was. Right where it belonged. He knew he definitely wasn't dreaming now. He was exactly where he thought he was, seeing what he knew he saw: He was in the Bishop's Garden on November 3, 2004, standing before the eyes of Christ, the Lord. This was—God's Name Be Praised! HIS TICKET TO THE WHITE HOUSE!!! And yes, of course, of somewhat lesser importance, the holy road to his personal redemption.

Next a crazy idea came over him. He had visions of a crackerjack CNN film crew hopping the garden wall at any second, and demanding an exclusive with his Lord of Lords. Notwithstanding the lunacy of his thinking, McClellan looked around, all very paranoid. But there wasn't even a cub reporter from WAMU radio station around. Let alone someone from the *Northwest Current*. There was only Jerry McClellan and you-know-who: The poster boy for humankind's salvation.

Christ commanded McClellan to rise. "Jerry, It's morning again in America. Now rise... Rise."

McClellan did as he was told. And as he rose up, his knees stained with grass, the Comeback Kid slowly walked toward him, a smile blazing like sunrise across his warm, inviting face. And he brought with him a confidence that could only be described as, well, Omnipotent. An Omnipotent confidence—that's what it was. Exactly. You know it when you see it.

And as he came closer and closer, McClellan momentarily spun into an awful panic. He was stricken with terror that his breath would reek of last night's alcohol and Christ, the Lord—100% pure—would smell it. So he reached into his pocket for the pack of gum and

551

extracting it, he tore off the wrapper, and popped a piece into his mouth as fast as you can say, "Karl Rove's history."

And as the Savior of the Democratic Party, and McClellan's ass, came up to him, he put his arm around him, and said with not a little irony and in a tone rife with conspiracy: "Now let's go show those Republicans a thing or two about winning a *real* Moral Values victory, shall we?"

McClellan, as gaga as it gets, nodded his consent.

As the two strode off across the great green lawn of the Bishop's Garden, headed for history, and a seismic triumph that would shape America forever, the Comeback Kid, in all his stardust glory, leaned in a little closer to whisper these few words to the once and future chairman of the DNC: "*I'm your guy for 2008.*"

April 9, 2010, Bangkok, Thailand

552

TABLE OF CONTENTS

First Electronic edition published 2012 by Americus Press, Washington, D.C.
under the title "My Name is Jesus Christ and I'm Running for President"
Copyright © 2012 Timothy Cooper
e-ISBN-13: 978-0-9619914-2-5, e-ISBN-10: 0-9619914-2-9
Second Electronic edition published 2015 by Americus Press, Washington, D.C.
Under the title "2020 or My Name is Jesus Christ and I'm Running for President"
Copyright © 2015 Timothy Cooper
e-ISBN-13: 978-0-9619914-2-5, e-ISBN-10: 0-9619914-2-9

Cover art to the electronic edition based on early Renaissance painting by Giovanni Bellini, Resurrection of Christ, Copyright © 2012 Timothy Cooper

DISCLAIMER

All characters and incidents appearing in this work from the beginning of time to the end of time, both in this life and the hereafter, are intensely fictitious, completely made up and most definitely invented for the sake of comic relief in a world fraught with too many politicians running for too few elected offices. Any resemblance to actual, factual, real-life, authentic, bona fide, genuine, tangible, palpable, concrete, honest-to-goodness, honest-to-God persons, either living or dead, is purely coincidental, and yes, absolutely accidental, inadvertent, serendipitous, fortuitous, unplanned, unexpected, unwanted and, I swear, unintentional. Well, sort of.

DEDICATIONS & ACKNOWLEDGEMENTS

For my brother, Gregory, confederate extraordinaire: champion of political satire and unwavering advocate for the completion of the Book. And to my mother and father, who never shied from a good political debate, and sat me down in front of the Fada T.V. as a child to watch the first-televised presidential debates.

To Ferdinand Ruge, author of *Ruge Rules*, and STA English teacher unparalleled: May he Teach in Peace (TIP); and to my other teachers over time: John Bloch, L.M. Reynolds, James Silke, Ted Walch, and John W. Wrigley—all believers in the power of the word. And, oh yes, to the author of that one magnificent book from which, according to Ernest Hemingway, all American literature flows—*The Adventures of Huckleberry Finn* by Mr. Mark Twain.

Deep appreciations go to Natalie Kimber, my agent, for her belief in Second Comings and literary miracles; to Elizabeth Garner, for her exuberant faith in the divinity of creativity; to my fellow Starbucks writers Page Evans, Lisa Fuentes, Rochelle Kainer, and Debbie Weil who pursue the high challenge of writing well; and to all the good folks at the Wisconsin Avenue Starbucks in Cleveland Park, including, but not limited to, Wendy Garner, Susan Green, Shadi Hamwi, John Hanrahan, Martin McMahon, and Nick Zakas, who put up with my monopolizing the corner table morning, noon and night for all those years.

And finally to Ian, Arran, Dylan, and Jo, who paid the price.

Made in the USA
Columbia, SC
30 January 2018